THE LAND OF BRITAIN

The Report of
The Land Utilisation Survey of Britain

EDITED BY
L. DUDLEY STAMP, B.A., D.Sc.

Part 86
SOMERSET

By

T. STUART-MENTEATH, B.A. (Oxon.)

WITH THE CO-OPERATION OF

THE SOMERSET FARM INSTITUTE, CANNINGTON

AND

THE SCHOOL OF RURAL ECONOMY, UNIVERSITY OF OXFORD

AND WITH AN HISTORICAL CHAPTER BY

S. C. MORLAND, M.A., C.C.

LONDON
PUBLISHED FOR THE SURVEY BY GEOGRAPHICAL PUBLICATIONS LTD
1938

NOTE

The publication of this Report has been made possible
by a grant from the Pilgrim Trust and by a donation
from the Patron for the County:

HIS GRACE THE DUKE OF SOMERSET, D.S.O., O.B.E., D.L., J.P.

Maps and Report are obtainable from
THE LAND UTILISATION SURVEY OF BRITAIN
London School of Economics, Houghton Street, London, W.C.2

Part 86

SOMERSET

By

T. STUART-MENTEATH, B.A. (Oxon.)

WITH THE CO-OPERATION OF

THE SOMERSET FARM INSTITUTE, CANNINGTON

AND

THE SCHOOL OF RURAL ECONOMY, UNIVERSITY OF OXFORD

EDITORIAL INTRODUCTION

ON May 16th, 1931, Mr. F. Burkinshaw, County Education Secretary of Somerset, wrote to the Director of the Land Utilisation Survey that his Committee had agreed for the survey of the county to be organised through the schools. The county is a large one and the set of 323 six-inch maps was purchased by the Education Committee. By June the maps had been allotted to schools and distributed. Although the headquarters of the Survey in London undertook to deal with all enquiries from the surveyors, the County Education Secretary reported on July 31st that his office had written also over 250 letters on the subject ! Completed maps began to come in from July onwards and by the end of 1931 a third of the county had been finished. But difficulties arose with regard to the remoter areas and it became clear that the whole county could not be reached from the schools. The work, however, went on steadily during 1932. On March 7th, 1933, a conference was held at Weston-super-Mare and the completion of the field-work discussed. The assistance of new volunteers was sought : during 1933 Taunton was surveyed through the schools of the Municipality ; a number of areas were surveyed by members of the Somerset Rural Community Council ; a tract by Sidcot School (Winscombe) ; a considerable part of the north by Professor S. H. Reynolds of the University of Bristol ; and a large area by Mr. C. H. Puckett, B.A., of King's College, University of London. During 1934 many of the remaining tracts were surveyed by Mr. L. W. C. Maidment, B.A., of University College, Southampton.

On July 16th, 1935, through the kind offices of Mr. J. N. L. Baker, M.A., B.Litt., of the School of Geography of the University of Oxford, an offer was received from Mr. T. Stuart-Menteath (then attached to the School) to assist in the work of the Land Utilisation Survey. After discussing the matter on July 22nd, Mr. Stuart-Menteath agreed to be responsible for the completion of the field-work in Somerset, the revision of all work already carried out, and the preparation of this Report. In the months which followed he travelled very extensively in the county, penetrating to every corner, covering hundreds of miles, interviewing scores of farmers and getting into touch with the Somerset Farm Institute (Cannington) whose Principal, Mr. W. D. Hay, B.Sc. (Agr.), has afforded unstinted help and made available his own unique knowledge of the county and that of his colleagues, Messrs. D. Rowe, J. E. Forshaw and F. R. Wallbutton. By the end of 1935 the Bridgwater–Taunton one-inch sheet (No. 120) was ready for publication, and once more the County Education Committee lent its support by a generous grant of £50 towards publication, the grant to be repaid in maps as published. Mr. S. C. Morland, the son of the Chairman of the Education Committee, has further contributed the historical chapter to this Report. The Report itself has been written at the School of Rural Economy, University of Oxford, where Mr. Stuart-Menteath has had the advantage of the co-operation of his colleagues and especially of the advice of Professor J. A. Scott-Watson, Mr. C. S. Orwin, Major G. D. Amery and Mr. J. N. L. Baker.

L. D. S.

TABLE OF CONTENTS

I. INTRODUCTION

THIS report is intended to be used with, and to be complementary to, the seven maps on a scale of one inch to the mile of the Land Utilisation Survey of Somerset.

The one-inch maps are based on a survey of the surface of Somerset recorded on some 323 quarter-sheets of the Ordnance Survey Six-inch Series, filled in on the ground, field by field, in part by volunteers from the Somerset schools, in part by various helpers, and in part by the writer, working on behalf of the Land Utilisation Survey of Britain.

A list of those responsible for the individual field-sheets and the dates of completion, etc., appears in the Appendix, but since the survey took a number of years to complete a check and revision of all important parts was made before producing the one-inch maps. This checking and revision was carried out by the writer in consultation with the headquarters staff of the Survey, who have been dealing with similar surveys from all over Britain for some years. Wherever difference of opinion, or doubtful interpretation occurred, the sheets in question were referred back to the field surveyors for confirmation.

Although the six-inch sheets varied in appearance widely according to the skill and care bestowed on them in the schools, the accuracy of the information supplied was extraordinarily high, and serious mistakes few. Only one sheet appeared to have been really carelessly done, and in that case probably the mistake was to fill in as " arable," land that was arable by tenure and not by present use.

The children of the Somerset schools may well be proud of their efforts.

The result of such a survey is a very full record of the surface pattern of the county between certain dates, with considerable information in the form of notes, accurately related to particular localities, but in a form which is too unwieldy to be generally useful. The object of this report, and the one-inch sheets, is thus to present the material collected in convenient form without sacrifice of the precision which the Ordnance Survey six-inch sheets makes possible. The report further amplifies the detail shown on the one-inch sheets and supplies such further information as is relevant to their interpretation. In this form it is hoped that the published survey will provide a useful basis for further close study of the County, as well as serve as a work of reference. The report is the result of co-operation between the School of Rural Economy, Oxford— members of which have been responsible for compiling material and general research—the Somerset Farm Institute, Cannington, the staff of which have supplied unique and valuable information, and have conducted local research, and the Land Utilisation Survey at the London School of Economics, where the illustrations have been prepared and general editing undertaken.

The reduction of the six-inch sheets to a convenient scale of one inch is the vital link between the collection and recording, and the publishing of the material, and this has been done by the staff of the Land Utilisation Survey. A full map, corresponding in size to a single sheet of the Ordnance Survey one-inch " Popular " edition requires from seven to nine weeks for completion, by a single person to ensure uniformity of treatment.

The small maps on the folding plate have been prepared from tracings of the various separate utilisations on the one-inch sheets, reduced photographically, and thus are accurate both in scale and detail. It is a simple matter to draw the rectangles on any of the maps to indicate the position of the six-inch sheets of the original field-survey, after which the Ordnance Survey Sheet Index Map on a scale of $\frac{1}{4}$-inch to the mile provides quick reference to the parishes, the smallest units for which statistical information is available.

5

Completing and checking the field work was made both quick and pleasant by the universal courtesy and helpfulness of the people in all parts of the county, many of whom were already familiar with the scheme through the activities of the local schools, and the successful completion of the Survey is due to their kindness and forbearance, since lack of time often prevented those engaged in the work of checking and revision from obtaining permission to enter private land.

It is impossible to particularise all those who helped the work forward by information and advice, but the author wishes particularly to thank the following residents in the county for the

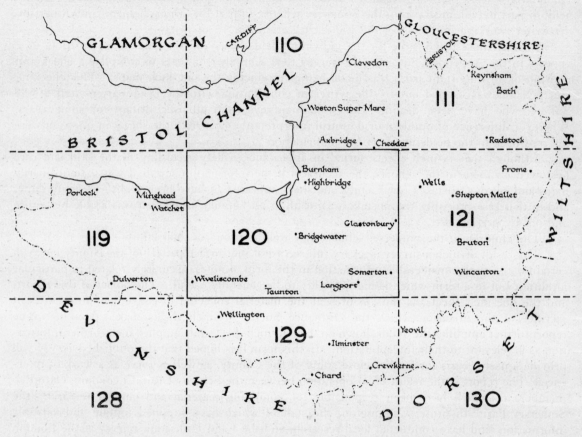

FIG. 1.—Map showing the position of the one-inch Land Utilisation Sheets and the principal towns of Somerset.   Sheet 120, Bridgwater and Quantock Hills, was published in 1936.

time and trouble they have taken, for introductions given or other help.   Reference to contributions has been made in the text.

Roger Clark, Esq., Street; S. C. Morland, Esq., Glastonbury; the late R. Neville-Grenville, Esq., Butleigh ; A. L. Hobhouse, Esq., Lamyatt ; Captain D. Cruikshank, Wells ; Sir Charles Miles, Bart., Gordano; Captain Hippisley, Wells; F. B. Goodman, Esq., Bridgwater; J. Duncan, Esq., Bridgwater ; W. H. Haile, Esq., Nottingham ; J. T. A. Sheppard, Esq., Glastonbury ; T. Barrington, Esq., Bridgwater; J. Evans, Esq., Taunton; A. W. Ling, Esq., Bristol; Captain J. Roseveare, Ministry of Agriculture and Fisheries, London.

A preliminary revision of the material was carried out by Professor J. A. Scott-Watson of the School of Rural Economy, Oxford.

II. AN OUTLINE OF THE PHYSICAL BACKGROUND

A. THE LAND SURFACE OF SOMERSET

THE County of Somerset comprises lands situated at a meeting place of most of the geological formations found in England, the older rocks surrounding, or appearing through, wide, level tracts of river and tidal deposits of alluvium and tracts of peat which occupy the central and northern lowlands.

With the exception of these alluvial or " Moor " areas, and tracts of recent marine and downwash deposits, the geological beds are little obscured by deep drift and therefore variations in relief often correspond closely with geological outcrops.

The accompanying map (Fig. 2) gives a much generalised view of the chief geological divisions of the county. Only two drift sheets[1] have been published by the Geological Survey and no others are at present being prepared. Apart from an area of about 80 square miles about Langport, of which a soil survey has been made by the Long Ashton Research Station, and the special work in connection with pasture improvement done by the Somerset Farm Institute, there are no detailed soil studies available for the county, and the map (Fig. 2) is therefore based chiefly on the Old Series (Solid) Geological Sheets first prepared in the last century.

There are seven outstanding geological outcrops which correspond broadly to regions based on distinctions of surface features.

1. The Devonian Beds of the West

These form high, down-like ridges, separated by deep valleys. The area can be further divided into a northern portion, rising to greater heights and providing poor soils and a southern which, displaying the same mountain and hill forms, and still reaching considerable heights, affords more fertile soils.

The main line of heights, chiefly on the Lower Devonian Beds, lies roughly east to west along the geological division, from Wood Barrow to Dunkery Beacon, at levels from 1,300 feet to over 1,700 feet. From Dunkery the land slopes down eastward to the Porlock–Timberscombe–River Avill line of low levels, beyond which, to the east, though the Devonian Beds are repeated in Bossington Hill (1,014) and North Hill (900) and the heights west of Dunster, the levels are in general lower.

South of the dividing line between the Lower and Upper Devonian Beds, the long, whale-backed ridges of hill masses tend to lie north-west to south-east, the levels falling gradually towards the east ; to the west of the line of the Quarme and Exe rivers only the surface of the narrow river valleys falls below the 1,000 feet level ; east of this line only Croydon Hill (1,258), the Brendon Hills and accompanying slopes, Haddon Hill (1,164), and a few isolated knolls rise above the 1,000 foot level, although the general level, except in narrow river bottoms, is above 600 feet.

To the east of the Permian and Trias-filled trench which makes so useful a gap to the coast from Taunton, rises the steep, faulted escarpment of the Quantocks, not so high as the western hills, but reproducing on a smaller scale the same features and forming an inlier of the same Devonian Beds. The division occurs between the Lower, and Upper and Middle Devonian

---

[1] Sheet 311 (Wellington) ; Sheet 295 (Taunton). Obtainable through booksellers or from Ordnance Survey.

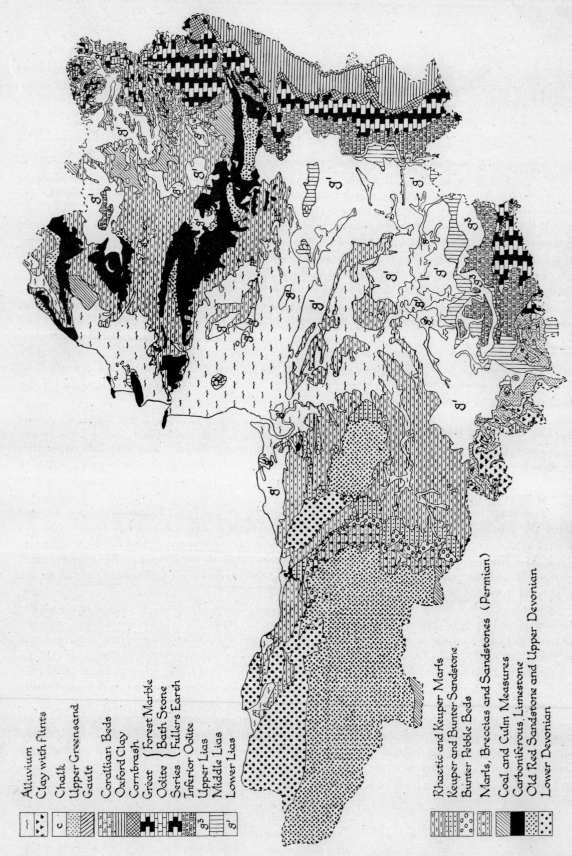

Alluvium
Clay with Flints

Chalk
Upper Greensand
Gault

Corallian Beds
Oxford Clay
Cornbrash
Great ⎰ Forest Marble
Oolite ⎱ Bath Stone
Series ⎰ Fuller's Earth
Inferior Oolite
Upper Lias
Middle Lias
Lower Lias

Rhaetic and Keuper Marls
Keuper and Bunter Sandstone
Bunter Pebble Beds

Marls, Breccias and Sandstones (Permian)

Coal and Culm Measures
Carboniferous Limestone
Old Red Sandstone and Upper Devonian
Lower Devonian

FIG. 2.—An outline Geological Map of Somerset. Scale : 8 miles to one inch.

Beds, and the former, as in the west, form the highest points. The steep westward-facing escarpment rises over 1,000 feet along a regular line of heights from Cothelstone Hill in the south to Beacon Hill in the north, steeply falling towards the east and south-east on the northern Lower Devonian Beds, and on long, gentle slopes on the Upper and Middle Devonian slates and grits to merge with the swells of the surrounding Trias, so that eastward of the narrow line of heights above the scarp only a few hilltops rise above the 1,000 foot level.

2. The Cretaceous Beds, the Clay-with-flint Plateau and the Chalk Hills

The south-western border of the county from about Crewkerne to the region of the Wellington Monument consists of Cretaceous Beds, chiefly Upper Greensand and some Chalk, but often with a superficial covering of Clay-with-Flints. The narrow east-west ridge of the Blackdown Hills rises sharply from the Trias-filled trench south of Wellington to heights between 800 feet and 1,000 feet. The heights to the west are formed by a flattened capping of Clay-with-Flints forming a plateau of rolling downs and spurs on an underlying bed of Upper Greensand, which, where exposed at the edges of the clay, drops away steeply to the broad valleys of Keuper Marls and Lower Lias.

East of Buckland St. Mary and Whitestaunton the highest points are formed on chalk or the Clay-with-Flints which covers it.

3. The Jurassic Scarp and Vale Lands

The whole south-eastern and eastern border of the county from Crewkerne and Ilminster to the boundary north of Bath is formed by the southern extension of the Cotswold Country. The highest land, nowhere above 650 feet, until Bath is reached, is found on a north to south outcrop of Oolitic Limestones, narrow, but continuous to the south until the county boundary by Yeovil touches the Lower Lias. This Limestone belt does not exceed ten miles in width anywhere in the county. To the east, following the dip of the rock, lower ground is reached—first a narrow outcrop of Cornbrash and then a wider expanse of Oxford Clay. To the west the Oolitic escarpment overlooks the low ground formed by the underlying Lias Clays.

This Jurassic belt continues on a small scale the characteristics of Cotswold country—dry, rounded hilltops and tilted platforms dropping by steep, westward-facing scarps to the surrounding clays, which then descend by more gentle slopes or form broad vales.

A convenient division can be made where the county boundary by Mudford reaches the Lower Lias and breaks the continuity of the belt.

(a) *The Western Area* has a surface chiefly of Middle Lias Marlstone, Midford Sands, Forest Marble and a tract of lowland in the south-east, provided by a bed of fuller's earth. The absence of extensive tracts of Oolitic Limestones makes the aspect of the country generally more like that of the Lias, rolling instead of scarped.

(b) *The Eastern Area*, roughly from Milborne Port to Bath, is the true scarp and vale country, and the surface can be studied in detail on the Old Series (coloured) Geological Survey maps. The full list of beds exposed includes Marlstone, Upper Lias, Midford Sands, Inferior Oolite, Great Oolite (from which Bath Stone is obtained), fuller's earth rock, fuller's earth, Forest Marble, Cornbrash, Oxford Clay, Calcareous Sands (Corallian), and a small extension of Coral Rag, Gault and Upper Greensand, all squeezed into a narrow belt. The lines of the various exposures in the valleys are often so narrow that a reduced diagram is not practicable.

4. The Carboniferous Limestone (The Mendip Plateau and Northern Coastal Heights)

This old, hard formation extrudes through the surrounding Trias and Lias to form the

Mendip plateau, three hills on the coast to the west, isolated patches in and about the southern Quantock region, and less extensive plateau regions to the north of the Mendips.

Through the surface of the Mendip plateau rise smooth, rounded slopes of still older and harder Old Red Sandstone, forming Blackdown, North Hill, Pen Hill and Maesbury Beacon, whilst at intervals on the Mendip plateau are Jurassic outliers.

From the Mendip plateau the descent to the plains to the south is abrupt, the upper slopes of Carboniferous Limestone and conglomerates broken into coombs and craggy gorges (e.g., Cheddar) and dry valleys, the lower slopes of fertile marls and clays descending more gently.

The northern edge is also steep, but less imposing as it is shut in by the northern hills beyond the comparatively narrow vales of the Yeo and Chew Rivers.

The numerous tributaries of the Frome River break up the eastern flank so that it loses its plateau character and becomes a succession of hills and valleys that descend to the rivers.

5. The Lower Lias

These beds extend westward from under the Jurassic Limestones and Marls and are widespread throughout the county, forming rolling country, the important low ridges which rise above the alluvial flats, and, capped by harder Middle or Upper Lias, the characteristic knolls and isolated hills which break the alluvial levels. In the remote past these beds must have formed a relatively soft cover over large areas of central and north Somerset, and have been worn down to base level by the agents of denudation and weather, leaving only vestiges and traces in the shape of the familiar hills and ridges, the lower tracts now being covered with alluvium and peat.

6. The Rhaetic-Trias Beds

(Rhaetic Beds, Keuper Marls, Keuper and Bunter Sandstones, Bunter Pebble Beds, Marls, Breccias and Sandstones.)

This widespread and important series provides very different types of surface, and does not allow of such generalisation as the beds already mentioned.

About the Quantocks, where there are comparatively large areas of the red Keuper Marls and Keuper Sandstones, two published drift maps (see p. 7) show the nature of the surface in detail with the Gravel and washdown deposits in valleys and hollows. North of the Polden Hills, however, there are no drift sheets available, and on the map (Fig. 2) the areas lying about the Mendips shown by the Rhaetic and Keuper Marl symbol are much generalised. Actually the area presents many different surface aspects, and includes small areas of conglomerates, breccias, etc. The Geological one-inch maps often indicate the nature of a locality in lettering without defining the exact limits.

West of the Polden Hills, the Triassic Red Keuper Marls and Keuper Sandstones form swells and slopes below the surrounding heights.

About the Mendips the Keuper Red Marls form the lower, gentler slopes of the Mendip plateau, and low steep hills and valleys.

The Breccias and conglomerates usually appear, as indicated on the diagram, in the west, as the higher and steeper slopes above the marls, lying against the flanks of the heights of the Devonian Sandstones in coombs and steep valleys.

The Rhaetic Beds appear usually as narrow outcrops, often steeply scarped between the Trias and the Lias, a typical example appearing to the south-east of Taunton Vale in the long, steep scarp that marks the division between the Red Marl and Lower Lias. This is not shown in the map (Fig. 2) but may be observed clearly by the thin line of woodland running roughly north-east from the Clay-with-Flint country, on the folding-map.

Where necessary to an understanding of the differences in surface utilisation, these differences in composition and structure of geological beds have been more fully treated in later sections.

7. The Alluvium

River silt of varying composition, peat and tidal deposits form the widespread level plains and " moor " areas which occupy the central portion of the county. They extend from the coast of the Bristol Channel far inland, following the windings of the Rivers Parrett, Brue and Axe, Yeo and Kenn, and their tributaries. These areas, and the problems connected with them are dealt with in detail in a later section.

PHYSICAL LAND-USE REGIONS

The map (Fig. 3) provides a key to the physical regions of Somerset for convenient reference throughout the report. This map was drawn after careful consideration of the available data, provided by the physical maps, the geological and drift maps, Land Utilisation maps, the parish statistics collected by the Ministry of Agriculture, and information acquired locally in Somerset.

A few regions, such as the Western Highlands, the Quantocks and the Levels, admit little dispute, although they might be further refined and subdivided; other regions are more or less arbitrary and separated from adjoining regions with respect only to a few characteristics ; they could be further divided, or arranged in other ways. Accurate, detailed study of the surface of each area indicated can be made on the one-inch Land Utilisation maps. The least satisfactory " regions " are the " Mendip " area and the " North Somerset Hill and Valley region," the former because it includes small but important tracts of special cultivation on sheltered ground of the south slopes with the high plateau land, and the latter because of the number of small tracts of different geological formation and the absence of " drift " sheets to show the true surface deposits of the valleys. Each region, however, has some distinct characteristics of composition, topography or land use, and the divisions have met with the approval of practical agriculturalists in the county.

The physical land-use regions are as follows :

1a. *The " Old Devonian " Heaths.*
The old high Devonian mountain masses of heath and rough pasture.

1b. The lower, but similar, mass of the *Quantock Hills.*

1c. *Exmoor–Exford Region.*
The " Upper Devonian " heath and pasture and arable region, of high downlike hill and mountain heaths, and deep valleys, with good pasture and scattered arable fields.

1d. *The Croydon, Brendon and Haddon Hills* pasture and arable regions.
Similar in character to 1c, but generally lower altitude, and with a higher proportion of arable.

2. *The Porlock Vale.*
Alluvium, fertile Red Marls and Keuper Sandstone soils. Hill spurs, low hills and alluvial flats.

3. *The Minehead–Watchet Coastal Lowlands.*
Alluvial levels about Minehead to the east ; low rolling country chiefly on Red Marls and Sandstone soils and some Lias Clay.

4. *The Fault Corridor.*
Rising from the coast, and from the Taunton Vale to a water parting at about 400 feet to

500 feet in the region of Crowcombe. Shut in on the west by the Devonian and Permian Slopes, on the east by the steep scarp of the Quantocks. A region of spurs and downlike slopes.

5. *The Vales of Wellington and Taunton Deane.*

A highly fertile area of rolling lowland forming an irregular basin opening to the alluvial levels in the east, composed on the surface chiefly of Red Marls, Downwash, Gravels, the alluvium-filled valleys of the River Tone and its tributaries ; the western rim rising first to fertile Keuper Sandstone slopes and then to the valleys and hills of the Pebble Beds, conglomerates

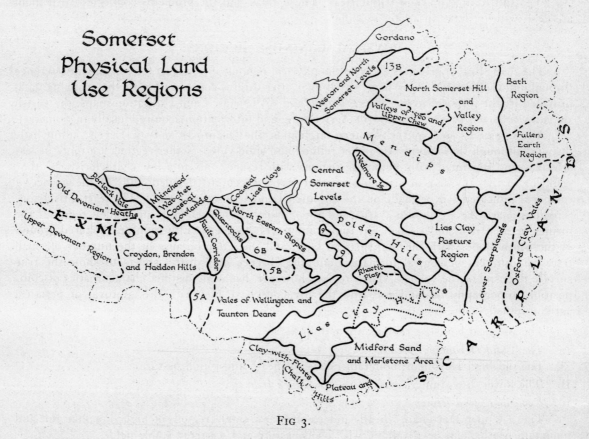

Fig 3.

and Permian Lower Red Marls, Breccias and Sandstones, (5a) ; to the north, rising on to the fertile Devonian slopes, (5b) that grade, at first steeply, and then gently, down from the southern extension of the Quantocks ; to the south, ending abruptly against the steep scarp of the Blackdown Hills, except where the county border crosses the narrow extension of the vale south into Devon ; and to the south-east, terminating against the Lias Clay hills and the Low Rhaetic scarp.

6. *The North-eastern Slopes.*

A continuation on gradual sloping folds of fertile Upper Devonian (6b) and Red Marls and Sandstones of the eastward tilt from the Quantock scarp.

6a. *The Coastal Lias Clays.*

A lowland area of undulating land.

7. *The Clay-with-Flint Plateau (to the West) and the Chalk Hills.*

Rounded or flat-topped hills dropping by steep scarps and slopes to the north and to the valleys.

8. *The Lias Clay Arable and Pasture Hills.*

This region consists of typical low rolling or flattened swells and hills penetrated in the centre by extensive tracts of alluvial and washdown flats following the upper courses of the Rivers Isle, Parrett, Cary and tributaries (marked in broken line). To the north-west the area terminates above low but steep Rhaetic scarps of Limestone and Shales, or falls to Alluvium and Red Marl slopes.

8a. *The Rhaetic Plateau.*

A small platform of White Limestone, Gravels, Sands, Shales and Clays.

9. *The Marine Deposit Islands.*

Chedzoy, Weston Zoyland, Middlezoy. Low flattened banks of quite fertile deposits of shelly and gravelly silt, of comparatively recent origin compared with the main geological formation.

10. *The Polden Hills.*

Consisting of northern slopes and folds of Lias Clay, and southern miniature vales and hills and scarps of Red Trias and Rhaetic exposures.

11. *The Lias Clay Pasture Region.*

Consisting of the vales and rolling clay lands of Upper Brue and tributaries, the Shepton Mallet clay hills and the Glastonbury–Ditcheat ridges, the latter forming steep slopes capped with Middle Lias Marlstone and Upper Lias Clay.

12. *The Midford Sand and Marlstone Low Relief Arable Area.*

Consists of the wide gently sloping vales of the Upper Parrett tributaries, the general low levels broken only by occasional miniature scarps and small abrupt limestone-capped hills, the western remnants of the Oolitic scarplands.

12a. *The Lower Scarplands.*

Steep westward-facing scarps, ridges, and gently tilted plateaus.

12b. *The Oxford Clay Vales.*

Broad, gently sloping, rolling vales.

12c. *The Fuller's Earth Region.*

High, flattened downs, and steep narrow valleys.

12d. *The Bath Region.*

Consisting of the Vale of Bath (Clays, Alluvium and Washdown) and surrounding Great Oolite (Bathstone) high downs, and deep narrow valleys exposing narrow fertile strips of Marlstone and Midford Sands.

13. *The North Somerset Hill and Valley Region.*

As will be seen from the geological diagram, this region is composed of various geological beds, forming the Limestone region of plateaus and coombs; the Limestone-capped, clay mass of Dundry Hill; the steep low hill and narrow valley region of the red Marl, Coal Measures and Lias Clay.

13a. *Marks the Valleys of the Yeo and the Upper Chew.*

Narrow and shut in by steep hills.

13b. *Yatton, Flax Bourton Red Marl Slopes and the Ashton Vale.*

14. *The Mendip Area.*

Consists of the high Limestone plateaus, the emerging rounded Old Red Sandstone masses, the surrounding scarps, coombs, gorges and water eroded valleys and the lower Marl and Wash-down slopes. The area has been extended to the west to include the similar heights of Bleadon Hill.

15. *The Wedmore Isle.*

The Trias area consists of steep Rhaetic (Wedmore stone) Hills, with a narrow eastern slope of Red Marl. To the west lies the Lias Clay miniature vale of Chapel Allerton, and clay hill slopes.

16. *The Gordano Area.*

A depression filled with Alluvium, Sandstones and Marls, Conglomerates and Grits, open to the mouth of the Severn and enclosed to the west and south by Limestone heights.

17. *Weston-super-Mare and the North Somerset Levels.*

18. *The Central Somerset Levels.*

B. DRAINAGE

The Alluvial Levels

The lowlands of Central and North Somerset, indicated on Fig. 3, which shows the Internal Drainage Districts, comprise approximately 158,710 acres, forming " moors " and " levels " lying about and following far inland the windings of the Rivers Parrett, Tone, Isle, Cary, Axe, Yeo and Kenn, with a northern tract stretching south-west from the mouth of the Bristol Avon.

The greater levels are open towards the Bristol Channel, gradually rising to higher elevation as they approach the sea-coast, attaining an average height of from 6 feet to 8 feet above the central districts.

The special problem presented by these low-lying tracts results from three geographical factors ; the flatness and low level of the land, relative to mean sea level, with its tendency to rise in elevation towards the coast and consequent slight fall of the main rivers ; the fluctuations of a relatively high rainfall on extensive surrounding watersheds comprising high ground, well drained and with a rapid run-off ; and the great variation in rise and fall of the tides in the con-stricted Bristol Channel, liable to be increased by westerly gales.

The low level of the land may be appreciated from the following extracts taken from the Engineer's report[1] for proposed improvements to the main waterways.

> " The bed of the Parrett at Langport Bridge is 15·55 feet O.D. and under existing circumstances floods every year attain a height of 28·13 to 28·38 O.D. at which height the water invariably overflows the banks both above and below Langport, . . . the water in the river at 26·63 O.D. is much too high for the moors above and below Langport, with a gravitation discharge only, to drain into the river. . . . An evenly graded line from the bed of the river at Langport to the bed of the river at Bridgwater, gives a fall of 12 inches per mile."

The approximate distance from Bridgwater to Langport, as the crow flies, is ten and a half miles (the distance by river being more on account of curves), and at Bridgwater, some five miles from the sea at the mouth of the estuary, high tide level at the Town Bridge gauge is 25·96 O.D. On the River Tone, if the bed of the river were evenly graded from its confluence with the

---

[1] Report of C. H. G. Clayton, Chief Inspector, Board of Agriculture and Fisheries for the Somerset War Agric. Com., afterwards sent to the Somerset Drainage Commission for their meeting of March 13th, 1918.

Parrett at about 10·00 O.D. to a point immediately below Ham Mill, a fall would be allowed of 12 inches per mile.

The King's Sedgemoor Drain and Cary River from the Dunball Clyse, at 5·04 O.D. would permit of a drain to a point near the 18-foot rhine between 7 miles and 8 miles above Dunball Clyse having a depth of 6 feet of water and a fall of $6\frac{1}{2}$ inches per mile.

On the Brue, with the sill of Highbridge Clyse, approximately 2·50 feet *below* O.D., the bank of the river immediately above White's River at 14·30 O.D. and the bank of White's River 14·07 O.D. as controlling points, if the bed of the river at White's River were to be lowered to 4·00 O.D. a waterway would be permitted 10 feet deep with a fall to Highbridge Clyse of 8·4 inches per mile. The bed of the river at Pons Perilis Bridge is 16·62 O.D. and an evenly graded line from Clyse Hole to White's River gives a fall of 22·62 inches per mile.

These are ideal grades, not at present functioning.

The normal range of the tides at Portishead is 42 feet, at Weston-super-Mare 37 feet, and much of the low land has therefore been brought into use only by the provision of artificial barriers along parts of the coast and bordering the outlets and lower courses of the principal rivers, thus improving on a process begun by natural forces through tidal alluvium and blown sand.

The protected area on the coast begins at Brean Down and extends to Burnham, where adequate defence is provided by sand-hills, and thence to Stoeford. From Burnham up to and above Huntspill there is a stone-built sea wall needing constant watching. Higher up the rivers sea walls give place to earthern embankments, sometimes close to the river, and sometimes at a considerable distance from it, since the fall in these lower reaches is so slight that provision must be made for flood-water to expand.

On the Parrett, the influence of the tide is felt as far up as Langport ; on the Brue, the main source of control and regulation is at Highbridge, where there is a Stoney sluice ; there was no barrier to the tide on the Axe until 1807, when tidal gates were put in at Bleadon.

On the inland areas, periodic flooding from the rivers and other water channels has similarly raised the banks and bordering regions by deposition of alluvial materials ; so that in general the " moors " form shallow basins, in some cases on or about the level of the beds of the adjacent main waterways, surrounded by rims which would tend to the level of the highest floods, except that those rims have been artificially raised by the products of dredging and cleaning the drainage rhines and streams.

Nature of Rivers, Valleys and Watersheds

The *River Parrett* takes its rise in high ground about Crewkerne and Pendomer and flows in a north-westerly direction towards the Bristol Channel, being joined in its course, together with minor tributaries, by the River Isle at a point near Thorney, and further on by the River Yeo about half a mile above Langport Bridge.

This portion of the river from its source to Langport is known as the Upper Parrett.

Proceeding towards Bridgwater, the river is joined above 5 miles below Langport by the River Tone, then passes Bridgwater and continues north-west till it goes into the Bristol Channel at a point beyond Highbridge. At Dunball Clyse about 3 miles below Bridgwater, the King's Sedgemoor main drain, discharging the Cary Valley basin, enters the Parrett.

The drainage basin of the Parrett and three tributaries above named is about 362,860 acres, of which that of the Upper Parrett, with the Isle and Yeo, is about 186,880 acres, that of the Lower Parrett with the Tone, 175,980 acres.

The whole valley is geologically " Alluvial "—River and Marine Deposits overlying Peat, and with surfaces of Peat. Deposition of river silt has generally taken place on the borders of the sea and banks of the tidal rivers, and the deposits are commonly on a level with the highest tides and floods and cover the Peat. Inland the Peat is the prevailing soil at lower levels and forms large plains, in many parts covered by flood waters some months in the year.

Immediately adjoining the slopes of high and rising ground round about and intersecting these plains there is a deposit caused by the washing down of the soil on to lower ground.

The deposit along the course of the Parrett within the area subject to tides is a fine sand combined with a small portion of clay, and of this the Bath bricks, building bricks, drain pipes, tiles, etc., are made.

The *River Isle* rises on the north of the Blackdown Hills in the high lands between Devon and Somerset, passing Ilminster on one branch and Beer Crocombe and Isle Abbots on the other. The whole course of the river passes through Lias and Marlstone and the land is in general excellent quality, being (except in the valleys, which are in grass) mostly arable.

The *River Yeo* has its source in high ground by Yeovil on the borders of Somerset and Dorset and flows through Ilchester. There are large areas of fine pasture on both sides of the river. It joins the Parrett about a mile above Langport Bridge. The river takes its rise in Lias and Marlstone, but for the greater part of its course flows over Alluvium. The extent of low, flat lands on either side is much greater, and flooded further up towards the source, than with either the Upper Parrett or Isle.

The *River Cary* is strictly a tributary of the Parrett, but joins the latter so near the sea in a broad tide-way, that the drainage basin is really distinct and has no real connection with that of the Parrett.

The river takes its rise in high ground about Castle Cary, chiefly supplied from high ground to the north of its course and passing north of Somerton, flows into the plain of King's Sedgemoor by Henley Corner. It was diverted at the time of the King's Sedgemoor Award (31 George III, 1791) into the large King's Sedgemoor Drain then made, which intersects the moor, passing the north side of Weston Zoyland and Chedzoy, and continuing by a deep cutting to Dunball Clyse on the Parrett.

The *River Brue* is formed principally by the confluence near Bruton, of several streams rising in the high lands in the neighbourhood of Wincanton, Bruton and Batcombe, and flows between Baltonsborough and Butleigh and between Glastonbury and Street, at which place it turns due north to near Glastonbury, whence it continues due west past Cold Harbour, leaving Meare and Westhay on the south, then passing through Burtle Heath and Mark Moor to Crip's Corner. Thence it was adapted for navigation to the tide-way below Highbridge. From Crip's Corner eastward up the valley to Cat Bridge and south-east to Cossington Hatches is a watercourse now known as the South Drain.

Into this length the drainage of the valley as far as the foot of the Polden Hills is discharged.

The remains of the old canal up to Glastonbury form a drain for a great part of that valley towards the Brue.

Near Cold Harbour a stream joins the Brue from the north near the Hartlake Stream, descending from the north-east from high ground near Pilton.

At Meare, the Brue receives drainage from Wells and Dinder, and from the south slopes of the Mendips.

The valley of the Brue is bounded on the north by the eastern extremity of the Mendip Hills and by the high land between Wells and Wedmore ; on the south principally by the Polden Hills, which form the watershed between it and the Cary.

From the mouth of the river to Crip's Corner the soil consists of high alluvium overlying the peat. The remainder of the main valley and also the minor valleys converging into it exhibit the same soil as the other valleys described—a general surface of peat, with alluvium near the rising ground; but on the south side of the valley the peat land on Ashcott Moor attains a greater elevation than elsewhere, and so is not covered by floods.

For about five miles from Highbridge on the line of the River Brue the land on both sides is high, and is not subject to floods, but from this point for about seven miles further up the land is about 4 feet to 5 feet below the top flood level, and a large area is subject to flooding at the slightest increase of rainfall.

The *River Axe* rises in the Mountain Limestones of the southern slopes of the Mendips between Wells and Westbury, and flows in a westerly direction, passing Wookey, Axbridge and Bleadon, discharging into the Bristol Channel on the north of Brean Down 7 miles from the mouth of the Brue and 2 miles from Weston-super-Mare.

The whole valley is bounded on the north by the Mendip Hills, contracting to a point at the eastern end. The southern boundary is formed by high ground extending from Wells past Henton and Wedmore to Badgworth, thence by the public road to Brent, from which place to the sea, the watershed between the Axe and Brue is indefinite.

Numerous streams discharge into it from the valleys of the Mendips, the largest being Cheddar Water.

The geological formation is Peat, underlying Alluvial soil of greater or less thickness.

The river is confined within raised banks on either side for some distance from its outlet upwards. The bank on the south side starts at the point of the Ridge of Brean Down ; the northern one abuts on the high ground on which Uphill stands. These confine the tidal waters as far as the railway bridge where there are tidal gates protecting the low land.

For some distance further up the river is embanked and afterwards further confined between the rising ground of Weare and the Mendips for several miles. Further up, to the south of Rodney Stoke and Westbury, is a low, wet district where floods are the most extensive, frequent and persistent in this valley.

North Somerset Rivers Area

The (Congresbury) Yeo is a small stream springing from the Mendips near Compton Martin and traversing the marshy district of Congresbury level, whence it falls through a tidal sluice to the Bristol Channel near Wick St. Lawrence. Near the mouth it receives through an artificial channel the waters of the River Kenn, a small stream which flows through the adjacent moor. From the outfall sluice as far as Congresbury the land is defended by raised banks.

A rivulet, rising at Backwell Hill, traverses Nailsea Moor and part of North Marsh, and flows into the sea north of Woodspring Bay.

The three drainage districts of this area (Fig. 3)—West Mendip, North Somerset, Gordano Valley—were included under the Somerset Rivers Catchment Board set up by the Ministry of Agriculture and Fisheries under the powers of the Land Drainage Act 1930. The area has the same general characteristic as that to the south of the Mendips. The seaward portion is more elevated than the south-westerly portions lying under the hills. There is, however, enough fall for satisfactory gravitational drainage in conjunction with the fall of the tides, when improvements to the existing channels have been effected, such as widening of rhines, removal of obstructing bridges and provision of appropriate sluices.

At present the inlying moors, Nailsea Moor, Kenn and Congresbury Moors suffer from restricted drainage and are consequently of use as pasture for only three or four months of the year. (On May 20th, 1936, Kenn Moor was still waterlogged after winter flooding.)

B

Floods

Under such general conditions it is obvious that flooding of certain lands cannot be entirely prevented except at great expense though it may in normal seasons be controlled, and the land drained when the flow of water in the main channels permits.

" In wet periods the water pours off the hills and comes down by the various rivers on to the low-lying land, with the result that, as the rivers are not large enough, or with sufficient fall, to carry off the water, the land must flood, because large areas are below the level of high spring tides.

" There are two forces working—the tide coming in from Bridgwater Bay and the flood waters pouring down from the hills. In the course of centuries those two forces have battled, and where they met at a point where they tended to balance, the deposit took place of material in suspension. Through the deposit taking place on the seaboard there is higher land than inside, and the natural gradient of the land is not towards the sea. There are deep depressions in the land and once they become flooded it is difficult for the water to get away because the drainage still goes on from the hills and keeps up the level of the water in the main river. Man has attempted to use the levels two or three thousand years too early. During the summer, thousands of tons of silt are left in the lower reaches of the Parrett by the spring tides ; this accumulation is normally washed out by the flood waters at the beginning of winter, but the result is that periodically the river channel becomes constricted, and makes some measure of flooding inevitable."[1]

This summary of the position as regards the Parrett, is true generally for the Somerset rivers of the Drainage Areas. According to Mr. Haile and the late Mr. Neville-Grenville,[2] the problem of drainage is one of control rather than prevention, to free the land of water when possible, in days or weeks, instead of months ; to deal with exceptional floods, always possible through a combination of excessive rainfall, on-shore winds and high tides ; to deal with normal seasonal flooding and spring and summer " freshes " ; and, of equal importance, to maintain during dry seasons the level of water in rhines and ditches to " keep fence " and to water stock, without which provision the moor pastures would be useless at the time when they should be invaluable in the economy of the county.

Drainage

The Authority for the drainage system in southern Somerset up to 1931 was the Somerset Drainage Commissioners, set up by the Somerset Drainage Act of 1877,[3] and having 16 Internal Boards. The Somerset Commissioners of Sewers had jurisdiction in the northern part of the county. Under the Land Drainage Act 1930,[4] all these areas were brought under the Somerset Rivers Catchment Board which took over the powers previously held by the Commissioners.

The Catchment Board, besides possessing general powers of oversight, and providing skilled advice and assistance as required or requested by the Internal Drainage Boards, are directly responsible for the inspection and maintenance of sea walls and defences and the " Main Rivers."

The duty further devolves on them of studying the drainage as a whole, and formulating such plans as are necessary for general improvement, which may, or may not, then be adopted subject to confirmation by the Ministry of Agriculture and Fisheries.

[1] From a lecture on the 1929–30 floods on the Parrett, by Mr. Haile, engineer to the Somerset Drainage Commissioners. Printed in *Bridgwater Mercury*, March 5th, 1930.
[2] Late Chairman of the Catchment Board.
[3] 1877 was a local Act only.
[4] The General Land Drainage Act of 1930.

The Internal Drainage Districts are, in practice, separate and distinct administrative areas, each dealing with its own problem according to the real or supposed advantage of a large number of smallholders owning rights, usually freehold, on the moors and levels. Technique of dealing with flood-water, rhines, waterways, etc., varies in different localities.

The work of managing pumps, sluices, the cleaning of rhines and ditches, and in some cases the ordering of removal and entry of stock, devolves on an official appointed by the Internal Drainage Board, known as the expenditor, who receives a small fee for his services, and may be a local farmer, business man, solicitor or surveyor. On his experience and energy really depends the state of the district.

There is no general co-ordination, except as amongst neighbours, between one district and the others, or between the Catchment Board officials and Expenditors of Internal Drainage Districts. Records, other than those dealing with expenditure, are kept, if at all, according to the interest of the Expenditor. Much information possibly was lost some years ago, when on the death of Mr. Combe all the papers relating to his work for Commissioners of Sewers were inadvertently destroyed. But drainage matters in Somerset have until quite recently been the concern of local land occupiers, essentially practical men with intimate local knowledge of restricted areas under their care, jealous of outside interference, and concerned to keep down expenses. Grantham, Grenville and successive engineers have deplored and struggled against the tendency to work in " water-tight compartments " on a problem which should be treated as a whole ; and even now, as has been stated, the Catchment Authorities, who alone possess rights of general supervision and interference, with the trained staff at their disposal to make it effective, act as far as possible on a policy of non-interference, natural enough when any intervention must cost money which is already hard to find for the work they have normally to do.

Rhines and ditches in the areas must be cleaned annually, and this is done either by letting contracts to local small-holders and labourers, by directly engaging labour, or by the occupiers of holdings working under the supervision of a foreman dyke-reeve—a system which was formerly widespread with authority for fines provided by Act of Parliament where work was not satisfactorily carried out. In certain districts the 1930 Act, by making no provision for such fines, has temporarily upset the whole internal management, since the change from a traditional practice involves higher expenditure and consequent rating, while among a number of smallholders there are always a few who nullify the effect of the work of the majority by delaying or omitting to clear the weeds from their sections of drainage channels.

Rating

The Catchment Boards are empowered to levy a precept on the County Council up to 2d. in the £ of annual value on all land within their jurisdiction, exclusive of interest on loans, and to issue precepts on the various Internal Drainage Districts for such amounts as they consider fair and reasonable.

The Internal Drainage Boards levy rates on all occupiers of land within Internal Drainage Districts to cover estimated expenses for the year as well as Catchment Board precepts which are raised by rates on owners. The rates fluctuate according to the nature of the seasons,[1] and the efficiency of machinery and administration. Those areas which require clearance of flood-water by pumping are under a disadvantage, rates being liable to sudden increases. On one moor pumping charges alone vary from 2s. to 10s. per £ of annual value, and the operation of drainage machinery must often be balanced against the expense to the many occupiers of small parcels of land.

[1] Rating for 1935 ; see below.

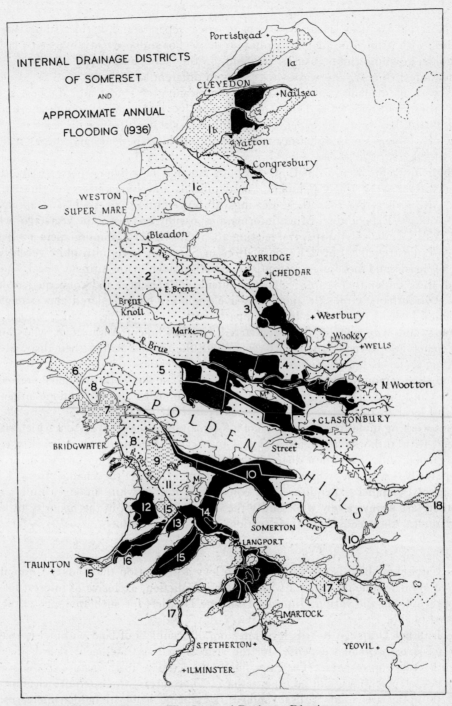

FIG. 4.—The Internal Drainage Districts.
Approximate areas flooded annually in black.   Scale : 6 miles to one inch.

1a. Gordano Valley	1b. North Somerset	1c. West Mendip
2. Lower Axe	3. Upper Axe	4. Upper Brue
5. Lower Brue	6. Stockland	7. Cannington
8. Bridgwater	9. Chedzoy	10. King's Sedgemoor
11. Othery Middlezoy	12. North Moor	13. Stanmoor
14. Aller Moor	15. West Sedgmoor	16. Curry Moor
17. Langport		

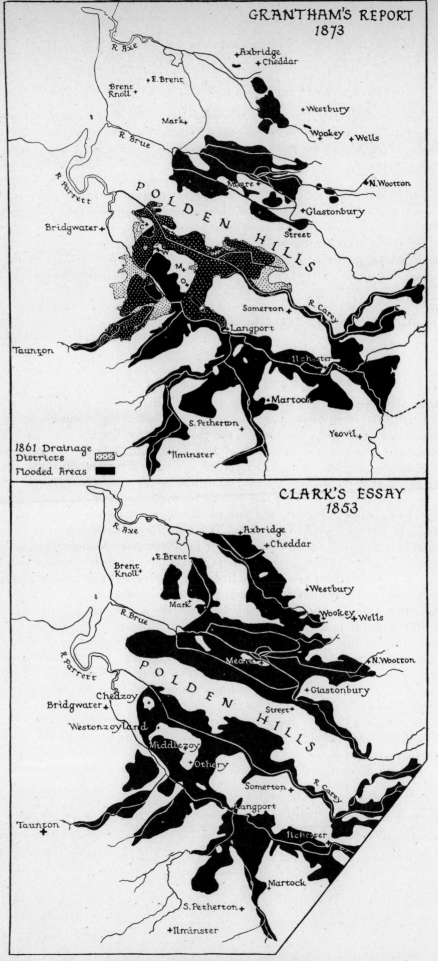

FIG. 5.—Scale : 6 miles to one inch.

This liability to fluctuating charges acts as a deterrent to improvement, since those areas where the liability is already heavy would most benefit by improvements suggested by the engineers, such as regraded water-ways, raised stop-banks, extra sluices and pumps, the initial cost of which is at present high.

A recent semi-official publication, *The Somerset Survey*, produced for the County Planning Association by W. Harding Thomson, F.R.I.B.A., gives a list of 16 Drainage Districts followed by the statement that " the above-mentioned districts embrace all land for rating purposes up to a height of eight feet above the highest known flood," which is, however, a serious mis-statement of fact. This became clear during the process of collecting information for this Report, when it was found that responsible drainage authorities[1] in Somerset knew nothing about an " 8-foot contour " level, and were certainly not contemplating any such extension of the present Districts.

Actually, there has always been some confusion of thought with reference to the contour levels fixed for Internal Drainage Districts.

Before the 1930 Act it was understood that the areas in Somerset had been defined by a contour level of 2 foot above the highest ascertained floods, although there was no available documentary evidence to prove this, and the practical experience of the engineers disproved it in many instances.

The 1930 Act states (Part I, para. 5) that " The Districts . . . to be constituted as drainage districts under this Act shall be such areas as will derive benefit or avoid danger as a result of such drainage operations," and subsequent to the passing of that Act the Ministry of Agriculture issued certain rules regarding the formation of Internal Drainage Districts which set out, *inter alia*, that the damage avoided, or benefit received was generally to be illustrated by a level of 8 feet above the level of the highest ascertained floods.

This " 8-foot level " is a working rule framed by the Ministry of Agriculture, in particular for drainage areas outside Somerset, and one to which the Ministry would agree where local Internal Drainage Boards wished to adopt it. The 8-foot level is not at present in operation in Somerset, and its adoption is entirely a matter for local Somerset Authorities to decide.[2]

The limits of the present Drainage Districts are set out on official maps, which the various Acts instance as being the final proof of the limits and extent of the Drainage Districts, and in many cases it is not precisely known at present what relation exists between these limits and the local floods, although no doubt it soon will be since the Catchment Board Engineers are at present (1936) engaged in making a survey of the levels.

The only available survey of a general flood was made by Grantham's order in 1873 (see Fig. 5). The highest recorded flood level is that at Bridgwater, when a combination of wind, tide and flood-water has overtopped for a short period the flood-bank there.

Records even of the serious flooding in 1929 are available only in the accounts written in the *Bridgwater Mercury* at that time.

Moreover, since the levels of the moors vary widely, and some are not flooded at all, while others form self-contained drainage areas flooded through sluices and cleared by pumping ; and as the tidal fluctuations make remarkable and strictly local flood-levels, to bring an " eight foot level " into general operation, will in any case be a matter of considerable difficulty.

[1] The late Mr. Neville-Grenville, Chairman of the Catchment Board, with whom I had the great good fortune of discussing the matter, knew nothing about it, and considered the statement to be nonsense. (T. S.-M.)
[2] Further information on the point can be found in the *Journal of the Ministry of Agriculture*, September 1936.

FLOODS

Exceptional Floods

A very much larger area than that suffering seasonal flooding lies under the threat of exceptional circumstances of wind, tide and rainfall, or the breaking of banks and sea defences.

This includes the relatively high land between the estuaries of the Parrett and Brue, and north to a point beyond Burnham, protected from high tides.

Mr. Neville-Grenville,[1] and Grantham,[2] recount that there are records of disastrous floods at the end of the fifteenth century, and that in January 1606, in 1687, 1703 and 1811 owing to high tides and rain, and the breaking of sea walls at the tidal entrance of the Brue, the floods reached from the coast to the Church of St. Benignus in Glastonbury 14 miles inland. Sir William Dugdale, in his *History of Imbanking and Drayning*, published in 1662, gives the following description : " The rich and spacious marshes below Wells and Glastonbury (since by much industry drained and reduced to profit) sufficiently manifest . . . the overflowings both of the sea and fresh rivers. For, considering the flatness of those parts at least twelve miles eastward from the sea, which gave way for the tides to flow up very high, as also that the silt and sand thereby continually brought up did not a little obstruct the outfalls of those fresh waters which descend from Bruton, Shepton Mallet and several other places of this shire, all that great level about Glastonbury, and below it [then ' Brentmarsh '] was in time past no other than a very fen ; and that place being naturally higher than the rest, accounted an island by reason of its situation in the bosom of such vast waters."

The map given on p. 21 (Fig. 5) copied from the plate in the Prize Essay on the Somersetshire Levels, reprinted by permission from the *Bath and West of England Agricultural Journal* of 1854, gives a fair, if rough, idea of the land subject to flood at that date, and before the first Internal Drainage Districts were formed under authority of the Land Drainage Act of 1861. In particular, the line of weakness leading from the Brue mouth and Parrett estuary is clearly indicated.[3]

In 1873, R. B. Grantham compiled a report on the floods in Somerset in 1872-3, for which the actual limits of flooding in the valleys of the Parrett and tributaries, the Cary, Brue and Axe were properly surveyed, and the resulting map (Fig. 5) may be considered as showing the extreme limits of probable flooding at the present time, since after that date the Act of 1877 provided for the formation of further Internal Drainage Districts and created the administrative position very much as it is to-day, since the 1930 Act has hitherto made very little, if any, difference, though allowing for modifications which will doubtless be effected in time.

The floods were exceptionally severe, the average rainfall for the basin in 1872 having been exceeded only once, in 1821, since 1818. From October to December 1872, rain fell on 67 days, and for the last quarter of 1872, and first quarter of 1873 combined, the average rainfall for the combined basins of the Yeo, Parrett, Isle, Tone, Brue and Axe, was 24·74 inches compared with an average for the same period during three previous winter seasons of 16·31 inches. Given below (p. 31) is a summary of the basins affected with the areas flooded. The floods on the Parrett, Isle and Yeo commenced in October 1872 and continued to nearly the end of March 1873.

On December 11th, 1929, after heavy continuous rainfall, and during a strong westerly gale, the River Tone burst its right bank by Athelney and flooded the land for miles around.

[1] R. Neville-Grenville, " Somerset Drainage," *Som. Arch. and Nat. Hist. Soc. Proceedings*, 1926.
[2] R. Bloxham Grantham, " Report on the Floods in Somerset in 1872-73. Presented to the House of Commons, July 16th, 1873 (*Min. Agri. and Fish. Library*), pp. 71-72.
[3] Whether the plan was surveyed or filled in from observation and inquiry is not stated. J. Aubrey Clark, the writer of the essay, was a land surveyor, however.

The break occurred at a point where a gap had been repaired years before with piles which had rotted, and the gale blew the flood-waters on to soft garden soil on the landward side of the bank, wearing it away.

Athelney and the country about King's Sedgemoor, West Sedgemoor, Aller Moor and the moors above Langport were immediately affected. At Athelney, the waters flowed over a shed ten feet high.

The G.W.R. Main Line to Taunton and the West was put out of action. The branch line from Durston to Athelney was flooded, and Lyng station under water. By December 18th the floods had increased enormously, the roads from Athelney to Stoke St. Gregory and Burrow-bridge were impassable, and the whole of Stanmoor was flooded to a depth of several feet. The expanse of water covered some 10,000 acres.

Every house was flooded in Curload, Athelney, Stanmoor and Stathe, and the Baltmoor Bank which runs across the valley in the Burrowbridge area, protecting ten miles of country running to Bridgwater, had nearly twenty feet of water against it.

On January 29th when many refugees had returned to their silted homes the temporary bank which had been erected with great difficulty burst at Athelney, and the flood waters again poured out on the surroundings lands.

The conditions were exceptional, since in October 4·65″, in November 7·24″ and in December 6·13″ of rain fell, and was almost continuous through November and December over most of the catchment area.

The approximate limits of normal seasonal flooding at the present time (1936) are set out on the accompanying map (Fig. 4) which was drawn for the present report by Mr. Duncan, Assistant Engineer to the Catchment Board, with no special survey, but from his knowledge of local conditions.

These areas are expected to be more or less under water during part of each winter, according to conditions of rainfall and evaporation, in parts to the practice of admitting flood-waters charged with silt or for the protection of flood-banks against dangerous pressure. Parts where it is possible to keep the land free by pumping, are nevertheless allowed to flood in preference to incurring the expense of working pumps during a period of the year when such herbage as remains after summer cutting and grazing is of little value, and the surface soft and liable to be spoiled by treading.

The management of the drainage districts varies greatly according to the requirements, physical and economic, of each locality. Even with skilful management it is not always possible to control flood-waters to the best advantage at the present time owing in part to incomplete drainage arrangements—flood-banks too low, inadequate or inefficient sluices, badly graded channels and old pumps—and in other areas, owing to the divergent views of large numbers of small freeholders, previously mentioned, as to the benefit of flooding or the needs of stock.

In general, stock is off the moors liable to flood by the end of October, and may not return until late in April, for some time must elapse after the waters are clear for the ground to dry out and herbage to become well established.

Access to the moor allotments, which are " fenced " by ditches and rhines in which water is maintained by closed sluices where possible in the dry part of the year, and which are often at some distance from the farmstead which is on rising ground, is by roads and trackways known as " droves," many of which are little better than strips of the surrounding pastures, and liable to the same conditions of flooding and consequent softness of surface, making parts of the moor areas, particularly on the peat lands, inaccessible for some time after flood-waters have disappeared.

The following is the printed notice published annually by the Curry Moor Drainage District, and posted up in the last few days of October :—

THE LAND DRAINAGE ACT, 1861 AND 1930

CURRY MOOR DRAINAGE DISTRICT : IRRIGATION OF MOOR

Notice is hereby given

That the lands under the jurisdiction of the C.M.D.D.B. will be flooded as soon after the date of this notice as the state of the River Tone will permit, and all Owners, Occupiers and other persons interested are hereby warned to remove their cattle and all moveable produce and effects from the moor liable to receive damage from flooding.

Dated the first day of November 19 .

Thereafter, when conditions permit, the sluices are opened and the land flooded to a depth of several feet (during the winter of 1872–3, 7 feet deep) in which condition it may remain all winter. The moor is cleared of water by pumping some time in March, usually in the first week (in 1933 it was not clear until March 28th) and a further period of some weeks must elapse before the ground is firm enough for stock.

The expenditors of other moors leave clearance and stocking to the discretion of individual farmers. On Curry Moor, however, there are some special conditions, since the floods in the Tone come down rapidly, and there is danger of the flood-banks protecting Curry Moor being broken by the force of water on one side only. Moreover, sudden increase of level is liable to be brought about through the manipulation of weirs at the Paper Mills below Taunton, which apparently takes place without warning being given.

During the growing season, freshes are watched for by the expenditors, with the aid of a rain gauge interpreted according to their experience of local conditions, and, where possible, the moors are kept free by pumping. Rainfall alone is no clear indication of liability to flooding, since the degree of rain necessary to cause flooding varies with the season, and consequent evaporation and possibility of absorption by the ground.

Increased Liability to Sudden Floods

Reports and commissions since the eighteenth century stress the increasing rapidity and volume of run-off due to improved drainage in surrounding higher lands. In their undrained, or partly undrained state, the moors acted as reservoirs for flood-water and traps for silt, which now are more swiftly conducted towards the main drainage channels. Better drainage has produced new problems, especially in dealing with sudden floods.

One authority on the Tone[1] states that floods which in 1914 took three days to appear on the lower reaches, now appear in six hours. These facts seem to justify the contention that rating for the work of drainage should be spread more widely than at present.

The problem is further aggravated by the tendency of the peat lands, notably the Sedgmoors, to sink when dried out, and thus increase the liability to sudden flooding.

Effect of Flooding

The Parrett and Brue, and their tributaries, bring down during floods great quantities of rich silt which acts as a valuable fertiliser to grassland.

Of the moors on the Upper Parrett, John Aubrey Clark wrote in 1854 : " The desideratum required by the landholders of these moors is a certain command of the water in order to avail themselves of the benefit of the floods in the winter months without injury from their too long continuance in the spring and summer to the lands.

[1] Mr. Ames.

" The meadows which have been gradually formed by the deposit of the floods above Long Sutton are proverbial for the quality and proof of the herbage, the nutritive quality of the hay which it produces being considered equal to that of corn."

Of the Brue level he says, " The principal soil of the Brue level consists of a large district of bog or peat upon which, in the immediate neighbourhood of the principal rivers, and at the higher levels bordering the sea, a deposit has been formed of sandy loam varying in depth from half a foot to 8 feet by the tides and land floods . . . the thinner soils bordering the rivers are suitable for dairy purposes . . . but it is to be noticed that this fertility is maintained by constant deposits from the floods, and when from over-drainage this deposit ceases, the lands are deteriorated in value. . . .   That this advantage was understood at a very remote period is shown by the existence of a custom of right to cut gaps in the banks of the river for the purpose of flooding the lowlands three weeks and three days before Christmas, and gaps to be closed on receipt of proper notice. . . ."

Instances are also given of the successful use made by private individuals, constructing sluices at their own expense, of the silt of the Brue, at Glastonbury, Burtle and Burtlet. Stagnant and thin waters lying during the summer months, however, are a positive evil, encouraging the growth of waterweeds and rushes.

It is otherwise, however, with the waters of the Axe which he considers " hard and un-fertilising from the influence of the swallets or interior streams which constitute its principal supply."

Mr. Haile refers to the injurious effect of water lying too long on the land, causing the growth of waterweed, damaging the grass, and killing earth-worms.

Deep floods are preferred to shallow ones, however, since the former tend to compress the light spongy soil of the peat moors, and on smaller moors give a sufficient body of water to dilute the evil effect of flushing from septic tanks and night-soil pits.

There seems to be little doubt that on the Brue and Parrett, engineering improvements to create, where necessary, proper control of land drainage, and unity of action among land-holders, would result in much wider annual benefit from flooding.

Present Difficulties

The chief difficulty at present is that, although the Catchment Board Engineers know exactly what needs to be done, and have worked out plans in detail for doing it, the present price of agricultural produce, particularly hay, does not warrant the extra capital charge on these lands of five or six pounds an acre which would be necessary if the districts were to finance their own improvements. As will be seen from the accompanying maps, large areas do not suffer from flooding, and of those areas flooded, some have already satisfactory arrangements ; so a large sum of money is necessary for an improvement scheme, which must be general, to benefit particularly only a small proportion of the lands rated, and a small percentage of the farming population.

At the present time (1936) a large subsidy is being sought from the Government towards the cost of a general scheme of improvement, and the opportunity seems a good one for recon-sideration of methods of control of certain areas which will be most benefited.

While it is not the business of this report to suggest means, it may be pointed out that the geographical factors allow the possibility of (a) making use of silt brought down by rivers if the latter are properly controlled by banks and sluices, and if an over-riding authority has power to act at the right moment. (b) Transporting silt, dredged from the main channels and estuaries, to low areas which could eventually be raised to a satisfactory level.

The present system of Internal Drainage Districts was arranged at a time when transport was not so quick or easy as it is now, when it is possible by motor and telephone to exercise oversight and control quickly over large areas.

It is unlikely that the rough moor areas, if left as at present, will again enjoy such a measure of usefulness as they have had in the past, since the disappearance of the horse from general use has made the coarse pasture of these areas almost useless. (Hay on West Sedgemoor was offered recently at £1 to £1 5s. a ton. Twenty acres was offered, and refused, for £2 the lot, if the buyer would cut it.)

NOTES ON THE DRAINAGE DISTRICTS OF SOMERSET

Internal Drainage Districts (See Fig. 4)

1a. *Gordano Valley District* (two sub-districts) :

Area east of Portbury Railway Station, 436 acres annual value £659 ;
Area west of Portbury Railway Station, 2,020 acres, annual value £35,65.

Contains Walton Moor, Weston Moor, Clapton Moor. Drainage by gravity. Flooding is due to incomplete construction, narrow obstructed channels, poor grading, tight bridges and low banks. Soil on the moors is poor, including some peat in portion marked as flooded, and some yellow should appear on the Land Utilisation Sheets in the sub-district No. 2 (West of Portbury Railway Station). The eastern area has some rough and marshy fields, which, however, have been marked green as the vegetation consists mainly of grasses. The saltings (marked yellow on Land Utilisation Survey sheets) south of the mouth of Bristol Avon, carried a good grass cover when observed on 26th May, 1936.

1b. *North Somerset District* (constituted since Act of 1930).

Sub-districts : Yatton, 7,782 acres, annual value £21,096.
Nailsea, 4,080 acres, annual value £17,602.

Yatton Sub-district (West of Clevedon–Yatton Road) contains area of low-lying pasture land and Congresbury Moor.

Nailsea Sub-district (East of Clevedon–Yatton Road) contains Clevedon Moor, Tickenham Moor, Nailsea Heath, Nailsea Moor, Kenn Moor, Hilsea.

Drainage is all by gravity, and requires considerable improvement (sluices widened, some regrading, obstructions removed) for full effect. At present much land is waterlogged which could be rich summer pasture. Floods are bad from October to March.

Kenn Moor and Hilsea Moor. Much " marginal " land. Some areas have been marked yellow on Land Utilisation Survey sheets to indicate this, but the field survey is often a matter of opinion and needs explanation. The moors provide good, rich summer pasture when the seasons and inadequate drainage allow. Kenn Moor is typical. On 21st May, 1936, it was still unstocked and plashy, with water in the rhines at or about field level. On the tarmac surface of minor roads which had apparently just dried out, there were in places numbers of water snails. Large areas were covered thickly with rushes. In general the land provides good summer pasture for cattle for three months in summer.

Nailsea and Tickenham Moor. Along the boundary rhine there is an area of peat. Much of the land in May 1936 looked all rushes and swamp. Where clay overlies the peat the pasture is better. " Snake-pipe " grass is present. The rough pasture is available for from two to four summer months. Conditions on these low lands are further complicated by the presence at Chelvey of a well from which the Bristol Water Board is empowered by Act to pump water. Three and a half million gallons a day should flow over the weir on the Kenn, however, to maintain sufficient water on the moors in summer.

The weir was dry from April 1933 till beginning of December 1934, owing to the exceptional weather.

During dry seasons, also, the pumping has the effect of drying out the peat so that the lands about the Kenn River sink.

1c. *West Mendip District Drainage Board.*

Area 14,478 acres. Annual value £84,895.

Contains Worle Moor, Puxton Moor and large area of low, flat pasture land. Orchards and farms widespread on flats.

Drainage by gravity through rhines and ditches. A fair fall allows the drainage to function and the land consists in general of good pasture. Inland by the hills there is some winter flooding which, however, is not serious. There is some marshy land tending to flood in winter, about the River Yeo.

2. *Lower Axe District.*

          Area 18,091 acres. Annual value £60,991.

    Contains Bleadon Level, Allerton Moor, Binham Moor and large tracts of level pasture land of good quality. Drainage by gravity. This district is not subject to serious flooding, though in parts low and liable to become waterlogged. Sea and tidal river protection already noted. Soil, alluvium and clay of more or less thickness over peat.

    Bleadon Level. Good land which will flood for a short time during an exceptional tide. Drainage presents no difficulty.

    Allerton and Binham Moors are liable to floods, which, however, are not of serious extent or duration, and are adequately removed by gravity drainage. On Allerton Moor there is liable to be a shortage of drinking water in summer.

3. *Upper Axe District.*

          Area 7,146 acres. Annual value £19,525.

          Sub-district : Parishes of Rodney Stoke and Westbury, 1,239 acres. Annual value £2,468.

    Contains Cheddar Moor, Oxmoor, Monkmoor, Draycott Moor, Stoke Moor, Wedmore Moor, Westbury Moor, Panborough Moor, Knowle Moor. Soil, alluvium over peat. Drainage by gravity along rhines except in Rodney Stoke sub-district where there is a pump. Floods heavily from surrounding hills. An average daily rainfall of 0·5 inches (24 hours) for four or five days continuously will cause floods. Cheddar Moor, Draycott Moor, and part of Wedmore Moor are subject to floods. South of Rodney Stoke and Westbury is a low, wet district where floods are most extensive, frequent and persistent in this valley. On Stoke Moor a large area was still under flood when observed 3rd March, 1933. There is some swampy and rushy land, but in general the area provides very good summer pasture. A large new reservoir is in the course of construction on Cheddar Moor for the Bristol Water Works Company. Most of the area is very good land and drainage arrangements are in satisfactory condition. On parts of Cheddar Moor and Draycott Moor cattle can remain on ground all winter.

4. *Upper Brue District.*

          Area 22,265 acres. Annual value £38,729.

    Contains Westhay Level, Westhay Heath, Shapwick Heath, Meare Heath, Ashcott Heath, Glastonbury Heath, Walton Heath, South Moor, Kennard Moor, Butt Moor and low ground to Wheathill, Westhay Moor, Godney Moor, North Moor, East and West Backwear, Crannel Moor, Common Moor, Queen's Sedge Moor, Splotts Moor, Hearty Moor. Drainage all by gravity. Most of area (see Land Utilisation Survey Sheets, and Fig. 4) floods badly. River section insufficient, and floods overtop to Mark Bridge. Considerable areas of peat with overlying alluvium near main waterways and washdown by hills.

    On both sides of the Old Glastonbury Canal there is peat cutting which has in many places lowered the surface of the land to the level of the water-table, rendering large areas waste. Along the Meare–Ashcott, and the Westhay–Shapwick Roads, houses, such as Sand Drove House, and detached portions of land may be observed on elevations eight or ten feet above the general level of the ground lowered by peat digging over generations.

    The Land Utilisation Survey sheet 120 shows much land south of the Brue marked as heath and rough pasture. Also alongside peat cuttings often small patches of garden cultivation for subsistence vegetables are found.

    Much of the land is, however, improvable with drainage works and control. Knowle Moor, in the Upper Axe District, used to be something like Shapwick, but is now in good condition. In normal seasons, stock is all off the Drainage District by the end of October which is not restocked until May (1935 all clear of water by 19th May). After May, water must be " penned " by closing sluices to preserve drinking supply and " keep fence." In places, notably Queen's Sedge Moor, the surface is soft and cattle or laden carts can break through the dry crust to peat bog below. There are some two hundred and fifty miles of internal drainage channels to be kept in order.

5. *Lower Brue District Drainage Board.*

          Area 22,778 acres. Annual value £86,105.

    Containing (south side) Huntspill Level, Huntspill Moor, Puriton Level, Woolavington Level, Edington Heath, Edington Moor, Catcott Heath, Chilton Moor ; (north side, west to east) Burnham Level, Blackford Moor, Mark Moor, moor known as Aller Moor, Tealham Moor, Tadham Moor. There is much flooding north and south, east of junction of old Glastonbury Canal, and River Brue. Mark Moor, Tealham, Tadham, Aller, Huntspill, Chilton, Edington and Catcott. From mouth of River Brue to Crip's Corner the soil consists of high alluvium overlying the peat. Remainder of the main valley and also minor valleys converging into it exhibit general surface of peat with alluvium near rising ground. For about 5 miles from Highbridge on line of River Brue land on both sides is high and is not subject to floods, but from this point for about 7 miles further up, land is about 4 to 5 feet below top flood-level and large area subject to flooding at slightest increase of rainfall.

6. *Stockland District.*

Area 2,740 acres. Annual value £5,329.

Containing moor known as Wick Moor and low land between Stockland and Combwich, portion of the lower Parrett on the west side, and Stert Flats. Drainage by gravity; no serious flooding except possible danger from high tides. Good pasture land.

7. *Cannington and Wembdon District.*

Area 4,289 acres. Annual value £16,868.

Contains area north of Bridgwater and (detached to south) Risemoor and Stock Moor. Drainage by gravity. Risemoor and Stock Moor both subject to seasonal flooding. Fair quality pasture.

8. *Bridgwater and Pawlett District.*

Area 5,944 acres. Annual value £32,974.

Contains north of Dunball about Pawlett Hill, Pawlett Level; west and south, low land lying in loops of the River Parrett; south of Dunball, Horsey Level and land about Bridgwater. Drainage by gravity, no serious flooding. "Round Pawlett Ham, enclosed by earthen banks up to Bridgwater, a considerable tract of probably the finest pasture in the Kingdom."

9. *Chedzoy District.*

Area 3,076 acres. Annual value £8,660.

Contains South Moor, Long Moor (western extension of King's Sedgemoor) and low ground about Chedzoy rise. Drainage: South Moor drained by pumping; otherwise by gravity along rhines. Long Moor heavily flooded from Barty Bridge to Bondenham Farm.

10. *King's Sedgemoor and Cary Valley District.*

Area 12,372 acres. Annual value £18,679. Per £ of annual value 2/-.

An extensive district containing, west by north to east by south, along King's Sedgemoor Drain and continuation in River Cary, Bawdrip Level, West Moor, King's Sedgemoor and Somerton Moor, and continuation of low land up River Cary.

Drainage by gravity. Flood-water takes about three months to run off. Extensively flooded throughout.

King's Sedgemoor drain accomplished by 31 George III, 1791; also setting out certain areas subdivided and allotted among several proprietors having rights of common in the respective parishes. Thirty-two allotments set out on a map and rights in the whole number 1,798. Limits of enclosure extended 1865 under Land Drainage Act 1861. One thousand acres surrounding added. Area comprised within jurisdiction of former Commissioners of Sewers, 11,259 acres.

King's Sedgemoor. Bounded on north by high ridge of Polden Hills; on east by high ground of Compton Dundon, and by those of Somerton and High Ham Town on south as far as Beer Door, where skirted by elective district of Aller Moor; thence by rising ground on which stand Middlezoy and Westonzoyland; from latter place drainage District of Chedzoy forms part of southern boundary to Perchay, from which place the drain to Dunball Clyse takes water to the Parrett. Soil: The greater part of the soil is peat with some alluvium where the surface is slightly elevated above the ordinary level. The moor is intersected by several streams from high ground north, east and south, discharging into the main drain. Basin of whole district, including Cary proper, 44,930 acres (1873) heavy and continuous flooding for years past owing to insufficient outfall through main drain at Dunball; totally inadequate at present when quantity of water much increased by *more effective drainage* over whole watershed. Flooded area 1872-73, 13,958 acres—rain nearly all fell October, November, December. Floods have become more serious of recent years. Peat land is still ploughed north of Compton Dundon, but much has been put to grass on account of the increased flooding.

11. *Othery, Middlezoy and Westonzoyland District.*

Sub-districts: Old District. Area 1,501 acres. Annual value £4,329.

Added Area. Area 620 acres. Annual value £2,101.

Southlake. Area 401 acres. Annual value £1,014.

Contains Weston Level, Earlake Moor, Nether Moor, Southlake Moor. Drainage: Southlake has pump drainage only ; Weston Level and Earlake Moor drained by gravity assisted by pumping (the area would benefit by an efficient pump). Otherwise by gravity. The lands are frequently overflowed as in certain seasons the water in the river is considerably higher than the surface of the land.

12. *North Moor District.*
>   Area 3,200 acres. Annual value £5,935.

Contains Hay Moor, Horlake Moor, North Moor, and flat land known as " Hitchings." Drainage by pump. Land floods extensively. Peat surface in interior low lands, at the foot of the rising ground overlaid by washdown deposits ; alluvium by the river.

13. *Stanmoor District Drainage Board.*
>   Area 790 acres. Annual value £1,994.

Award of enclosure of the several parishes made 37 George III. Flooded and freed by pumping assisted by gravity. 1929, break in river, moor flooded to 10 feet.

14. *Aller (" Alder ") Moor District.*
>   Area 1,927 acres. Annual value £4,425.

Contains North Moor, Aller Moor, Middle Moor.

Drainage by gravity through North Moor to King's Sedgemoor Drain. " Board has power of admitting flood-water of River Parrett to irrigate the district, by which means mud (a valuable manure) is deposited " (Grantham, 1873 Report). Soil : alluvium over peat, carries pasture of excellent quality. Liable to be heavily flooded. " Aller Moor is in a more difficult position than any other moor ; as the flood-bank had to be kept a little lower than Langport's, to protect the town. It is liable to flood within twelve hours of the first rain to fall after a dry spell." (From *Bridgwater Mercury* account of floods in 1930, 19th February.)

15. *West Sedgemoor District.*
>   West Sedgemoor. Area 3,811 acres. Annual value £3,991.
>   Sub-districts : Upper Curry Moor. Area 628 acres. Annual value £2,085.
>   Saltmoor. Area 611 acres. Annual value £1,728.

Drainage : West Sedgemoor, gravity drainage ; the moor acts as a collecting basin for a watershed of about 11,840 acres, receiving all the water round it, which is eventually carried away by two main drains to two sets of clyses on the Parrett. The interior surface is peat, with washdown and alluvium at the foot of the high grounds and near the River Parrett.

The whole area is in grassland of varying quality and in ordinary seasons produces large crops of grass mixed with various waterweeds, providing summer pasture for three to four months' duration. Special difficulties are the softness of much of the surface, making ingress and egress along the " droves " difficult, and the flooding and drying out of the peat. One authority, particularly well informed, and owning land on the moor, states that " to own an acre on West Sedgemoor is to own the lot, the land being practically common in a dry summer owing to the drying out of ditches."

Upper Curry Moor. Drained by gravity. River overtops between Hamwear and Bathpool where there are no flood-banks.

Saltmoor. Drained by gravity assisted by a pump.

16. *Curry Moor District.*
>   Curry Moor. Area 1,320 acres. Annual value £3,457.
>   Sub-districts : Westmoor. Area 140 acres. Annual value £371.
>   Charlton. Area 360 acres. Annual value £950.

Contains Lyng Moor, Curry Moor, Hook Moor, West Moor, Hay Moor.

Drainage. Curry Moor (see p. 25) an area of good pasture land. Grantham's Report states : " During whole winter (1872–73) since October the flood remained at times 7 feet deep. In eight days the engine could have thrown the water out." The District is now excellently managed, with an improved pump. Hay Moor drained by gravity assisted by pumping. Otherwise by gravity.

17. *Langport District Drainage Board.*
>   Area 12,797 acres. Annual value £28,907.

A widespread area following the windings of the Isle, Parrett, Yeo and tributaries.

The area on the Isle extends south of Ilminster. Contains *River Yeo*, West Moor, King's Moor, Witcombe Bottom, Ilchester Mead.

River Parrett, Thorney Moor, South Moor (part), West Moor (part), Stapleton Mead.

River Isle, South Moor, West Moor.
Together with other areas of low-lying land along rivers.
All liable to heavy floods and drained by gravity.
River Isle : lias and marlstone—land in general and excellent quality, valleys in grass.
River Yeo : large areas of fine pasture on both sides of river—greater part of course through alluvium.
Grantham Report 1872–73. " Floods in (Upper) Parrett, Isle and Yeo commenced in October and continued to nearly end of March injuriously affecting grass, chief product of valley lands. On 16th March heavy rain for several hours and resultant floods rose within 12 hours."

SUMMARY OF WATERSHEDS AND FLOODED AREAS OF RIVER VALLEYS OF CENTRAL SOMERSET

| River Valleys | Watershed | | Flooded Area |
	sq. miles	acres	
Upper Parrett (above Langport Bridge) :			
Parrett Proper	67	42,880	—
Isle	67	42,880	—
Yeo	158	101,120	—
Total Upper Parrett	292	186,880	24,137
Lower Parrett :			
Proper	115	74,864	—
Tone	158	101,120	—
Total Lower Parrett	273	175,980	15,135
Total Parrett	565	362,860	39,272
Watershed discharging through :			
Staith	310½	198,720	—
Cary	79	44,930	13,958
Brue	207	136,850	13,576
Axe	98	62,720	2,266
Summary :			
Parrett	565	362,860	39,272
Cary	79	44,930	13,958
Brue	207	136,850	13,576
Axe	98	62,720	2,266
Total	949	607,360	69,072 (107 sq. m.)

These figures have been taken from the Grantham Report 1872–73. Flooded areas are those referred to in the report and indicated on the accompanying map (Fig. 5), specially surveyed at that time. In view of subsequent legislation for the co-ordination and improvement of drainage in Somerset the acreage of flooded areas may be considered as maxima. Except see Shapwick area.

C. CLIMATE

In speaking of climate it must be recalled that the County is an administrative, not a geographical unit, and therefore only the general conditions, which help to make local climate, position of the County, winds, etc., are uniform. The climatic factors which are most important for local land use within those broad general conditions, vary considerably.

The General Conditions

The northern boundary of the County is the Severn estuary, and the body of water has the usual effect of lowering summer temperature along the coast and keeping up winter temperature.

FIG. 6.—Maps supplied by the Air Ministry, Meteorological Office, British Rainfall Organisation.

Fig. 7.—Maps supplied by the Air Ministry, Meteorological Office, British Rainfall Organisation.

C

Moss[1] points out, however, that the waters of the estuary are colder than those of any other English estuary so far south, and compare with those of Humber Mouth. The effect is, however, appreciable as may be seen from the temperature table (page 39) and almost certainly increases towards the west.

The climate generally, as elsewhere in England, is greatly affected by the winds, bringing both rainfall and warmth from the south and west, and cold from the east and north particularly in winter, spring and late autumn. Coastal climate is particularly affected by the sea but it is not easy to define in figures. There are five more or less distinct areas of local climate in Somerset.

1. The Western Highlands

This area corresponds roughly to areas 1a, 1c, 1d on the Physical Regions Map (Fig. 3) and to Production Areas, Nos. 1 and 2 (Fig. 14).

2. The Coastal Belt

This is difficult to define since comparable figures are not available for the various parts and shelter from easterly and southerly winds is an important factor, probably the most important since two well-defined specially favoured spots, Porlock Vale, where New Zealand plants will grow, and Cheddar, a well-recognised " early " district noted for strawberries, are both well protected on the north and east.

The Cheddar Valley because of its topography and southern aspect, for growing of strawberries is always reckoned to be at least a fortnight earlier with the harvest than the strawberry districts of Gloucestershire, Herefordshire, Wiltshire and Worcestershire.[2]

Weston-super-Mare also has shelter from the north and a favourable exposure to the south, and so can hardly be considered typical for the exposed coastal flats, and the important distinction for this division lies in what happens to the temperature when easterly and north-easterly winds blow.

This area of climate is suggested therefore rather than proved, except for the Porlock Vale, Minehead and locally, and Weston-super-Mare. The " Fault trough " (Physical Area No. 4) may belong to the area also, being sheltered from easterlies. Good soils are found on most parts of the coast, and with Wales opposite for cheap coal, more definite information on the local climate of the coastal area would be valuable, since with modern transport which makes light of distance there seems no particular reason why Somerset should not share much more fully in the market for early special crops grown under glass.

3. The Mendip Area

There is a well-defined area of high rainfall embracing the Mendip country and the environs. Average temperatures vary slightly with elevation and exposure, and sheltered nooks such as the Cheddar region may be specially favoured. As can be seen from the rainfall charts, the rainfall area varies with the season. On the Mendip plateau exposure to the full effects of northerly and easterly weather is probably the most powerful climatic factor, but the moorland character of parts of the surface are due to tracts of poor soil rather than to local climate. In the western hills, on better soil, much land is regularly under cultivation at as high, or higher levels than those of the Mendips.

[1] *Vegetation of Somerset.*
[2] University of Bristol. Bulletin No. 8. " An Economic Inquiry into the Production of Strawberries." C. W. Dawe, M.Com., and H. T. Horsman, B.Sc., N.D.A., Dipl. Agric. Printed for private circulation, 1933.

4. The Chalk Hills

This corresponds to the western half of Physical Area No. 7 (Fig. 3). The sudden scarp gives rise to an increased rainfall; the height probably makes a slight difference to average temperature, but no figures have been obtained in proof of this.

5. Central Somerset

This area embraces Physical Areas 5, 6, 8, 9, 10, 11, 12 and much of 18. Rainfall is low, and a general idea of the range and nature of temperatures is provided by the statistics for Street. Hill country towards the south and south-west will naturally provide local differences due to altitude, exposure or shelter, but temperature statistics which are comparable are not available

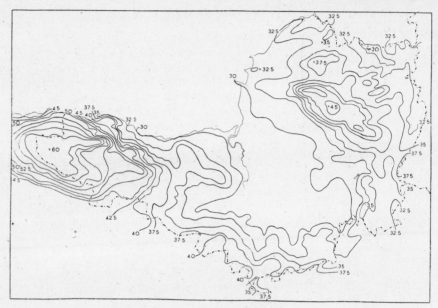

Fig. 8.—Mean Annual Rainfall.
Map supplied by the Air Ministry, Meteorological Office, British Rainfall
Organisation.

for such detailed study. If the present utilisation of the land is a guide, these should be fairly uniform.

These five areas are more or less distinct though one shades into another and it would be sheer guesswork to define the areas on a map with the few figures available, and they are not so much separate climates as local variations of one climate due to height and disposition of the country.

The Jurassic belt (see Fig. 2 and Fig. 3, Physical Areas 12a, b, c, and d) varies greatly in altitude and exposure. Statistics are available for Bath, but the city lies in a sheltered hollow and the exposed plateau and down-like hills of the region would probably have different temperature averages, more like those of Mendip.

Rainfall

The diagrams supplied by the Meteorological Office give the mean annual rainfall (Fig. 8) and the average annual rainfall by months (Figs. 6 and 7) over a period of years.

Naturally rainfall will vary in different years, but the diagrams give a good indication of the proportion of rain which will normally fall on the different parts of the County ; of the rain falling in any normal year, most will fall on the western Devonian hills and mountains increasing towards Exmoor ; the Mendip Hill region will normally rank next, closely followed by the Greensand–Chalk region of the Blackdown Hills, while the Parrett-Brue lowland area will receive least rain.

While this is the normal distribution, heavy local falls due to cyclonic disturbances, always possible in the latitude of the British Isles, may occur, the distribution of two such local storms being shown on diagrams (Figs. 9 and 10).

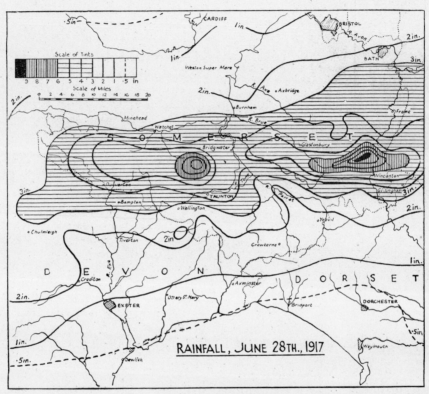

RAINFALL, JUNE 28TH., 1917

FIG. 9.—Map supplied by the Air Ministry, Meteorological Office, British Rainfall Organisation.

Heavy falls on any one day are usually the result of thunderstorms in the summer and early autumn months ; heavy monthly rainfall, excepting the few occasions on which " freak " falls such as those of 1917 and 1929 have taken place, are more usually the result of a number of days of steady, relatively low rainfall.

In the low country, the low rainfall area, falls of an inch or more in 24 hours are rare ; in the high country of the west, and to a less extent on Mendip and the Chalk Hills, heavy short showers make up much of the summer total.

The following table (page 38) gives the monthly average rainfall, the highest monthly fall, the average number of raindays and the highest number of raindays per month at Street, centrally placed in a relatively low rainfall area of the County.

The figures relate to the period between 1892 and 1922. Number of raindays and particularly depth of falls will be proportionately higher in areas of higher rainfall as shown on the diagrams (Figs. 6 and 7).

" Raindays " are days on which ·01 inches of rain or more fall during the 24 hours. Much is still left to the imagination, since sunshine and evaporation, prevalence of fog and mist, as well as the manner in which the rain falls are necessary for a clear picture of the weather. Land utilisation depends to a great extent on what the rain does to the ground after it falls, which, again, depends partly on the surface, whether porous or impervious, and partly on the season— a fall of rain which in summer may be ignored, in winter and spring, when the land is saturated and evaporation low, will make the Expenditors of Drainage Districts anxious.

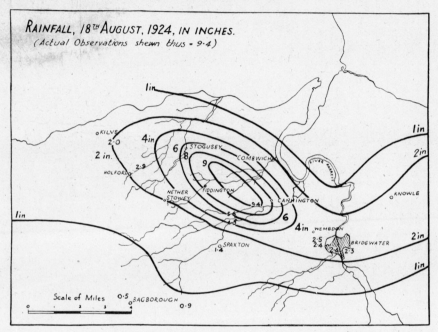

Fig. 10.—Map supplied by the Air Ministry, Meteorological Office, British Rainfall Organisation.

Temperature

Temperature is commonly expected to vary with altitude, or height above sea-level, but in Somerset especially in the late autumn, winter and spring, the temperature depends to a great extent on the direction of the wind. The westerlies blow in from comparatively warm seas and " import " warmth to the hills and plains, exercising a levelling effect on temperature. In still weather, or northerly weather, altitude has more effect. The effect of easterly winds is different in summer and winter.

For this reason, and also because reliable temperature records are far fewer than those for rainfall, a useful temperature chart of the County cannot be drawn on the assumption that the high country will be uniformly lower in temperature at all seasons than the low country. What is more probable is that average temperatures in the high country are lower owing to occasional very low temperatures when weather conditions allow the altitude to have full effect. For land use in Somerset, the most important factor of weather is the local variation in rainfall.

For instance, wheat grows satisfactorily in the parish of Exford, but the very uncertain ripening season, due to showers of rain, makes harvesting a matter of luck.

Month	Lowest monthly fall, inches	Highest monthly fall, inches	Number of rain days (a)	Number of rain days (b)	Average rain days	Highest number of rain days	Lowest number of rain days
January .	0·48	4·82	5	24	17·5	25	5
February .	0·16	4·93	3	27	14·6	27	3
March .	0·28	5·25	9	26	15·9	28 (2·48)	4
April .	0·10 (4)	4·9	4	22	13·5	22	4
May .	0·16	4·08	6	20	12·3	21	4
June .	0·55	6·53 (5·09)	7	15 / 17 (1·51 fall. Th | largest under)	12·2	23	3 (see note)
July .	0·49	4·67 (5 thunder-storms. 0·56 in. largest fall)	7	18	9·5	23	1 (1911) (1 in. in 1 day. Thunder)
August .	1·1	6·76 (5 thunder-storms. 0·76 in. largest fall)	6	24	15·7	26 (6·69)	6
September	0·19	5·42 (storms)	4	28	9·4	28	4
October .	0·93	7·38 (0·82in. steady rain great-est fall)	7	29	17·4	29	7
November	0·68	5·51	6	24	16·2	24	6
December	1·0	7·12	11	27	20·0	28	11

Note : 1917, 5·13 ins. in 24 hours. Thunderstorms afternoon and evening.
(*See pages* 36 *and* 37.)

To give some idea of the temperature variations in Somerset, the following statistics have been taken from the records kept for over 70 years (1858–1936) by Roger Clark of Street and members of his family.

The climatic conditions which they represent in detail for a particular area, are general to the County, and variations somewhat similar to the variations shown on the rainfall charts would probably show if sufficient figures were available.

The temperature figures used are those shown on two thermometers, one recording the lowest temperature in 24 hours, the other the highest, both temperatures being read at or about 9 a.m.

Columns 1 to 4 are made up from daily readings between 1908 and 1936 ; columns 5 and 6 from daily readings between 1858 and 1908 checked on to 1936. The thermometers, properly screened, stand at 100 feet above sea-level. The letters in columns 1 and 3 refer to the direction of the wind observed at 9 a.m. on the day the reading of the previous 24 hours was taken. In July, August and September, the wind direction is not so important as the land has had time to get warm. The direction of wind, observed locally, often does not give its true character for temperature, since the drift air from the warm west usually advances in circular whirls or

TEMPERATURES IN DEGREES FAHRENHEIT

Month	1 Lowest Temp. for Month	2 Highest Low Temp. for Month	3 Highest Temp. for Month	4 Lowest High Temp. for Month	5 Average of Daily Low Temp. for Month	6 Average of Daily High Temp. for Month	7 Possible Monthly Range of Temp.
	degrees	degrees	degrees	degrees	degrees	degrees	degrees
January .	12 E.	50	59 S.	26	32	45	47
February .	12 W.	50	59 S.E.	30	32·5	47	47
March .	9 N.	49	75 N.E.	32	34	51	66
April .	20 N.	49	74 W.	34	37	58	54
May . .	26 N.E.	59	84 W.	49	42	64	58
June . .	31 S.E.	62	90 W.	54	48	70	59
July . .	35	62	93 N.W.	54	51	73·5	58
August .	31 N.W.	64	92 S.W.	55	50·5	72	61
September.	26 N.	62	90 N.E.	45	46	67	64
October .	17 S.E.	57	81 S.E.	42	41	59	64
November.	12 E.	55	69 N.W.	32	35	50·5	57
December .	12 E.	52	60 S.W.	28	32·5	45·5	48

The letters refer to the direction of the wind at the time when the temperature reading was taken (9 a.m.).

cyclones, so that the wind drifting from the west may box the compass in a few hours. Many examples of this can be observed from the records. For instance, when the high temperature for March, 1929 (75°) was observed, the wind direction was N.E., the previous day had been N.W., and the day following was W., which probably meant that a circular wind was moving up from the south-west.

The following figures for Street and Weston-super-Mare show, amongst other things, the

TEMPERATURES IN DEGREES FAHRENHEIT

Month	Mean Maximum Temperature		Mean Minimum Temperature		Monthly Mean Temperature	
	Weston	Street	Weston	Street	Weston	Street
January . .	45·0	44·1	+36·3	30·64	40·7	37·4
February . .	46·2	47·1	+36·5	31·76	41·4	39·4
March . .	49·0	49·4	+37·6	32·61	43·3	41·0
April . .	54·3	56·3	+41·4	35·34	47·9	45·8
May . . .	60·2	63·4	+46·5	41·24	53·4	52·3
June . . .	65·4	67·8	+52·0	45·7	58·7	56·7
July . . .	67·9	70·8	+55·6	48·64	61·8	59·7
August . .	67·6	70·4	+55·2	47·7	61·4	59·0
September . .	64·4	65·1	+51·5	42·7	58·0	53·9
October . .	57·0	58·6	+45·9	39·3	51·5	48·9
November . .	50·9	49·6	+41·1	31·9	46·0	40·7
December . .	46·9	47·8	+38·0	33·0	42·5	40·4

The figures for Weston-super-Mare have been taken from the *Book of Normals*; the figures for Street from those kept by R. Clark, Esq. Both sets refer to the period 1881–1915.

effect of distance from the sea. Street is approximately 15 miles from the coast as the crow flies, but the screen in which the temperatures have been recorded stands at 100 feet above sea-level, which makes a slight difference, and is perhaps not so well sheltered from the important Northerlies and Easterlies. It will be noted that daily high temperatures at Street are slightly higher on the average than those at Weston, except in November and January, while all the year round daily low temperatures at Street are considerably lower. The water has the effect of checking slightly the daily rise in temperature due to the sun, and checking even more the drop at night.

Weather Records at Cannington

Weather records have been kept at Cannington since 1928 at the Somerset Farm Institute. Rainfall and temperature records are so close to those of Street, where there is the added advantage of a very much longer period of observation, that only two extracts are included here dealing with ground frosts, and sunshine recorded.

Below is also given a table of the " accumulated temperatures " for the period 1929–36.

The period of observation is short, but figures give an accurate, if limited, basis of comparison with other parts of the country.

SUNSHINE (IN HOURS)
RECORDED BY CAMPBELL-STOKES'S INSTRUMENT AT SOMERSET FARM INSTITUTE

Month	1929	1930	1931	1932	1933	1934	1935	1936	Averages
January . .	45·1	59·0	72·3	54·1	85·3	56·6	56·8	42·1	58·5
February .	62·0	59·2	77·4	67·6	96·5	98·8	68·0	70·3	74·9
March . .	202·1	128·7	128·6	145·6	183·2	126·4	121·9	84·5	140·1
April . .	179·2	138·4	114·5	133·1	179·2	143·9	145·6	156·4	148·0
May . .	248·4	147·5	143·2	118·7	207·2	227·1	166·2	205·7	183·0
June . .	251·3	239·5	197·5	243·6	252·2	227·8	208·1	165·7	223·2
July . .	253·6	191·7	143·1	150·0	243·3	283·0	267·3	148·9	210·0
August . .	203·2	199·2	150·1	193·4	245·2	198·4	208·9	229·9	203·5
September .	202·9	140·9	109·3	121·7	158·5	154·9	151·9	115·5	144·5
October . .	110·5	108·5	120·6	115·6	92·5	76·2	89·8	110·4	103·0
November .	75·6	83·1	77·2	53·5	81·3	22·1	68·0	48·4	63·7
December .	77·2	42·3	50·1	42·5	50·3	41·4	53·0	61·4	52·3
Totals . .	1911·1	1538·0	1383·9	1438·8	1868·4	1656·6	1605·5	1439·2	1605·2

GROUND FROSTS
DAYS ON WHICH GRASS MINIMUM THERMOMETER REGISTERED 30·4° F. OR BELOW

Month	1929	1930	1931	1932	1933	1934	1935	1936	Averages	Extremes
January .	17	14	18	13	22	14	9	19	15 to 16	9 & 22
February .	18	19	14	19	14	20	7	20	16 to 17	7 & 20
March . .	18	18	18	19	14	19	18	12	17	12 & 19
April . .	10	3	3	9	14	8	5	15	8 to 9	3 & 15
May . .	5	4	2	4	0	1	7	6	3 to 4	0 & 7
June . .	0	1	0	0	0	0	0	0	0	0 & 1
July . .	0	0	0	0	0	0	0	0	0	0
August .	0	0	0	0	0	0	0	0	0	0
September .	0	0	0	0	0	0	0	0	0	0
October .	4	1	8	3	1	1	5	11	4 to 5	1 & 11
November .	10	10	6	5	11	8	17	12	9 to 10	5 & 17
December .	12	14	9	12	22	1	12	11	11 to 12	1 & 22

TABLE OF ACCUMULATED TEMPERATURES ABOVE AND BELOW 42° F. FOR 8-YEAR PERIOD, 1929–1936, AT CANNINGTON

Months	1929		1930		1931		1932		1933		1934	
	Above	Below	Above	Below	Above	Below	Above	Below	Above	Below	Above	Below
January . .	25	194	111	39	59	110	141	57	53	182	83	93
February .	31	248	15	138	60	61	20	127	85	101	29	119
March . .	181	89	97	59	93	122	97	98	189	26	95	58
April . .	165	51	214	7	172	12	140	23	230	30	185	23
May . .	355	16	326	6	350	3	308	9	392	0	369	5
June . .	448	2	569	0	522	0	506	2	564	0	581	0
July . .	634	0	591	0	565	0	609	0	725	0	757	0
August . .	602	0	610	0	569	1	718	0	729	0	565	1
September .	623	0	512	0	410	3	491	2	558	2	515	0
October. .	326	9	358	5	296	34	279	12	315	7	357	4
November .	184	55	161	54	185	19	146	19	110	48	108	32
December .	135	47	85	65	124	66	105	73	5	234	213	3
Yearly Totals .	3,709	711	3,649	373	3,405	431	3,560	422	3,955	630	3,857	338

Months	1935		1936		Average for 8 years		Extremes			
							Above		Below	
	Above	Below	Above	Below	Above	Below	Lowest	Highest	Lowest	Highest
January . .	82	57	74	73	79	101	25	141	39	194
February . .	124	43	34	128	50	121	15	124	43	248
March . .	142	61	161	39	132	69	93	189	26	122
April . . .	214	14	129	45	181	26	129	230	7	51
May . . .	315	15	371	9	348	8	308	392	0	16
June . . .	543	1	513	2	531	1	448	581	0	2
July . . .	703	0	579	0	645	0	565	757	0	0
August . .	659	0	624	0	635	¼	565	729	0	1
September .	498	1	532	1	517	1	410	623	0	3
October . .	300	11	261	18	312	13	261	358	4	34
November . .	135	43	125	59	144	41	108	185	19	59
December . .	58	115	117	55	105	82	5	213	3	234
Yearly Totals .	3,773	361	3,520	429	3,678	462	3,405	3,955	338	630

" *Accumulated Temperature* "—a term which is used to denote the combined effect of the amount and duration of the excess or defect of air temperature above or below the base temperature of 42° F.

It is expressed in units of day-degrees Fahrenheit. It is a " scalar " quantity, so that amounts for individual days can be added together to obtain the amount for all the days together.

The above figures are worked out from daily values of maximum and minimum temperatures in the screen, using specially prepared Meteorological Office tables.

D. SOILS

Fig. 2 showing the chief geological formations in Somerset gives a very general indication of the distribution of the basic material from which the soils are developed. In some regions the massive beds which form the " bones " of the County are directly related to the thin, complex layer of cultivated soils, but in others, what is really important is the presence of a few feet of " drifted " material, which may vary from field to field, or even in parts of the same field.

Nor does it follow that similar soils will be used in the same way in different parts of the County, as economic, social and even personal factors all have a part in determining the particular nature of agriculture in a district which, once developed, tends to be fixed by the size of fields, surrounded by fences, walls or hedges, the type of farm buildings and the area of holdings, all of which represent expenditure of capital, and, perhaps most important, by the local skill and knowledge of farmers and labourers, often handed on from father to son and depending in part on intimate association with particular fields in all seasons and weathers. These things cannot be quickly changed to take advantage of a change in markets, even where the soil material is suited to a change in farming practice.

Cultivated soil is a complex and changing material, which must be considered not as the unchanging hills, but like an electric battery, which is charged to do work and then runs down, the " charging " process in the case of the soil being the cultivation and manuring, or management with stock.

The Land Utilisation Survey sheets provide an accurate if limited commentary on the soils ; where large tracts of plough ground appear it can be taken that soils are naturally fertile, or that they can be made so at reasonable cost. The largest continuous tracts of plough ground are found on light, sandy soils (Midford Sands or Upper Sandstones, or Marine beds), which are " quick turnover " soils, where easy and quick cultivation allows a margin for heavy and comprehensive manuring. As the soils must receive manures, rotation can be disregarded and profitable catch crops slipped in between staple crops. But it does not follow that where no ploughland appears soils are infertile ; grass is also a crop of high value, and in many areas leases have special clauses preventing[1] the breaking up of permanent pasture. Moreover, some areas are unsuited to other crops owing to winter flooding, or to slope.

A knowledge of the soils is therefore presented in this Report indirectly, through the facts collected as to values, treatment and products under present conditions of farming in the various districts, and it is hoped that the Report and the Land Utilisation Survey maps may be of use as a rough and ready reference for a scientific study of the soils in the County at a future date.

The farms selected for detailed study (see Section IV) have been chosen each to represent the practice and policy on a particular type of soil material as shown by the Geological or drift maps available, but it will be seen that the soils which develop on these various beds form, for practical purposes, a much smaller number of groups.

The form of questionnaire was designed to show the nature of the soil material, the treatment it received in order to keep it productive, the nature and roughly the amount of the produce, and the approximate value of the land.

---

[1] In the sense that if permanent pasture is broken up without the landowner's permission, compensation must be paid at outgoing. All that a lease can do is to lay down an agreed rate of penalty. With improved "seeds" mixtures available, landlords are now willing in most cases to waive the restriction clause if the farmer is prepared to break up and re-sow later with an up-to-date seeds mixture. There seems little doubt that the reason for the clause in most leases was that previous to the present knowledge of seeds mixtures it took 8 to 12 years to make a pasture,—in those days, " to make a pasture was to break a man " and naturally landlords objected to farmers breaking up a pasture and "cashing the fertility " without putting anything back in return.

The result has been perhaps to stress the personal, social and economic factors with regard to all but certain types of land which are definitely poor, such as the Lower Devonian, the Carboniferous Limestone and Old Red Sandstone, and some of the Upper Jurassic Beds; or the factor of rainfall, as in the Western Devonian Hills. The soils over much of the County cannot be estimated by value, except very roughly, without constant reference to the distribution of small-holdings, nor can the grassland be valued by productivity (i.e., weight of hay) without reference to the quality of the grass produced, and the manuring necessary. The factors of skill and management are seen to be enormously important ; judgment in the matter of applying capital and labour in relation to available markets, and to the demands of the soil, which may be more or less fixed according to type.

Nevertheless, a picture is created of certain conditions as they are in the County, which, if studied with the maps, gives a basis of comparison between the different districts, and with other parts of Britain.

The farms studied in Section IV have been called " specimen " rather than " typical " for reasons which are indicated above, and also because in general farms above the average size have been chosen, where operations have not been handicapped by insufficient capital, but they have nevertheless been chosen as typical as far as possible of farming practice in the several districts.

III. THE LAND UTILISATION OF SOMERSET

A. GRASSLAND

The importance of the grasslands in the County can be appreciated from the fact that out of a total acreage of about 900,000 acres of agricultural land, 660,000 acres are under permanent pasture, with a further 97,000 acres scheduled as rough grazing. (See folding map.)

" Permanent Pasture " is a rather misleading term as it includes the very rich dairy land of mid-Somerset, the grazing pastures such as those in the Pawlett Hams and various intermediate types, gradually deteriorating to herbages which in their present state could justifiably be classified as " Rough Grazing."

In the extreme west—Brendon Hill, Porlock, Exford, Dulverton, etc., really good permanent pasture is rare and can be found only in the valleys and a few fields adjoining the homestead. The fields further from home are often very poor, with a very rough herbage, composed largely of *Agrostis*. The long temporary ley is fairly common, and since the introduction of good seeds mixtures has become more highly thought of than all but the very best of the local permanent pastures.

Except in the case of the very worst pastures, i.e., those carrying bracken, etc., tremendous improvement can be made by the use of Basic Slag, provided there is a small amount of wild white clover present. In many cases, however, ploughing up and reseeding appears to be the most economical way of improvement.

Travelling east into the Vales of Wellington and Taunton, the long-term ley is less common, the farms consisting of permanent pasture and arable, the latter carrying clover for one year, or at the most two years, in each rotation. Here again there is a great variation in the value of the pastures. Some are excellent, both in appearance and effect, whilst others are poor and neglected. Phosphates are not used to any great extent although it has been abundantly demonstrated that great improvement can be obtained by both slag and superphosphate. Quite a considerable area laid down to grass comparatively recently appears to be " run out " and would benefit by being ploughed and cropped for a short period and then reseeded with a good mixture. This practice is becoming more popular with progressive farmers and should ultimately result in a great improvement. On the average the pastures are " stronger " than those of the west country, with the result that fattening of cattle and milk production are more extensively practised, the west country being devoted mainly to stock-rearing.

The hilly Chalk and Clay-with-Flint area that follows the County Boundary roughly from Wellington to Chard, carries a type of pasture which approximates somewhat to that of the west country but is considerably more productive. The effects of proximity to the homestead however, are just as marked as in the west country. Bracken and bent (*agrostis*) are only too common in many fields which could comparatively easily be improved.

It is true of Somerset as of other counties that the best fields are treated too well at the expense of others. It is very probable that infectious diseases such as contangious abortion, Johne's, etc., are propagated by the intensive stocking to which the more productive fields are subjected.

On the Lias lands which lie roughly within the triangle bounded by Taunton, Yeovil, and Shepton Mallet, there is a very productive area carrying excellent grass suitable for milk or beef production. Unfortunately much of this land is what is known locally as " teart "[1] and

[1] See below, p. 46.

causes cows and young stock to scour badly, so that they have to be removed to land which is sound. On the whole this area is well farmed and the pastures well managed, although quite a considerable area is suffering from water-logging due to the failure of the drains. Tussock grass (*agrostis vulgaris*), rushes and sedges are common weeds, and soon increase if not regularly cut. Little artificial manure is used and does not appear to be necessary on the heavily stocked farms, using large amounts of feeding-stuffs.

Along the coast from Pawlett right up to Clevedon and extending several miles inland there is an exceptionally good belt of pasture land. This is now chiefly devoted to milk production although not many years ago it was largely a cattle-fattening area. The soil is chiefly a rich alluvium and if well stocked and well managed does not appear to need artificial manure. Its value can be gauged from the fact that quite large farms (for Somerset) are rented at £2 to £3 per acre. Drainage is largely by surface gripes with pipe drains in some cases. On the average this land is well farmed but there are many instances of bad management. Neglect to clear ditches and to cut rushes, etc., soon tells a tale, and in three or four years first-class pastures become practically worthless.

In the north and north-east of the County, i.e., Frome, Bath, Keynsham, etc., there is a tremendous variation in the pastures. Here again the effect of proximity to the homestead can be seen, and in addition there are various soil types, elevation and aspect all playing some part in determining the value of particular fields. There is a great deal of land carrying a weedy, benty (i.e. with *Agrostis*) type of herbage, due largely to starvation. Superphosphate or slag is badly needed, with farmyard manure or sheep. On the other hand there are large areas of really good pastures, productive and healthy.

Speaking of the County as a whole, it is probably true to say that pasture land is gradually deteriorating in value. This is due to the switch-over from mixed stocking with sheep, fattening cattle, cows and young cattle to what is now in many districts, wholly and solely, milk production for sale as whole milk. The additional drain on the phosphatic reserves of the soil has not generally been accompanied, as it should have been, by a more liberal use of phosphatic fertilisers, and the land suffers in consequence.

On the majority of farms, there are fields which are mown every year and to these the bulk of the farmyard manure is applied. Without doubt a great improvement could be made if some system of rotational manuring was adopted, which would allow some of the farmyard manure to be applied to other parts of the farm. Late mowing is also too common, with the result that Yellow Rattle (*Rhinanthus crista-galli*) and other weeds of similar habit considerably reduce the quality and quantity of the yield.

With regard to artificial manures, there is no doubt that phosphate in some form (depending upon type of soil) could with advantage be used to a much greater extent than it now is.

Although lime may slowly improve the herbage on acid soils, the visible return does not appear to justify its use when compared with the effect of basic slag on similar soils.

Potash also seems to effect no visible improvement on the majority of Somerset soils.

Drainage is an important problem and one that merits considerable attention. There is the large area in the valleys of the Parrett, Brue, etc., which could be greatly improved if the flood nuisance could be overcome ; but apart from this, which is in the care of the Drainage Boards there are many thousands of acres which need attention being paid to field drains. Much field drainage was done about 40–50 years ago and every year more and more of these old drains cease to function, with the result that herbage deteriorates and the growing and stocking season is shortened. Attention must be paid to this question when improvement of this land is being considered.

The Teart Lands[1]

In the central parts of Somerset there are pastures on which cattle, more especially milch cows and young stock, are liable to suffer from a distinctive type of scouring during certain seasons. The scouring is persistent and continues, usually with increasing severity so long as the cattle are grazing, but ceases abruptly when they are removed.

The cattle lose weight, develop harsh, staring coats and go out of condition, but recover fairly rapidly if taken in immediately and given dry food.

The milk yield of affected cows falls rapidly and it is stated that these animals will suffer permanent injury if left on the pastures too long.

Fattening bullocks are more resistant, but the fattening process is delayed and the animals would " go back " if supplementary food were not given. Ayrshires are the least susceptible, and accordingly on teart farms there is a preference for this breed.

Horses are considered to be unaffected by the disease but their complete immunity has yet to be established.

The opinions of farmers differ as to the susceptibility of sheep, but on the worst teart pastures they do not thrive, although they are not injured to the same extent as cattle.

Teart pastures vary considerably in appearance, but as often as not would be rated as good grazing lands. The degree of teartness is not always the same, but varies from pasture to pasture, season to season, and year to year. It may, or may not, occur in May and June, but is frequently present, and always at its worst, during the months of August, September and October, particularly in those mild, damp seasons when the aftermath is growing rapidly. In very dry summers only a few pastures develop teartness.

Frost destroys teartness or decreases it so effectively that it is safe to graze even the worst teart pasture during the winter and early spring, and it becomes less also when the herbage is allowed to mature or become foggy.

Manuring, however, definitely increases teartness and therefore, beyond occasional dressings of lime, salt and farmyard manure, no fertilisers are applied.

Hay, made from well-cured mature herbage seems to have little teartness, and there is general agreement that after one year in the stack, hay from teart land does not scour at all.

Teart pastures are found scattered among perfectly sound fields, and it is not common to hear of a farm where all pastures are teart. Sometimes a teart, and a sound pasture may be found side by side ; sometimes the change from sound to teart pasture is gradual.

The conditions are not precisely known, and therefore it has been a difficult matter to identify teart pastures and to decide their degree of teartness.

Nevertheless, the limits of the teart pastures may be reasonably clearly defined. Very roughly they may be said to lie within the triangle set by the towns of Shepton Mallet, Yeovil and Taunton ; or, more closely, that they lie within and sometimes correspond in striking fashion with the boundaries of the Lower Lias formation (see Fig 2) and research has so far failed to establish the occurrence of teart land on any other geological formation.

Pastures reputed to be teart have certainly been found on soils developed on the alluvial deposits of Old River Terraces, but these are composed mainly of Lower Lias material, and blue clay lies within two feet of the surface.

The Lower Lias in Somerset stands up unmasked by any other deposits except in a few scattered places where it is covered by Alluvium, River Gravel and Boundary Drift, and it is pre-

[1] The main source of information is " The Teart Pastures of Somerset," by W. R. Muir, University of Bristol, Paper read at P.R.C., Bristol, 1935, published in *Agricultural Progress*, Vol. XIII, 1936. See also A. Clark, Prize Essay, *Bath and West Journal*, 1855.

cisely on similar places, where unmasked Lower Lias forms small escarpments, that other teart pastures are again found in Gloucestershire and Warwickshire.

All pastures on the Lower Lias are by no means teart. Many are perfectly sound, and, so far, this important fact is unexplained. Moreover, no report has ever been received, of harmless land becoming teart, altnough the reverse has frequently been recorded, such changes having invariably followed drainage improvements and arable cultivations for a period of years.

A. Clark, in a Prize Essay printed in 1855,[1] gives the following regions as containing teart pastures :—

" The upland and border pastures on the north side of Polden Hills and immediately skirting the moors forming the Brue Level ; extending southward on the heavy clays of Ilchester and the neighbouring villages ; eastward in the direction of Pilton, Pennard and Shepton Mallet ; certain pastures in the parishes of Butleigh, Street, the hamlet of Edgarly, and at Cossington ; in the neighbourhood of Walton, Shapwick, Edington, Baltonsborough, Pennard, Pylle, Barton St. David, Priddimore, Load, Othery, and other villages ; north of Horsey Slime Deep Drain lands also are very bad."

The northern and western parts of the County have little or no trace of teartness.

Gimmingham[2] has set down 20,000 acres for the area involved, and since mid-Somerset is essentially dairy country, it will be realised that the presence of teart pastures on a farm may cause considerable inconvenience and loss.

Long Ashton Research Station has more definite information as to the exact situation of teart pasture, but, naturally enough, since their work depends on the goodwill and co-operation of individual farmers, they regard such detailed information as they possess as confidential. But enough has been said to indicate that care must be taken, in acquiring land in whole or in part, on the Lower Lias in Somerset, at least to make sure of the proportion of teart pasture.

In spite of repeated and sometimes laborious investigation, no solution of the problem has yet been found, but two measures have been found to create improvement, drainage and ploughing. From the evidence available it does seem that efficient drainage has effected gradual improvement, but, on the other hand, ploughing up and reseeding has effected only temporary improvement and in the following years teartness has gradually developed to its former intensity.

B. HEATH AND ROUGH PASTURES

The folding-map at the back shows the distribution of heaths and rough pasture in the County as it appears in yellow on the one-inch Land Utilisation Survey sheets.

This includes various kinds of more or less natural heathlands covered with heather and ling or other heath plants ; bracken ; natural pasture and scrub bushes ; gorse ; forests cut and not replanted ; waterlogged land covered with rushes or water-plants ; and once cultivated fields which have been allowed to deteriorate to thistle, other weeds, and bracken mixed with coarse grass.

Considerable care has been taken by repeated checking of the six-inch field-sheets to ensure that good land temporarily appearing rough owing to understocking or other cause is not included, and much land which would locally be termed rough pasture has therefore been excluded and appears on the Land Utilisation Survey sheets coloured green as permanent pasture.

[1] *Journal Bath and West Society*, Vol. III, 1855, p. 52.
[2] C. T. Gimmingham, *Jour. Board of Agric.*, Vol. XVII, 1910, p. 529 ; *Idem, Jour. Agric. Science*, Vol. VI, 1914, p. 328.

Land has been included which, though poor in quality, may have considerable usefulness owing to proximity to alluvial meadows used only in summer, and certain tracts which repeated checking on the field-sheet has shown to need constant cultivation to prevent the growth of fern, gorse or weeds, and which will not naturally maintain permanent pasture.

Nevertheless, the lands shown in yellow depend in the first instance on a number of observers and while the general result is to indicate the less favoured lands of the County, it must not be taken in detail as an indication of value.

Especially is this true in the " moor areas " on the alluvium, certain parts of which have been marked yellow to indicate peat heaths and rushy or waterlogged land, but the moor survey is not complete in this respect on the Land Utilisation Survey sheets. A slight variation of elevation, the presence of peat, snake-pipe grass (*Equisetum*), or the drying-out of ditches locally in summer can vary to a great extent the value of fields on the same moor, while rich, valuable pasture, seen at an unfavourable time may appear to an observer without local knowledge to be useless.

The Western Area of High Land (including the Quantock region). (See Fig. 2 Devonian Beds, and Fig. 3 1a.c.d. See also rainfall, Figs. 6 and 7.)

Heather, heathland and " natural pasture " with areas of bog, occupy the flattened and rounded heights and spurs, which are either unenclosed commons or are divided into allotments containing hundreds of acres.

The typical method of enclosure on the higher, surrounding improved areas, is by stone-faced banks on which grow beech hedges, the whole forming a shelter of considerable height according to the growth of the beech. The fields thus formed, usually small, sometimes run right up into the heath so that there is marked contrast between the two sides of a fence. Where understocked or otherwise neglected the upper fields have reverted in many places to bracken.

The moor vegetation and bracken on the heights act as a sponge through which the water provided by the high rainfall percolates with slight evidence of erosion.

On the slopes below the heights, and in the valley bottoms, constant management is necessary, by stocking and cutting, to prevent the growth of bracken, particularly on north-facing slopes.

There is no detailed botanical account such as exists for the County east of Taunton, in the absence of which these lands may be classified roughly as :—

Heather moors.
Heather heath.
Natural pasture.
Moor pan areas, i.e., heath pasture with ganceturn, ling and bog cotton.

C. S. Orwin[1] notes that on the old Forest of Exmoor regular stocking through two centuries or more has destroyed the heather to a considerable extent, and that grass-heath has generally been substituted. There is, however, a considerable amount of ling on the uplands about Simonsbath, and on the slopes of Dunkery, and large areas could be described as heather heath rather than grass heath, and support a few grouse in some regions.

On the Quantocks, the northern area of heathland, with the associated forests and plantations, almost exactly coincides with the emergence of the Lower Devonian beds (Hangman Grits).

Where this area is not forested or under new plantations the surface is occupied by heather and ling, bracken, mosses and heath plants, and natural pasture ; the greater part would probably classify correctly as heather-heath.

[1] *The Reclamation of Exmoor Forest*, 1929, Oxford Univ. Press.

Some detached patches of heath lie to the south-east of the main mass, on small extensions of the old beds on Middle or Upper Devonian hilltops, or associated with small patches of Carboniferous Limestone, the former covered with bracken and heath, the latter with limestone heath or limestone pasture.

UTILISATION OF THE WESTERN HEATH AND ROUGH PASTURE AREAS

1. *" The Chains," Dunkery Hill, Porlock and Oare Commons and vicinity*

Rights to run stock on the rough pastures are attached to adjoining farms. Some hundreds of horn ewes, some cattle and ponies and deer are pastured, the sheep and cattle during the summer months. Stocking is generally restricted to the number of animals which can be wintered on a farm.

No treatment is given to the land and bracken appears to be spreading.

The sporting rights are let to a syndicate.

An area about Dunkery is now rented to the National Trust, but the rights of the adjoining farms are not affected.

2. *The Area North-West of Sherdon Water and South of Simonsbath*

The common is let with adjoining farms for grazing. Hundreds of Horn and Cheviot sheep, some Devon cattle and Exmoor ponies are grazed in summer. Some two hundred head of deer are maintained all the year round.

The land receives no treatment and bracken is apparently spreading.

Sporting rights are let to a syndicate.

3. *Withypool Common*

This is common land, all occupiers of land in the parish having the right to run stock, cut turf and bracken.

Sheep are pastured in the summer and horses throughout the year.

The ground receives no treatment.

Sporting rights are reserved by the Lord of the Manor.

4. *Winsford Hill and vicinity*

Some 1,290 acres of common land is let to the National Trust at 2/6 per year for 500 years.

Some farmers rent the grazing for about four months in the summer at £5 per year. This includes the right to graze 10 cattle, some 200 sheep, and to cut turf and ferns (for bedding, etc.).

The sheep and cattle are pastured from June to October, the cattle sometimes continuing during the winter.

Bracken is cut and some farmers still cut a few loads of turf.

Sporting rights for grouse, snipe and rabbits are let for a small sum. Stag and fox hunting is carried on.

5. *Commons about Croyden Hill*

(Croyden Hill let to the Forestry Commission. Withycombe Common, Rodhuish Common, Monkslade Common.)

Part of the land is common, part attached to farms and on part, grazing rights let separately.

The residents of Withycombe parish have the right to graze any stock on Withycombe Common. Rodhuish Common is let in part to a farm and in part planted by the Forestry Commission.

Sheep and bullocks are grazed all the year round.

The heath, bracken and rough grass is burned off, but the ground receives no other treatment.

Sporting rights are reserved by the Lord of the Manor.

6. *Dunster–Wooton Courtnay Area*

1. Grabbist Hill. 2. Ellicombe Common. 3. Wooton Common. 4. Hopcott Common. 5. Alcombe Common.

Only rights of way exist on Grabbist Hill. Ellicombe Common and Wooton Common are let with farms and sheep are occasionally grazed. Part of the grazing rights on Hopcott Common are let with a farm and part let separately.

Sheep are grazed throughout the year.

The grazing on Alcombe Common is reserved for Alcombe parishioners who run sheep and horses.

No treatment is given to the ground except for a limited amount of bracken cutting.

Sporting rights are reserved by the Lord of the Manor.

D

7. *Minehead–Hurtstone Point Area*
   The grazing rights are let with a farm.
   Sheep are pastured from mid-May to end of November.
   No treatment is given to the land but some bracken is cut for bedding.
   Sporting rights are reserved by the landlord.

8. *Treborough Common*
   Grazing rights on the common are let with farms.
   The pasture carries about 600 sheep from June to December.
   Bracken is cut for bedding and gorse and heather burnt if possible.
   Sporting rights are reserved by the landlord.

9. *Lype Common*
   The common belongs to two farms. About 250 sheep are carried for some four months during the best part of the year.
   A few ferns are cut for bedding.
   Sporting rights are reserved by the landlord.

10. *White Moor*
    The land is attached to farms. Two hundred sheep, 10 heifers and 3 colts are carried from June to October.
    Forty to 60 loads of bracken are taken for bedding.
    Sporting rights go with the farms.

11. *Skilgate Common.*
    The grazing rights are attached to a farm. Sheep are carried from July to October.
    Bracken is cut for bedding.
    Sporting rights are reserved by the landlord.
    (Haddon Hill is reserved for deer.)
    [Where rights to pasture stock on an undivided area are distributed amongst several farmers, over-stocking is usually controlled by the provision that only the number of stock that can be " wintered " on the farm may be pastured on the common ground. This rule appears to be general, and quite satisfactory.]

The Mendip Area (Fig. 3, Area 14).

It will be recalled that the area presents surrounding scarps, broken by coombs, dry valleys and gorges, falling sharply to gentler lower slopes of Marls and Clays; plateaus of Carboniferous Limestone on which lie small beds of younger deposits, including Lower Lias Clays at levels from 600 to 800 feet; and areas of Old Red Sandstone, the smooth rounded slopes of which rise to heights of from 900 to 1,068 feet.

The greater part of the whole area has been enclosed into large fields surrounded by dry-stone walls, the most extensive unimproved areas being towards the west. (Compton Hill area, Wavering Down, Dolebury Warren, Rowberrow Warren, Blackdown area).

The extensive tracts marked as heath and rough pasture vary from thick gorse and fern and small areas of land spoiled for stock by the effect of lead in the soil, to thin limestone pastures, with stony or with stunted scattered scrub bushes, and " improved " fields which have been neglected, and have gone back to fern, gorse, etc. The presence of old lead-workings is shown on the one-inch Land Utilisation Survey sheets.

Soils are in general thin. On the limestone, which appears in places through the surface, moisture quickly soaks away. Stocking, cultivation and manuring therefore are necessary to preserve the improvement of the land, and neglected fields quickly deteriorate so that one may see good turf or cultivation on one side of a wall, and barren ground with fern and gorse in an identical field on the other side.

While this distinction is clear in many cases, there is also much marginal land which has been marked as grassland.

Much of the rough, high country about Axbridge and Cheddar lets at from 4/– to 5/– an acre as winter store ground for stock which must be moved from the rich flats liable to flood.

The areas where no improvement by cultivation has been attempted can be distinguished on the Land Utilisation Survey six-inch sheets by the Ordnance Survey rough pasture and heath symbols.

The accompanying map, Fig. 11, has been copied from the detailed report on the Geographical Distribution of Vegetation in Somerset, by C. E. Moss, published in 1906, and gives the exact nature of the areas marked in yellow on the Land Utilisation Survey sheets. Moss marks more " natural " pasture on the scarps than is shown on the Land Utilisation Survey sheets, where " marginal " land, improved by constant stocking has in most places been shown as " grassland." This is always a difficult matter to decide in the course of the field-work, and the interpretation on the Land Utilisation Survey sheets has usually arrived at a compromise after much discussion and exchange of opinion between the man on the ground and the checking and reducing staff in London.

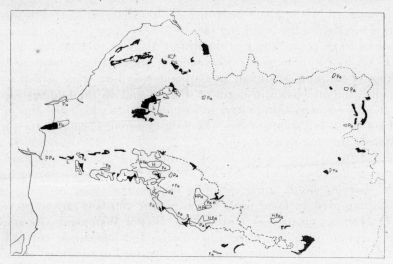

Fig. 11.—Natural Vegetation in East Somerset (after C. E. Moss).

Interpretation of Fig. 11.

In black. Ash woods, or woods in which ash is chief species.
    Pa   =   Natural pasture.
    L   =   Limestone heath.
    HPa =   Heath pasture.
    PaH =   Heath pasture and heather.
    H   =   Heather moor.

MENDIP AREA

1. *Brean Down*
    This is a bird sanctuary, there are no grazing rights.

2. *Pen Hill*
    The land is attached to farms, which run sheep on the rough grazing during the summer months.
    The sporting rights belong to Tudway estate.

3. *Rough Pastures about Cheddar and Draycott*
   The only common land is Priddy Green, on which neighbouring farms have grazing rights. All the rest of the land marked as rough pasture and heath is attached to farms.
   Sheep and young stock are pastured.
   Some bracken is cut.
4. *Bleadon Hill*
   All the land is fenced and rented or owned by farmers.
   Young cattle and sheep are grazed all the year round.
   There is a shortage of water in summer.
5. *Fry's Hill*
   Some land is common and some is let separately to farmers.
   Sheep and young cattle are pastured from May to mid-September.
6. *Wavering Down*
   Grazing rights are attached to neighbouring farms. Sheep are pastured on the rough hill herbage from May to September. There is no water on the Down.

South Bristol Area   (Fig. 3.   13, 13a, 13b, 16, 17.)

This area is bounded by the Mendips on the south, the sea on the north-west and the Lias Clays or County Boundary on the north and east.

Except for the saltings at the mouth of the Bristol Avon, and the patches marked on Nailsea and Kenn Moors to show waterlogged, rushy land, the largest area of heath and rough pasture appear on outcrops of the same Mountain, or Carboniferous Limestone as that which forms the plateaus of Mendip, and are shown in detail on Fig. 11 and on the folding-map.

In general these areas carry thin pasture of varying quality which dries up in summer, with local patches of low scrub and stunted trees, where the limestone is close to the surface, or where there are miniature scarps and rough coombs.

The smaller, scattered areas include (*a*) old unimproved common and heath areas, shown on the Land Utilisation Survey sheets by the presence of the Ordnance Survey heath and rough pasture symbols, carrying heath, gorse, scrubby bushes and trees, natural pasture, bracken and bramble ; (*b*) improved enclosed fields which require constant care to prevent the growth of rushes and bracken (as on patches north of the Bristol Waterworks Reservoir No. 3) and locally on steep slopes in numerous places ; (*c*) forests and plantations cut and not replanted or otherwise tended (as in the triangular patch on the Bristol Road north of Ashton Hill Plantation, where a strip along the road has been built on, the remainder of the estate being scrub and waste at present.)

SOUTH BRISTOL AREA

1. *Wrington Warren and Backwell Hill*
   The land is very rough and there are no rights of stocking.
   Some bracken is cut and there are no sporting rights.
   On all the Mendip rough pasture areas rabbits are apt to become a nuisance if not continually kept down.

Cretaceous Area   (See Fig. 2 and Fig. 3, Area 7.)

This small area contains a considerable amount of marginal land besides that marked as heath and rough pasture.

The downlike higher surfaces are found chiefly on a covering of Clay-with-Flints and Chert, providing heavy soils, waterlogged where drainage is impeded. The steep slopes at the edges of this formation are on exposures of Greensands, narrow to the west, broader and less steep to the east by Chard and Combe St. Nicholas, where there are small exposures of chalk.

The Greensands, the character of which is shown by old quarries, sand and gravel-pits, receive the drainage of the heights as from a roof, a constant seepage which keeps them wet and leached, fostering the growth of bracken, rushes, bramble and scrub.

Where the surfaces of the Greensands exposures are less steep, and receive less direct drainage, by Chard and Combe St. Nicholas, the character of the surface improves. One large patch of heathland above Churchstanton lies mainly on the clays, and where a patch of plough appears, shows a black soil. Elsewhere it is covered with rush, gorse, bramble, bracken and coarse grasses.

In general the area provides poor soils which require constant care to preserve fertility.

The Rhaetic Scarp (Fig. 3, Area 8a and Northern edge of 8.)

Along the line of low but steep scarps overlooking West Sedgemoor, Aller Moor and North Moor, King's Sedgemoor and Somerton Moor, an exposure of Rhaetic beds (White Limestones, Black Shales and Marls, with Washdown and Sands below) appear from under the Lias Clays, and a fringe of poor land appears on the Land Utilisation Survey sheets bearing thorn, bramble, scrub, bracken and natural pasture of poor quality.

Crowcombe Heathfield (Fig. 3, Area 4.)

The heath lies on Pebble beds and Conglomerates bearing gorse, bracken, rushes and grass-heath and some areas of cut forest which have reverted to scrub and bracken.

An area west of the station has recently been improved into grassland, orchard and house property with gardens.

Other small, scattered areas and fields on the Land Utilisation Survey sheets are sufficiently explained either by the text on the sheets (golf-courses, local names, as " sheep slight " marking limestone pasture) by position on steep slopes under woods (almost always bracken on the Clays and Marls) or by the presence of quarries as at Hamdon Hill.

Small areas of natural pasture indicated by Moss and not included in Fig. 11, appear at the following points on the Land Utilisation Survey sheets :—

South-west of Dundry, Knowle Hill, Stantonbury Hill, Stoney Littleton, East of Combe Down (Monkton Combe), Dulcote Hill (Dinder), Creech Hill (Lamyatt), East of Stoney Stoke, South-east scarp of Polden Hills, North of Dundon, East of Dundon, West of High Ham, South-east of Corton Denham.

Coastal Areas and Alluvial Levels

Along the coast and about the river-mouths strips of yellow appear on the Land Utilisation Survey sheets marking lands which vary greatly in utility, from agricultural waste, sand dune and sand-dune marsh to good seasonal pasture, known as saltings.

About the mouths of the rivers these take the form of muddy salt marshes and salt-marsh pastures. Good examples of the latter are found on the south bank at the mouth of Bristol Avon, at the mouths of the Kenn, Axe and Parrett, by Minehead and at Porlock.

From Burnham along the coast north to Brean, sand dunes, and a drained dune marsh form the golf links, indicated on Land Utilisation Survey sheet 120. For an account of the vegetation see page 55.

The levels have the character of reclaimed salt marshes. The drier pastures, where neglected, become infested with the field thistle, the damper ones with the glauceous rush. Except on the peat areas, scattered fields shown as yellow on the Land Utilisation Survey sheets, notably in the region of Kenn Moor and Nailsea Moor, usually indicate the presence of glauceous rush.

The area shown as yellow, between Edington Burtle and Glastonbury, marks the Turf Moor area of heaths and peat diggings. The portion of the peat moors which remain in their natural condition are dominated by *Calluna*, *Erica tertralix*, *Myrica* or *Molinia*, or by an association of these plants. Such spots are locally termed " Heaths " and the place-name survives in land now under pasture. The peat is at least 12 feet deep and except in certain hollows or pits, it is comparatively dry. *Calluna* is dominant in the driest places and often occurs to the exclusion of almost all other plants. The bog-bell occurs as a dependent species about stems of the heather. The damper portions of the heath are dominated by the sweet-gale (*Myrica*), the blue moorgrass (*Molinia*) and the cross-leaved heath (*Erica tetralix*), either singly or in company. Rushes and sedges are abundant and after fires in newly drained places the French willow-herb, or the bracken, springs up in abundance. The hollow places left by the peat cutters develop into peat-bogs, with *Juncus squarrosus*, cotton grass, and a host of other marsh plants.

While the fluctuating tides, swift currents and westerly gales in the Severn Estuary create considerable turbulence, it is yet probable that in certain areas, notably at the mouth of the Parrett reclamation work could be profitably undertaken on the lines of operations on the German coast, where fence structures are pushed out onto the mudflats to trap silt and mud, and eventually establish salt marsh which can be further reclaimed.

The sea grass (" rice grass," *Spartina Townsendii*) which has successfully established itself at Southampton, might also be tried.[1]

THE HEATH AND ROUGH PASTURE AREAS OF THE COASTAL REGION AND THE ALLUVIAL AND PEAT LEVELS

1. *Catcott Heath*
   All except 10 acres is let to neighbouring farmers with their farms. Ten acres is common to the parish for turf cutting.

2. *Shapwick Heath*
   All let with farms.

3. *Street Heath*
   All fenced and privately owned. There is very little stocking (one or two cows). The land is used chiefly for peat drying and growing potatoes.

4. *Saltings—Wall Common (beyond Combwich, Stolford and Catsford)*
   There are 42 rights of stocking each for 20 sheep, running from 1st April to 31st December (with no right to put out ram). Rights for four months are sometimes sold. The right to Wickmore runs from September to January. The mowing rights of Wickmore are let to a farm.
   " Flukes " are present.

5. *Saltings—Easton in Gordano*
   Grazing rights are attached to farms in the parish, and must not exceed one and a half sheep per acre of holding in the parish. The pasture is available in spring, summer and autumn.
   The land is sea-washed.

---

[1] See " The Economic Possibilities of Rice Grass (*Spartina Townsendii*)," *Agricultural Progress*, Vol. XIII, 1936.
   Rice Grass is a robust plant with erect stems two or three feet high, and extensive, underground creeping stems.
   The natural range extends from the high-water mark of spring tides downwards to a level about six feet below that line. The soil must consist of mud or clay, or have these materials as a basis. Many of the mudflats now occupied by Rice Grass have hitherto been quite bare. At the same time it has shown its ability to extend over " saltings."
   The grass, once established, has the capacity to fix shifting mud, and to raise the bed on which it grows by arresting silt. In Holland, the surface of mudflats has been raised at a rate of from 6 to 10 inches a year.
   In Essex, the plant has been tried with success for coast protection.
   Rice grass is readily eaten by grazing animals, either cut green or in the form of hay, and they do well on it.
   The value for the Somerset saltings, and mudflats such as at Stert, should be obvious.

6. *Saltings—Fenning Island (beyond Combwich)*

The land belongs to two farmers, carrying about 150 sheep for three months in summer. The land is covered at spring tides and is apparently diminishing. The area is approximately 60 acres, and is reported to have been about 100 acres at an earlier period.

Agricultural "Waste"

Some of the heathlands (marked yellow) merge in places into land practically waste, and the Shapwick heath area has very small patches where peat diggings are being worked, or are abandoned and full of water. Full reference has, however, already been made to the heathlands.

NATURAL VEGETATION OF CENTRAL AND EAST SOMERSET[1]

1. The Coast Region

The Dune Formation. Conditions favouring the accumulation of sand-dune—prevailing winds at right angles to the coast, and expanses of mud and sand uncovered at low tide—are found south of Clevedon, though extensive dunes are only found between Burnham and Brean. In some places their formation is prevented by the building of embankments and walls, from which the sand is removed as it accumulates. In other places, the dunes have been reclaimed and converted into sandy pastures. The dunes have been laid down over tidal mud, and appear to be very recent in origin.

2. The General Salt Marsh Association

This occurs over the landward side of the association of *Salicornia herbacea* and the association of *Glyceria maritima* and *Triglochin maritimum*. The mud is scarcely ever tide-washed, and hence the conditions of plant-life are much more favourable. Though the ground is often wet or damp, periods of drought occur, when the surface is baked hard by the sun, and huge cracks are formed. This association is of the intermediate or mixed type : there is no one dominant plant, but instead a number of smaller vegetation units which may be termed plant societies ; and the number of species in the whole association is comparatively large. The whole furnishes an association with a dominant halophytic form, with both halophytes and hemi-halophytes among the secondary and dependent species.

Dominant and Subdominant Species

Aster tripolium, L. var. discoideus.	Armeria maritima, Willd.
Statice limonium, L.	Plantago maritima, L.
	Glyceria maritima, M. and K.

Abundant Species

Buda marina, Dum.	Beta maritima, L.
B. media, Dum.	Suaeda maritima, Dum.
Artemisia maritima, L.	Juncus Gerardi, Loisel.
Chenopodium rubrum, L. (agg.)	Triglochin maritimum, L.

3. The Salt Marsh Pastures

In many cases the salt marsh is grazed over by cattle, sheep and horses, and then the character of the association becomes greatly changed. The larger plants are kept down by the cattle, and

---

[1] Abridged from C. E. Moss, *Geographical Distribution of Vegetation in Somerset*, 1906. See also Fig. 11. The nomenclature of the *London Catalogue of British Plants*, 9th edition, is followed, except in the case of aggregate species, marked " agg.," when the nomenclature is that of Hooker's *Students' Flora* (3rd edition). Species in inverted commas are taken from the Rev. C. A. Murray's *Flora of Somerset*.

the coarser ones dug up occasionally by the farmers. In extreme cases, the plants are so closely cropped as to render their diagnosis a matter of difficulty. Drains or rhines are sometimes constructed, and thus the marsh becomes drier, and agricultural weeds appear. In the rhines dense tangled masses of *Ruppia* and *Zannichellia* occur. The extensive Levels of the district are muddy salt marshes reclaimed and now wholly given over to agriculture. At the mouths of the rivers, there is every possible gradation to be seen from the *Salicornia* association to the rich alluvial pastures of the Levels. An excellent bird's-eye view of a transitional area may be obtained from the south-west of Brean Down, looking towards Brent Knoll. In addition to the species occurring in the salt marsh (any of which may occur here and there), the following may also be found in the partially reclaimed salt marsh, and it is interesting to note the intrusion of pasture plants. An association of plants which owes its existence to the influence of man has been called by Dr. Smith, a substituted association. The pastures of the Levels are examples of such associations ; and the partially reclaimed salt marsh is a transitional stage from the natural salt marsh association to the substituted or artificial associations of the Levels.

Trifolium squamosum, L.	Chenopodium, spp.
T. hybridum, L.	Atriplex, spp.
T. repens, L.	Polygonum aviculare, L.
T. fragiferum, L.	var. arenastrum (Bor.).
Bupleurum, tenuissimum, L.	Alopecurus pratensis, L.
Caucalis daucoides, L.	Agrostis palustris, Huds.
Achillæa Millefolium, L.	Poa pratensis, L.
Matricaria inodora, L.	Agropyron repens, Beauv.
Leontodon autumnalis, L.	var. barbatum, D.-J.
Plantago Coronopus, L.	Hordeum secalinum, Schreb.

4. Peat-Moor

The following are the characteristic members of the dry and damp heaths of the peat-moor.

Dominant Species

Calluna Erica, DC.	Myrica Gale, L.
Erica Tetrallix, L.	Molinia varia, Schrank.

Subdominant Species

Epilobium angustifolium, L.	Pteris aquilina, L.
Salix cinerea, L.	Lastræa Thelypteris, Presl.

Abundant Species

Rubus idæus, L.	Scirpus cæspitosus, L.
Potentilla silvestris, Neck.	Carex paniculata, L.
Galium saxatile, L.	C. Goodenowii, J. Gay.
Rumex Acetosella, L.	C. binervis, Sm.
Juncus squarrosus, L.	Deschampsia flexuosa, Trin.
J. communis, L. (agg.)	Festuca ovina, L.
Luzula erecta, Desv.	Nardus stricta, L.

5. Heath Pasture

The uncultivated grasslands of the Sandstones are dominated by rough heathy grasses (e.g., *Agrostis* spp., *Festuca viona*, *Deschampsia flexuosa*, *Nardus*, *Molinia*), and small shrubby plants, among which dwarfed ling, heather and whortleberry are characteristic, and often abundant. In other words, these tracts belong to the heath type of vegetation. Many examples are met with on the Sandstones of the Mendip Hills. One example is at Stratton Common, on the

Coal Measures ; but this particular tract is well pastured, and is in some places hardly to be distinguished from the ordinary permanent pasture of the farmland. This is the same difficulty as the distinction between " H " and " M " on the Land Utilisation maps. On the igneous outcrops, too, this type of vegetation occurs, although the large Downhead Common is now largely covered with a plantation of conifers. Heath pasture also occurs on the exposed summits of the Old Red Sandstone, and on other places on the Mendip Hills rendered rough and uneven by ancient tumuli, old pits and pit refuse. On a small tract of land adjoining Alfred's Tower (on the Greensand) on its south side, and surrounded by woods, the ling is almost abundant enough to justify the vegetation being classed with the heather moor type. When well-pastured and manured, many plants of the heath pasture are partially eradicated, and plants of the permanent pastures and meadows enter the association as invading species. The following species are characteristic of the heath pasture of this district :—

Polygala serpyllacea, Weihe.	Rumex acetosella, L.
Linum catharticum, L.	Luzula erecta, Desv.
Ulex europæus, L. (agg.).	Carea pilulifera, L.
Rubus fruticosus, L. (agg.).	C. binervis, Sm.
Galium saxatile, L.	Anthoxanthum odoratum, L.
Cnicus palustris, Willd.	Agrostis vulgaris, With.
Vaccimium Myrtillus, L.	Deschampsia flexuosa, Trin.
Calluna Erica, DC.	Holcus mollis, L.
Erica cinerea, L.	H. lanatus, L.
Erythræa Centaureum, Pers.	Molinia varia, Schrank.
Euphrasia officinalis, L.	Briza media, L.
Pedicularis sylvatica, L.	Festuca ovina, L.
Thymus Serpyllum, L. (agg.).	Nardus stricta, L.
Teucrium Scorodonia, L.	Pteris aquillina, L.

6. Upland Heather Moor

Association of *Calluna-Erica*. The only upland heather moor of the district occurs around Blackdown Beacon (1,068 feet) on the Old Red Sandstone. The heather is dominant over an area nearly 2 miles long and 1 mile broad. The term " moor " in Somerset is confined to wet ground, often peaty, but not necessarily so, such as the Turf Moor around Shapwick, the peaty but now drained Sedgemoor, many non-peaty and now drained parts of the Levels, such as Curry Moor, and wet upland peaty tracts, such as Exmoor. Ecologically the term Heather Moor is used to designate tracts of land dominated by *Calluna* or species of *Erica*, usually covered with peat. The summit of Blackdown is exactly such an area, and resembles the upland heather moors of the Pennines and of Scotland more than the lowland peat moors of Somerset previously described. Although the heather moor at Blackdown is the only good example in the central or eastern parts of the County, upland heather moors and heaths are well represented in the south-west of Somerset, as on the Quantocks, on Brendon and on Exmoor. Cotton-grass moors are not represented on the uplands of the east, but possibly occur on Exmoor. No species occurs on Blackdown which does not also occur on the Pennines, but several species found on the Pennines are absent from Blackdown. On the heather moors of south-west Somerset, however, some of these north of England species occur, and a few (e.g. *Agrostis setacea*) are found which are absent from the Pennine moors. The following species were noted on the drier portions of the heather moor on Blackdown.

Dominant Species

Calluna Erica, DC.	Erica Tetralix, L.	E. cinerea, L.

Subdominant Species

Vaccinium Myrtillus, L.   Molinia varia, Schrank.
Agrostis, spp.   Pteris aquilina, L.

Abundant or Frequent Species

Polygola serpyllacea, Weihe.   C. binervis, Sm.
Ulex europæus, L. (agg.).   Agrostis canina, Curtis.
Potentilla silvestris, Neck.   A. palustris, Huds.
Galium saxatile, L.   A. vulgaris, Wilb.
Veronica officinalis, L.   Deschampsia flexuosa, Beauv.
Rumex acetosella, L.   Sieglingia decumbens, Bernh.
Luzula erecta, L.   Festuca ovina, L.
Scirpus cæspitosus, L.   Nardus stricta, L.
Carex Goodenowii, J. Gay.   Lomaria Spicant, Desv.

In wet places the following occur :—

Ranunculus hederaceus, L.   Juncus effusus, L.
R. Flammula, L.   J. conglomeratus, L.
Viola palustris, L.   J. lamprocarpus, Ehrh.
Stellaria uliginosa, Murr.   J. acutiflorus, Ehrh.
Peplus Portula, L.   Potamogeton polygonifolius, Pour.
" Schollera Oxycoccus, Roth." Rare.   Eriophorum angustifolium, Roth.
Pedicularis sylvatica, L.   Carex panicea, L.
Narthecium Ossifragum, Huds.   Deschampsia cæspitosa, Beauv.

7. Natural Pasture

The uncultivated grasslands of the Yorkshire Pennines may be subdivided into two main types—Natural Pasture and Heath Pasture. Both types are met with in East Somerset, and heath pasture has already been described as commonly occurring on the Sandstones. Natural pasture may be defined as primitive grassland without heath plants, and is characteristic of the primitive grasslands of the Carboniferous Limestone, the Chalk, the Oolites and the Lias. The natural pasture is characterised by grasses of a higher agricultural value than the grasses of the heath pasture, and by plants which do not seem to flourish on soils containing humic acids. The soil is usually very shallow, and the plants so much cropped by sheep and nibbled by rabbits that it is often a matter of difficulty to determine the species. Shrubby and arboreal plants are practically absent. Several small examples of natural pasture occur on the Oolitic downs around Bath. These small but numerous tracts are vestiges of a much larger area, which has become greatly restricted owing to the land being brought under cultivation within the last hundred years. For example, Lansdown in Billingsley's time, in 1795, consisted of 1,000 acres ; but it is now almost entirely under cultivation. Other isolated examples of natural pasture occur on the summits of the Oolitic hills, as on Dundry Hill, Small Down and Creech Hill. The summits of the Poldens, on the Lias, also furnish excellent examples of natural pasture. Not much of the Chalk occurs in the present district ; but a very extensive Chalk area, including the Wiltshire Downs and Salisbury Plain, occurs to the east of the district. Good examples of Chalk downs in the present district are Long Knoll and White Sheet Hill, where the vegetation is identical with that of the uncultivated grasslands of the Oolites and Lias.

8. The Limestone Heath

This plant association is marked by the occurrence of *Calluna, Erica cincrea* and a few other heath plants growing amongst plants usually regarded as typical of limestone soils. It occurs on all the uncultivated tracts of the Carboniferous Limestone ; but it is scarcely universal on any of them, as natural pasture occurs where the subsoil is very shallow, or where there is much nibbling by rabbits or sheep. On the Carboniferous Limestone of the present district, the natural pasture is confined to uncultivated portions where the soil is very shallow ; and whenever the soil reaches a depth of about 3 inches or more, heath plants begin to assert themselves. On the limestone heath the phenomenon is thus presented of heath plants, such as *Calluna, Erica cinerea* and *Sieglingia (Triodea) decumbens*, growing side by side with plants characteristic of the natural pasture, such as *Spiræa filipendula, Helianthemum, Chamæcistus* and *Viola hirta*. On the plateau east of Cheddar Gorge, for example, for some distance along the top of the cliffs the soil is very shallow, and the vegetation is that of the natural pasture type ; but further from the cliffs, where the soil is deeper, the limestone heath is found. Even on the natural pasture, heather and heath plants are frequently found on old ant-heaps. The soil of the limestone heath is sufficiently moist to support such a plant as *Cnicus palustris*, which is abundant ; but on the whole, those heath plants, such as *Vaccinium myrtillus* and *Erica tetralix*, which are found in moist and peaty situations on heaths are absent. Again, the limestone heath may merge gradually into the limestone copse ; the passage occurs when the soil becomes still deeper and damper, and where the shade becomes more pronounced, conditions which occur at the base of cliffs and in the smaller gorges or coombs. The following is a selected list of plants from the limestone heath of Somersetshire.

Dominant and Subdominant Species

Ulex europæus, L. (agg.).
Cratægus Oxycantha, L. Dwarfed.
Calluna Erica, DC.
Erica cinerea, L.

Festuca, spp., and other grasses.

Besides the following, many plants of the ash copse also occur :—

Polygala vulgaris, L. (agg.).
Hypericum pulchrum, L.
Linum catharticum, L.
Lotus corniculatus, L.
Rubus, spp.
Peterium sanguisorba, L.
Rosa, spp.
Pipinella Saxifraga, L.
Galium saxitile, L.
Cnicus palustris, Willd.
C. acaulis, Willd.
Hieracium Pilosella, L.
Leontondon hirtus, L.
L. hispidus, L.
Erythræa Centaureum, P.
Veronica officinalis, L.
Euphrasia officinalis, L.
Thymus, spp.
Plantago media, L.
P. lanceolata, L.

Rumex Acetosella, L.
Luzela campestris, L.
Carex flacca, L.
C. pilulifera, L.
C. verna, L.
Anthoxanthum odoratum.
Briza media, L.
Phleum pratense, L.
Holcus lanatus, L.
Tristum pratense, Pers.
Avena pubescens, Huds.
Arrhenatherum avenaceum.
Sieglingia decumbens, Bern.
Bromus mollis, L.
Cynosurus cristatus, L.
Dactypis glomerata, L.
Briza media, L.
Festuca ovina, L. (agg.).
Pteris aquilina, L.

9. Parklands

Parklands occur in the vicinity of mansions and country houses, and are, as a rule, quite artificial in character. They are interesting as furnishing examples of exotic trees, and the grounds at Stourton House, Kilmington, and Victoria Park, Bath, are both excellent arboreta. The following exotic trees are often planted in the parklands of the district : *Magnolia* spp., *Lirodendron tupipifera* (tulip-tree), *Tilia* spp., *Rhus* sp. (sumach), *Planatus* spp. (plane-tree),

Æsculus spp. (horse-chestnut), *Quercus ilex* (evergreen oak), *Q. corris* (Turkey oak), *Castanea vulgaris* (chesnut) and species of *Juniperus* (juniper), *Cupressus* (cypress), *Thuja* (arbor vitæ), *Sequoia* (American big tree), *Picea* (spruce), *Abies* (silver fir), *Pseudotsuga* (Douglas fir), *Pinus* (pine), *Cedrus* (cedar, deodar), and *Larix* (larch).

C. FORESTS AND WOODLAND

The map showing the distribution of the woodlands and plantations of Somerset is combined with that of the heathland and rough pastures. (See folding map.)

On the Land Utilisation Survey sheets the woods appear in dark green, with the Ordnance Survey symbols representing coniferous, deciduous or mixed types of trees. Recent plantations, however, appear without the Ordnance symbols, except where woods have been cut down and replanted, which areas are almost invariably coniferous, chiefly Larch, Douglas Fir or Spruce. With the exception of certain Forestry Commission areas, new plantations are small, and considerable tracts of woodland have been cut and not replanted (the Great War was responsible for much of the cutting).   These are coloured yellow on the Land Utilisation Survey sheets and the area is in most cases indicated by the presence of the forest symbol on the tract under the Land Utilisation Survey indication of utilisation, usually yellow, (as at Shapwick Heath, and the woods above Sandford and Burrington), to mark rough heath, sometimes green, to mark grassland.

The Land Utilisation Survey sheets cannot, conveniently, be made to show hedgerow timber and the nature of fences (except on the " moor areas " where the chief rhines and ditches are shown), and the aspect of the country depends to a considerable extent on these.

There are four main types of fence in Somerset corresponding to different types of country : (*a*) the beech and stone-faced bank shelter fences of the west, corresponding in the main to the improved Devonian uplands, and repeated over a limited area of the Quantocks ; (*b*) the widespread blackthorn or hawthorn hedge, with or without banks, associated with oak, ash, holly or elm hedgerow timber, and found on the Trias, Lias, over most of the Jurassic beds, and the Coal Measures, in the valleys of the Devonian as well as on the alluvium where this attains sufficient height above flood-level ; (*c*) the stone walls, found on the Carboniferous Limestone, the White Lias stone, and the Oolites and slates ; and (*d*) the rhines and ditches of the alluvial levels, often lined with pollard-trees, chiefly willows.

The following general account of the woods and plantations has been based on the *Geographical Distribution of Vegetation in Somerset*, by C. E. Moss, M.Sc., and the Land Utilisation Survey sheets have been checked with the accompanying map, which shows few divergences in every case explained by the field-notes on the Land Utilisation Survey six-inch MS. sheets. Moss's account is out of print, and difficult for the general reader to obtain, and the information and conclusions reached are authoritative, so no excuse is needed for the considerable quotations here reproduced, but his survey finished on a north–south line running through Taunton, and so westward of this, information given in this account is derived only from the six-inch Land Utilisation Survey field-sheets. " Natural " woodlands have been presumed to be the same as on similar geological formations to the east, though on the high country about Exford and to the west the prevalence of beech in hedges, grown often to a height of 40 feet or more, and of birch in plantations, both established within the last hundred years, as well as considerable plantations of ash in the valleys below the 900-foot contour, suggests that a detailed botanical survey might amplify the conclusions which Moss based on a study of part of the Quantocks.

This western area has for a considerable period supported a more active forestry than is apparent in most other parts of the County, owing to the constant demand for pit-props in South Wales.

The Alluvial Levels and Peat Moors

Not a single example of natural woodland occurs and plantations are uncommon, though on the peat moors, birch, alder and oak may have been aboriginally wild (Moss). Clark,[1] however, states that in the Brent (Brue) Level are found the remains of trees in various positions and occasionally upright which have every appearance of antiquity and are probably the remains of a forest covering the extent of the plain consisting principally of yew, oak and alder ; the former predominating in the neighbourhood of Burtle, the oak near Sharpham and the alder in South, or Alder (Aller ?) Moor, so-called from the great abundance of those trees in the time of the Abbots of Glastonbury.

Plantations occur chiefly north and south of the Upper Brue (about Shapwick and Meare Heath and Tadham and Westhay Moors) and consist chiefly of birch, Scots pine, alder, spruce, oak and larch. None of those which appear on the Land Utilisation Survey sheet, north of the Brue, are to be found on Moss's map (published 1906) but they consist chiefly of shelter-belts. The heathland appearing north of Decoy Pool Farm was a coniferous plantation, cut and not replanted.

About Glastonbury Heath and Westhay Heath the new plantations (coniferous) are clearly indicated by the absence on the Land Utilisation Survey sheet (No. 120, published) of the Ordnance Survey conventional forest signs.

The Upland Area

From the standpoint of vegetation it has been found sufficient to subdivide the soils of the upland area into only three classes, Sandstones Grits and Slates, Limestones, and deep Marls and Clays.

The Sandstones. (With which are grouped the Slates and Grits of the Quantocks.)

These areas are indicated in the Geological map, Fig. 2 and include parts of the Mendips (practically without natural woods) ; the Coal Measures (north of Mendip) ; the Upper Greensand, a narrow belt of which is included within the County Boundary marked by a belt of woodland lying between Wincanton and Frome and another area by Chard ; and the Quantocks, with which it is assumed the Western Devonian high lands may be grouped at least with respect to the general observations on natural woodlands.

The ultimate plant formation of the Sandstones and Grits appears to be an oak wood, but almost all the primitive woods of these districts have been converted into farmland or have degenerated into heaths or moors.

An extensive series of oak woods occurs on the Greensand North of Penselwood and forms part of what was the Ancient Forest of Selwood. Much recent plantation is, however, coniferous. Moss marks the Witham Park region as coniferous (larch over 100 years old) for over 2 miles south of Gore Hill, and recently the Forestry Commission have added a further coniferous plantation over the whole extent of King's Wood Warren, overgrown with bracken, and natural copses of oak, birch and sallow, marked on Moss's map as Heath Pasture.

The Devonian Uplands

On the improved ground, this area gives an impression of being well wooded, owing to the high beech hedgerow timber. The heaths of the upper slopes are practically treeless over wide stretches.

[1] Prize Essay on the Somersetshire Levels, *Bath and West Agric. Journal*, 1855.

About Exford, and to the West, the small plantations consist chiefly of beech, birch, Douglas fir and larch. A small plantation of larch, made before 1904, and now about 15 feet high, stands south of Simonsbath at approximately 1,400 feet.

Southwards and westwards in the sheltered valleys of the Barle, Exe and Haddon, as well as beech (which appears chiefly in hedgerows), and birch, well-grown oak and ash appear, with some sycamore and plantations of Douglas fir, larch and other conifers.

To the North the large tracts of forest which appear on the seaward slopes consist of mixed coniferous and deciduous species of the same order. About Luxborough, deciduous and mixed forests run up to about 1,000 feet, and large comparatively recent (since 1904) coniferous plantations, chiefly larch, extend over Croyden Hill and south-west of Luxborough.

Two areas of recent plantation, the work of the Forestry Commission, appear on the Quantocks. The largest of these, West of Overstowey and Plainsfield, shows on the Land Utilisation Survey sheet the Ordnance Survey symbols for deciduous and mixed forest, but the old forest has been cut and the whole recently replanted chiefly with Douglas fir.

The other recent plantation, also coniferous, lies on the seaward slope of the Quantocks.

Other woods on and about the Quantocks are mixed, while oak, various conifers and old well-grown beeches appear in Bagborough Wood.

The woods of the Coal Measures are also naturally oak woods, except in low-lying, damp places where ash, alder and other trees share dominance with the oak. At the present time they are much mixed with coniferous and there is little evidence of replanting where they have been cut over.

On the Quantocks, hedgerow timber includes hazel, briar, holly, ash and elm. The two large areas, Great Wood, on the west centre, and the woods appearing at the seaward end of the heath country have been recently planted by the Forestry Commission with conifers. Great Wood, on the Land Utilisation Survey sheets, still bears the Ordnance Survey mixed symbol but most of the oak has been cut out, except around the edges, and the bulk replanted chiefly with Douglas fir.

Other woods on the Quantocks are mixed with oak and various conifers.

There is not (according to Moss) a natural beech wood of even moderate dimensions to be found in the district. Isolated trees and small clumps of beeches occur here and there, and small belts and plantations are not uncommon. Occasionally the specimens reach great size.

The Limestones   (See map, Fig. 2.)

The Carboniferous Limestone is, with the exception of a short break at Loxton, continuous from Elm near Frome to the coast, where it ends in the five rocky headlands, Brean Down, Anchor Head, Swallow Cliff, the cliffs at Clevedon and at Portishead Point. From Clevedon two arms of limestone extend inland, one terminating at Portishead Point, the other broadening out considerably in the neighbourhood of Wraxall where it curves northward to Bristol; and a large extent from Backwell Hill and from Congresbury to Dundry.

There are outcrops of Lias limestone in places, as in the vicinity of High Ham, but generally deep Marls and Clays prevail where the Lias comes to the surface.

Outcrops of Oolitic limestones are frequent in the east on the Jurassic belt (See Fig. 2)—especially abundant in the neighbourhood of Bath.

Chalk appears in the south-west in the neighbourhood of Crewkerne and Chard. Generally speaking the soil over the more massive limestones is a shallow Marl, whilst over the softer limestones the soil is a deeper and rubbly Marl.

The vegetation of the limestones is much more varied in character than that of the other rocks and soils of the district. The woods are dominated by the common ash, except in the case of recent plantations or replanting. Natural copses of ash are numerous, the larger of which possess many features in common with ash woods, while in others the proportion of trees, shrubs and shade-loving species becomes gradually smaller until the ash copse merges into limestone heath.

The chief ash woods, as noted by Moss, appear in black on Fig. 11, from which more detailed study can be made on the Land Utilisation Survey sheets.

The oak exists as a secondary species but it is not abundant, and beech, horse chestnut, yew and white beam are occasionally found.

Some of the ash woods are partly the result of modern forestry, and other trees are introduced, with the usual mixture of conifers ; some appear to be primitive, probably the scattered remnants of woods which existed in and around the historic forest of Mendip, the dominant tree in which was probably ash.

In many of the ash woods there is a thick undergrowth of hazel, wych-elm or privet.

On the limestone slopes of the hills wherever the land is not under cultivation and a certain amount of shade is afforded, a spontaneous copse or scrub tends to become established, which is a characteristic of the coombs and gorges of the district. Ash is a prominent feature, but is usually dwarfed owing to the shallow soil, and shares place with hazel, wych-elm, hawthorn, yew and white beam, but where damper conditions are found the scrub or copse merges into ash wood. In drier and more exposed places the limestone copse becomes more scrubby until it merges insensibly into limestone heath. Frequent examples of this may be seen along the south Mendip Scarps, where the Land Utilisation Survey sheets are marked in yellow.

Deep Marls and Clays

This generalisation covers most of the County apart from the areas already mentioned, and includes a considerable part of the Jurassic belt from the south to the vicinity of Bath.

Oak–hazel woods are numerous, occurring extensively on the clay soils of the Lias, Bradford clay, Fuller's Earth and Oxford Clay, and of the Jurassic belt, those from Butleigh to Copley being excellent examples.

The small copses which spring up naturally on exposures of Lias limestone and in the Lias flagstone quarries are dominated by ash.

The oak–hazel woods are scattered throughout the district especially on the New Red Marl (Trias) and the marly clays of the Lias and Oolites. The oak is the dominant tree but in these woods it is not planted so thickly as on the Sandstones. Coppice trees, usually hazel, are planted thickly among the oak standards, and the hazel coppice is exploited regularly in many areas. Certain patches are cut to the stumps each year so that the whole coppice is renewed every ten years.

Many of these woods are nearly two centuries old, but others are more ancient and possess characteristics of primitive woodland.

It will be seen that three types of woodland may be distinguished in the County : ash woods on the Limestones, oak woods on the Sandstones and Grits, and oak–hazel woods on the deep Marls and Clays. The deep soils of the Marls, Clays and Greensand are favourable to *Quercus pedunculata* which species is abundant ; *Quercus sessiliflora* is found on the shallow soils of the Old Red Sandstone and Grits.

The introduction of coniferous trees into the woods of the County on an extensive scale has already been noted. Neither larch, pine, spruce nor Douglas fir is native to the district, but have been found profitable in re-afforestation and new plantation. There are no large spruce plantations but small ones exist.

Plantations

Besides the large plantations mentioned comparatively new small plantations are common, consisting chiefly of larch, spruce, Scots pine and beech. Although the larch is commonly planted it can scarcely be regarded as a successful introduction as the larch canker (*Peziza Wilkommii*) is often to be observed, in some plantations very prevalent. The numerous plantations and wind-breaks on the Mendip plateau consist chiefly of pine, spruce and larch, with a mixture of beech and sycamore, all introduced.

Hedgerows

These are better developed on the Marls and Clays, replaced on the rock formations by walls of white limestone (*Carboniferous Limestone*) or darker, from Lower Limestone Shales, and Grits and Sandstones.

In the east, particularly on Midford Sands, the high, rank hedgerows recall the Devonshire lanes. The oak, ash and English elm are the commonest three trees of the hedgerow, the elm being probably an alien introduced, since it is found only in hedgerows, in fields or about parkland. It does not produce ripe seed freely, and seedlings are quite rare, if not absent.

The wych-elm, however, is indigenous and is found in nearly all the primitive woods of the district, abundant in some.

The indigenous maple and introduced sycamore and horse chestnut are also common, and the beech frequent (almost the only one in Exford district), larch, Scots pine, spruce and fir are also common. Pollard trees are common in lowland districts chiefly willows, ash, oak, elm and lime.

Forestry Commission Land in Somerset

Details of the areas planted in Somerset by the Forestry Commission to date are set out below :—

Forest Year	Forests		
	Brendon (acres)	Bruton (acres)	Quantocks (acres)
1921	240	—	—
1922	168	—	253
1923	116	—	232
1924	44	—	240
1925	50	—	200
1926	95	—	252
1927	140	—	190
1928	207	—	122
1929	130	—	142
1930	101	76	56
1931	107	61	22
1932	88	101	—
1933	76	53	—
1934	48	54	4
1935	55	40	—
1936	52	19	5
Totals	1,717	404	1,718

FOREST WORKERS' HOLDINGS

Forest	No.
Brendon	2 completed
Bruton	Nil
Quantocks	2 completed

D. WITHY BEDS

The map (Fig. 12) shows the distribution of cultivated "withy" willows in Somerset, shown on the one-inch Land Utilisation Survey sheets by brown lines. While every field shown was under willows at the date when the survey was made, it is possible that a few fields have

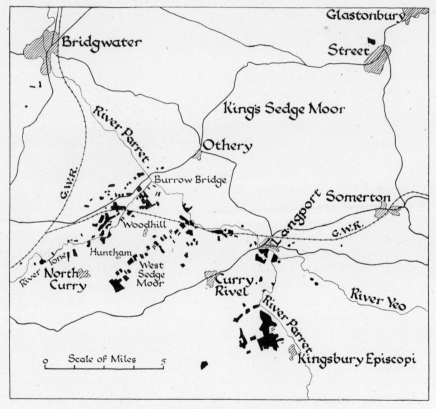

Fig. 12.—Withy Beds of Central Somerset.

Withy Beds are shown in black, towns and chief villages are ruled. Main roads are shown by lines.

been missed, as some areas were checked or surveyed when the land was under flood. Many fields, however, shown on the Ordnance Survey six-inch sheets as under willows, have been since rooted up and grassed.

The total area of the fields as shown is approximately 1,740 acres.[1]

[1] The area was computed from the 1-inch sheets by squared paper, a very rough method. The map is to scale and a closer estimate could probably be made.

E

Besides the willows planted and tilled in fields, a few cricket-bat willows are grown, chiefly in the neighbourhood of Street. Tree willows (pollards) used mainly for banking purposes, are usually cut every three years, giving a supply of stout sticks.

The following short account of willow-growing in Somerset has been taken from *An Economic Survey of the Somerset Willow-Growing Industry*[1] (July, 1932), in which is to be found also detailed information regarding the cost of growing willows, processes, marketing and prices obtained, pests and treatment, etc.

The bulletin gives the following total acreage of willows for 1932 :—

	Acres
West Moor, Kingsbury.	450
Langport	115
Wick Moor	70
Aller Moor	30
West Sedgemoor	385
Stanmoor	160
Curry Moor and Ling Moor	205
Hay Moor	75
West Moor, Knapp	30
Hitchings and Salt Moor	50
Total	1,570

The total acreage was made up for the Bristol Report, from the acreage of willows appearing on the twenty-five-inch Ordnance Survey sheets, and if the revision of these is not more up-to-date than is the case with the six-inch sheets, the total acreage for 1932 as stated is likely to be only approximate.[2] During the present survey (1935) the position and extent of willows grown were found to vary greatly from the position and extent as marked on the Ordnance sheets, many having been rooted up and the fields grassed down.

The cultivation of willows, confined to the limited area shown on the map, is of comparatively recent date. It is certain that withies were not grown in this area earlier than 120 years ago, probably being first used in the making of butchers' and bakers' baskets.

The first beds were planted in West Sedgemoor, but in most of the moors the first plantings are still within the memory of living inhabitants. On Curry Moor the original plantings could not have been more than 60 years ago.

The demand for wicker chairs greatly stimulated the willow-growing industry, but even before the War these were falling out of favour and the decline in demand has continued since. To-day there is some production of baskets of various sorts.

Even about 40 years ago there were only three people who sent willows to market. Around this nucleus developed the community of small growers dependent in some ways upon the large growers. In particular, the marketing of the produce of the smaller grower was done through the channels developed by the larger growers, who tended to accumulate the production of the whole area.

At the end of the War, the willow industry shared in the boom, and under the influence of high prices (reaching a peak of 27/– per bolt, where the 1932 price was 4/6) small men invested capital at inflated prices. The wave of optimism led not only to some growth in the numbers and size of small, independent undertakings, but to sharing in the profits by pieceworkers, to whom land was let by the large-scale growers.

[1] University of Bristol, Bulletin No. 9. C. V. Dawe, M.Com., and J. E. Blundell, M.Com.
[2] This appears to be the only statement in the bulletin which is open to serious criticism.

Sometimes these small-scale workers rented land ploughed but unplanted, sometimes both ploughed and planted, and became tenants having a common landlord and wholesale purchaser, but assuming the risks of production.

For some growers the cultivation of withies is only a part of their full occupation. There are general farmers in the district who have their own withy beds ; some carry the operations right through to preparation for market ; but frequently the withies are sold by auction, usually in half-acre plots, standing green in the beds, by owners who are either general farmers, or local business and professional men who have acquired beds as investments. The considerable labour involved in cultivating and preparing withies for market, and the local development of home industry in weaving baskets, etc., has in the past made the willow business a profitable part-time occupation for working people in the locality whose other occupations include glove-making, hay cutting, dredging and banking the drainage rhines and ditches, and farm labouring.

Acreage of Holdings

The following table is made up from statistics of willow acreage collected and analysed for 83 holdings :—

| | Holdings | | Willows | |
Willow Acreage	No.	Percentage	Acres	Percentage
Up to 5 acres	39	47	115	12
Above 5 acres and up to 10 acres .	21	25	117	18
Above 10 acres and up to 50 acres .	22	27	540	56
Over 50 acres	1	1	134	14
	83	100	966	100

Varieties

Of the total 966 acres surveyed, a classification according to variety of willows grown was obtained for 880 acres, the seven leading varieties being shown on the following table : —

Variety	Acres	Percentage of Total
Black (Mole or " Maul ") . .	582½	66.2
Champion Rod . . .	106½	12·1
Spaniards	95½	10·9
Osiers	29	3·3
Old French . . .	20	2·3
Red Bud (Dicky Meadows) .	15½	1·8
French New Kind . . .	10	1·1
Other Varieties[1] . . .	21	2·3
	880	100·0

The opinion, however, that the most common and well-established variety in the locality is for some reason deteriorating, is widespread.

[1] Amongst which are : Harrison, London Market, Black Rod, Blue Violet, Long Skein, Trustworthy, Pyramidalis and Wessender.

Establishing a Plantation

Considerable variety of opinion exists as to the best times for ploughing and planting, according probably to the strictly local conditions of shelter, and particularly, flooding on moor areas.

The consensus of opinion seems to favour either summer fallowing and planting in autumn, or late winter ploughing and planting from the end of January to March.

The ranks are planted on the average from 20 ins. to 2 feet apart, in Kingsbury, invariably 2 feet apart, but distance as low as 10 ins. has been mentioned.

The number of sets planted per acre is given from 16,000 to 20,000, with an average figure of about 19,000.

The withy " sets " are cut from specially sorted willow known as " drawn withies " which are more expensive per bolt, on an average (1932) 6/6 per 1,000 sets.

Cultivation

The amount of attention given to cultivation, particularly to weeding, makes a great difference to the crop obtained.

The principal item in the cultivation of the withybed is weeding which is accomplished either by " cleaning " with a hook, or by hoeing, the former practice being usual in the greater area, namely in the Stoke St. Gregory and Burrowbridge districts. July seems to be the principal season for this operation. Very often cleaning is done only once, either on account of expense or because some growers stock their plots with sheep in the spring which takes the place of one weeding. A second cleaning sometimes precedes cutting so that as little weed as possible shall get mixed with the bundles.

In the Kingsbury Episcopi district, weeding is regularly performed with a hoe, in April if dry enough, and again at the end of May, or even a third time in June or July. On Westmoor there are practically no facilities for stocking with cattle or sheep. Some horse-hoeing is done, and the rows are rather farther apart than in other districts.

Spraying

Practice of spraying to prevent blight varies considerably, but where it is done at all it is usually done twice.

Cutting the Withies

The cutting season lasts through the winter commencing as soon as the leaves have fallen in November or December, or may be delayed till the spring when a crop is said to be " Whitened off the stock." The advantage of spring cutting is that it keeps back the growth of the subsequent crop, or at least prevents a too-early shoot which is damaged by frost, but the grower who leaves cutting till the spring runs the risk of finding the weather unsuited to cutting. One of the main objects in autumn cutting is to get on with the process known as " buffing " during the winter months.

The rate of cutting varies, on the average between 30 and 40 " bundles " a day.

Crop Yields

The figures collected are consistent in placing an average crop at about 200 bolts[1] per acre, but the crop varies widely according to the soil, the age of the bed and especially the season and the management.

[1] In the Bristol Report there is confusion in the use of the terms " bolt " and " bundle " which appear sometimes to be synonymous and sometimes to refer to different stages of sorting and treatment. This presumed that " bolt " is sometimes used to refer to a marketable bundle only, and sometimes used loosely for bundle.

One grower provided the following figures :—crop grown in 1931, 150 bundles ; 1930, 188 bundles ; 1929, 103 bundles ; 1928, 171 bundles ; 1927, 251 bundles ; 1926, 220 bundles. (The figures are for a bed over 20 years old.)

Another, with a bed 12 years old in 1932 gave :—1930, 224 bolts per acre ; 1929, 317 bolts per acre ; 1928, 291 ; 1927, 334.

The figures show marked differences in average level between a bed of 12 years old and one of 20.

The best crops are likely to be obtained between the second and the seventh years of growth, and a reduction in yield occurs as a rule after the twelfth year, although this depends on the character of the soil.

Weather and Growth

Opinion is unanimous that the withy produces its best crop when the summer is hot and dry. In hot weather the growth may be put on at the rate of an inch a day. Rain is not wanted in the growing season. While the withy is maintaining steady growth it is less troubled by flies, while, if the season is detrimental to growth, spraying is also difficult, " button top " becomes serious and bushy tops are the consequence.

Yield of Green Bundles per Acre	Stoke St. Gregory, Burrowbridge		Kingsbury		Whole Area	
	No. of Growers	Acreage	No. of Growers	Acreage	No. of Growers	Acreage
Over 250 .	1	12	1	3	2	15
250 .	2	11	4	152	6	163
200–250 . .	4	56	2	50	6	106
200 . .	12	99	6	32	18	131
150–200 . .	8	49	1	3	9	52
150 . .	6	87	0	0	6	87
120–140 . .	7	93	2	13	9	106
100 and under .	7	32	0	0	7	32
	47	439	16	253	63	692

The yield is generally higher in Kingsbury than in Stoke St. Gregory and Burrowbridge. In Kingsbury the average yield is 212 bundles per acre ; in Stoke St. Gregory and Burrowbridge the average yield is 171 bundles.

The above table was compiled for the Bristol bulletin in order to calculate an average yield as a basis for cost determination and is the best available indication of yields.

Sorting and Tying

The bundles as brought from the withy beds are sorted into different lengths and unwanted material is cast out. As a rule sorting is done into four, five, six and seven-foot lengths. The girth of the withybed " bundle " measures 3 ft. 2 ins. As the large bundles are difficult to manage the sorted material is tied up into half-bundles or " wads."

Whilst rods badly cankered are rejected during the sorting, it is not the practice to sort according to quality, as there is no recognised standard except the discretion of the grower.

The average number of " sorted " bundles obtained per cent. from " withybed " bundles is in the neighbourhood of 72 per cent., while the average of " finished " or processed " bolts " is about 62 per cent.

Classes of Saleable Willows

Withies are sold finally in several different forms, principal amongst which are those known as " whites." If cut in autumn or winter withies for whitening must be " pitted," which consists in allowing the rods to stand in several inches of water, the whitening process commencing in spring when the sap is active and the rods begin to shoot.

When taken from the " pits " these withies are distributed to strippers ; large quantities are stripped with the help of domestic labour, though further large quantities provide employment, at piece rates, for women and girls who work in their own homes.

It is the general practice to strip the willows of their bark by hand, with a pair of " breaks " —two pieces of steel sprung together and contained in an iron or wooden frame. Some growers have experimented with petrol-driven stripping machines, but for various reasons these are not generally satisfactory.

Some withies are " buffed," which consists in boiling so that organic substances contained in the bark dye the wood. This process may proceed throughout the winter months after which the " buffs " are stripped in the same way as the " whites."

A few growers possess boilers of their own, but the majority depend upon getting their boiling done at a piece rate.

In addition to the market for " whites " and " buffs " there is a limited market for " browns " —the unstripped product, usually those which are not good enough for whitening, used for the making of yeast baskets.

After stripping, the withies are left in the sun to dry, and further drying is usually carried out under cover, since unless thoroughly dried the withies tend to mildew when tied in bundles. When dry the withies are again tied, and stored, ready for market, to await disposal.

E.   ARABLE LAND AND CROPS

The legend on the published Land Utilisation Survey sheets shows that rotation grass is included with the arable land, but under the particular circumstances of the Survey in Somerset, it has been impossible to be sure that all rotation grass is correctly shown. Complete accuracy would have entailed a farm-to-farm inquiry, for which there was not time ; moreover, in many cases where inquiry was made, the farmers themselves were not sure how long a particular field was to remain in grass.

There has in the past been extensive cropping where now only grassland is found, and in comparison with lands in other parts of the world there is very little land so poor, or under conditions so severe, that worse could not be found under cultivation.

Some observers have been able to include all rotation grass after inquiry, but in general it may be taken that what is shown on the Land Utilisation Survey sheets is what was apparent on the ground at the date of the survey.[1]

It is sometimes objected that this is a serious defect in the maps, since the ploughland shown will alter each season, but the picture presented is nevertheless correct within narrow

[1] See Appendix II.

limits—the actual fields may exchange from plough to grass, and back again, but unless an economic change[1] takes place, the proportion locally of arable to grass remains roughly constant.

Moreover, the limits within which the ploughlands may shift are particularly narrow in Somerset, since the agricultural holdings are generally small.

The following table gives the percentage of holdings within the various size groups as listed in the parish returns of the Ministry of Agriculture for 1935 :—

Total Number of Agricultural Holdings in Somerset above 1 Acre = 12,525							
Size groups . .	Acres 1–5	Acres 5–20	Acres 20–50	Acres 50–100	Acres 100–150	Acres 150–300	Acres 300+
Percentage of total holdings . .	18·4	21·5	20	18·3	9·6	10·3	1·9

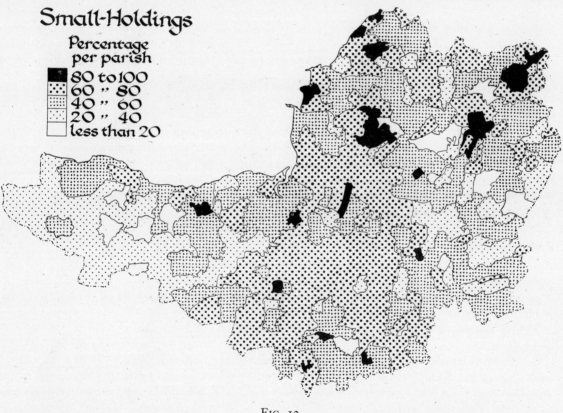

FIG. 13.

To show the distribution of these size groups accurately is a more difficult matter, since the statistics are drawn from parish returns which include lands lying within and without the parish of residence of the occupier. The returns are for total holdings and, particularly in the moor areas and those adjacent, often include detached portions.

[1] Such as through the wheat quota.

The map, Fig. 13, shows the distribution of holdings of 50 acres or less, expressed as percentages of the total number of holdings in each parish, that is, very roughly the areas where smallholdings are numerous or few. No account has been taken of physical features, the presence of heath, etc., which can be studied in detail on the one-inch Land Utilisation Survey sheets, or approximately on the folding map attached to this report.

The number of farms above 300 acres is distributed as follows :—

Size group . .	Acres 300–500	Acres 500–700	Acres 700–1,000	Acres above 1,000
No. of farms. .	208	21	6	1

On the one-inch Land Utilisation Survey sheets one square inch represents 640 acres, or a larger area than any farm in Somerset, except perhaps 7 or 10 farms, or a possible number of 28.

It is clear therefore, that even where rotation grass is not correctly shown, the ploughlands as shown on the Land Utilisation Survey sheets will vary annually within narrow limits, unless an economic change (such as occurred during the Great War) brings about the breaking up of permanent pastureland.

Crops

Wheat, fodder crops (including beans, peas, turnips, swedes, mangolds, kohl rabi, rape, cabbage, savoy, kale, carrots, lucerne and mustard) and oats, follow the ploughlands in varying proportion all over the County, and there are quantities, small or great, of potatoes grown in all but a very few parishes ; barley, beans, peas, potatoes and sugar beet show a distinct regional distribution, and crops for human consumption[1] and small fruit are restricted, in any quantity to a few neighbourhoods.

Production Areas

Partly on the basis of the distribution of arable land (see folding map) the County has been divided into sixteen areas of production which provide with the following table (page 74) a guide to regional distribution and a statistical summary of the chief crops produced on the ploughlands shown on the Land Utilisation Survey sheets.

The figures have been compiled from the Ministry of Agriculture returns for 1935 to coincide as closely as possible with the condition of the County on the completion of the field-sheets from which the Land Utilisation Survey sheets have been produced.

These areas were arranged in the first instance chiefly according to the grouping of the arable land on the Land Utilisation Survey sheets, and adjusted after study of the parish returns to include in the same group as far as possible crops of the same kind. Certain groups have, however, been kept separate from those surrounding to indicate a greater production per total acreage (as in No. 5) or to coincide with natural features (as in No. 9, which covers the Polden Hills. No. 11, the south-west scarps of Mendip. No. 13, north-east scarps of Mendip. No. 10, " Moorland " parishes). No. 7 groups a large area of scattered ploughlands, on hill country, which show little variation in distribution of the listed crops.

[1] Table of Crops in 16 Production Areas (see page 74).

The Western (Devonian) Uplands (Production Area No. 1. Physical Areas 1a, 1c, 1d.)

The division 1a marks the Lower Devonian heights which is an area of poor soils.

Ploughlands are negligible on these slates and grits except in two small areas—a narrow strip on the seaward-facing slopes from the region of Stoke Pero to the vicinity of Culbone, and the gap between Dunkery and Croyden Hills, roughly from Cutcombe to Timberscombe. These ploughlands, though of small area, are interesting as exceptions. The levels are considerably lower than the average for the exposure. The small patches on the seaward slopes may be due to the same moderating influences of the sea and of shelter from the easterly winds on local temperature, which in the Porlock Vale, produces, year after year, the finest samples of barley in the country.

The Cutcombe–Timberscombe valley ploughlands are possibly due to an extension of the same factors but the approximate nature of the divisions on the solid geology sheets and the absence of drift sheets or soil surveys, makes it probable that the surface beds in this small area are not correctly represented, and that beds of drift affording better soil material are present.

The Quantocks (1b.) show the same general features ; the northern mass of heath, rough pastures and forest shown on the Land Utilisation Survey sheet 120, almost exactly coincides with the exposure of the Lower Devonian beds (grits, slates, etc.) shown on the drift sheet. (Sheet 295. Geological Survey 5b., 6b.).

The " Upper Devonian " beds, although forming one production area, have been divided into two " physical areas," as there is a difference of altitude, and consequent climate, between east and west. The line drawn is merely a convenient one and much the same type of country can be found on both sides.

Isolated patches of land under plough are found as high as 1,500 feet, and considering the generally high levels, the amount of ploughland indicates the considerable fertility of the soil. Moreover, owing to the nature of the land forms, down-like spurs and hilltops and steep-sided shut-in valleys, the ploughland is found, in general, on the high land, and upper south-facing slopes.

Physical Area 1c. The small number of the thinly scattered ploughlands of the central parishes, lying roughly within a triangle based on the Cutcombe–Exton road and extending westward into Exmoor, is the result of the general high altitudes, high rainfall and uncertain ripening season, and also to the depredations, in root crops, of deer and rabbits.

A valuable record of the improvement of an extensive area of the high country about Exford, Simonsbath and Withypool, and the history of its subsequent use from 1830, when the experiment was begun, is to be found in *The Reclamation of Exmoor Forest*, by C. J. Orwin. This account explains the sharp division which occurs in this high region between improved and unimproved land, and indicates the possibility of further reclamation.

The soil of the present Parish of Exford is described as consisting of two types ; about half being a brown loam, naturally dry, covering a deep, yellow subsoil, the debris of the soft, Upper Devonian clay-slate rock, and occurring for the most part on the sides of the valleys. It has a natural drainage and requires only the addition of lime to make it fertile. The other portion of the Parish (which is co-terminous with the old " Forest " of Exmoor) is covered with a thin clay-and-iron pan impervious to water, on which the growth of centuries has laid a shallow layer of peat, for the greater part of the year saturated with water, except where deep subsoil ploughing has in the past been undertaken to break the " pan " and prepare for cultivation. A considerable area, some 2,500 acres, has been treated in this way and permanent improvement to good grassland effected.

TABLE OF CROP ACREAGE AND PERCENTAGES IN SIXTEEN " PRODUCTION REGIONS "

(SEE DIAGRAM NO. 14)

Production Region	No.	Wheat	Percentage of Somerset Totals	Barley	Percentage of Somerset Totals	Oats	Percentage of Somerset Totals	Beans	Percentage of Somerset Totals	Peas	Percentage of Somerset Totals
Western Highlands .	1	635	3·0	408	4·4	3,037	1·9	17	0·6	7	1·0
Western Coastal .	2	1,462	6·0	1,362	14·8	1,366	8·8	52	1·8	19	2·9
Taunton–Wellington .	3	4,874	20·0	3,857	42·0	2,459	15·9	598	21·0	291	24·0
N.E. Slopes, Quantock	4	1,793	7·0	938	10·2	818	5·2	294	10·3	185	15·0
Marine Islands and S. Bridgwater . .	5	1,725	7·0	1,075	10,6	526	3·4	201	7·0	428	36·0
Midford Sand and Marls Area . .	6	2,955	12·0	731	8·0	1,138	7·3	315	11·0	125	10·0
Chalklands and Jurassic belt . . .	7	3,454	14·0	379	4·1	2,025	13·1	228	8·0	13	1·0
Arable Lias, Clays and Marls . .	8	3,807	15·0	182	2·0	1,754	11·3	664	23·4	13	1·0
Polden Hills . .	9	1,033	4·0	36	0·4	521	3·3	258	9·0	13	1·0
Glastonbury–Burnham Levels . .	10	74	0·3	1	—	22	—	3	—	1	—
S. Mendip Slopes .	11	109	0·4	2	—	144	1·0	60	2·0	27	2·0
Pastoral Lias Clays .	12	158	0·6	23	0·2	82	0·5	23	0·8	—	—
N. Mendip Slopes .	13	213	0·9	29	0·3	162	1·0	6	—	4	—
S. Bristol Hills .	14	427	1·7	9	—	255	1·6	25	1·0	3	—
Bath Region .	15	1,248	5·0	115	1·2	724	4·7	56	2·0	29	3·0
N.W. Somerset Region	16	631	2·5	30	0·3	386	2·4	38	1·0	31	3·0
Total for Somerset .		24,598		9,177		15,419		2,838		1,189	

Production Region	No.	(1) Potatoes	Percentage of Somerset Totals	(2) Fodder Crops	Percentage of Somerset Totals	(3) Sugar Beet	Percentage of Somerset Totals	(4) Crops for Human Consumption	Percentage of Somerset Totals	(5) Acreage of Region as percentage of Somerset Area
Western Highlands . .	1	117	5·0	3,312	15·5	25	2·5	29	3·2	10
Western Coastal . .	2	89	4·0	1,905	8·9	4	0·4	16	1·8	4
Taunton–Wellington .	3	237	11·0	4,233	19·8	210	21·0	168	19·0	11
N.E. Slopes, Quantock .	4	56	3·0	1,116	5·2	4	0·4	17	2·0	4
Marine Islands and S. Bridgwater .	5	398	18·0	1,155	5·4	68	6·8	76	8·4	3
Midford Sand and Marls Area .	6	239	10·6	2,619	12·3	666	66·6	121	13·4	6
Chalklands and Jurassic belt .	7	167	7·4	2,922	13·7	24	2·4	49	5·4	20
Arable Lias, Clays and Marls .	8	69	3·0	1,180	5·5	2	0·2	10	1·1	6
Polden Hills .	9	56	2·5	469	2·2	—	—	66	7·4	3
Glastonbury–Burnham Levels .	10	59	3·0	188	0·8	—	—	4	0·4	5
S. Mendip Slopes .	11	123	5·5	297	1·0	—	—	44	5·0	6
Pastoral Lias Clays . .	12	12	0·5	165	0·7	—	—	2	0·2	5
N. Mendip Slopes . .	13	29	1·4	232	1·0	—	—	13	1·4	4
S. Bristol Hills .	14	88	4·0	375	1·6	—	—	33	3·6	3
Bath Region . .	15	219	9·2	627	2·7	2	0·2	110	12·2	4
N.W. Somerset Region . .	16	298	13·2	513	2·2	20	2·0	141	16·0	6
Total for Somerset. . .		2,256		21,308		1,025		899		

(1) Nos. 5 and 6 are the large-scale potato-growing regions. Elsewhere the totals are made up by small acreages in nearly all parishes.

(2) Fodder crops here do not include a relatively small acreage of " mixed corn."

(3) In some areas a few acres of sugar-beet are grown as a fodder-crop.

(4) This is usually made up of a number of small acreages in various parishes.

(5) Acreages for parishes taken from Census.

(6) The figures as supplied to the Ministry are filled in by farmers as from the parish of residence, and acreage may lie in one or several parishes. The returns are often inaccurate and while providing the best available statistical information for the County, and a fair idea of comparative production, the figures produced from them may contain a 2 per cent. to 3 per cent. error.

(7) Percentages following crop figures are approximate figures for the percentages of the Somerset Crop grown in the particular production region in 1935.

Physical Area 1d. The altitudes are generally lower though still high, and the plough-grounds more numerous. There is remarkably little evidence of erosion, considering the rainfall and steep slopes, due to the nature of the Devonian soils which absorb water almost as readily as the New Red Sandstone soils further east, and no doubt also to the stone and earth banks, topped by beech hedges, which surround the fields.

The Porlock Vale, Minehead–Watchet Coastal District, the Fault Corridor, Vales of Welling-ton and Taunton Deane, North-Eastern Slopes (of Quantock) and Coastal Lias Clays show a general similarity of production from arable land, the difference appearing to lie in production

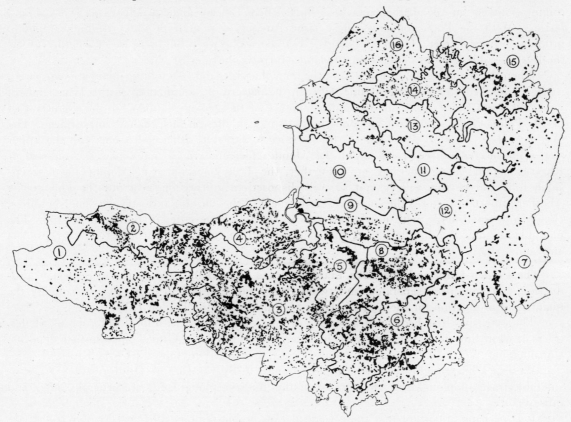

Fig. 14.—The Production Regions of Somerset.

Arable land is shown in black, the numbers are those of the regions given in the text. Scale approximately 12 miles to 1 inch.

of beans, peas and sugar-beet which are produced chiefly in the Wellington–Taunton district and the fault corridor.

Ploughlands are found on all the beds exposed, even occasionally on valley gravel and rainwash which naturally occupy depressions. The large continuous tracts of ploughland which show up on the "arable" diagram (see folding-map) lie on the Keuper Sandstones which provide light, fertile, easily worked and well-drained soils. Ploughlands on the heavier and less well-drained Red Marls are smaller and more scattered but still extensive. The coastal Lias is a heavy blueish clay and in parts the fields are inconveniently small.

The two Physical Areas 5b. and 6b. which show little difference in pattern of ploughlands from surrounding areas, are of basically the same material as the Western " Upper " Devonian hills, and have the advantage of generally lower altitude. South of Taunton a triangle of plough-lands appears, on generally low-lying Red Marls and washdown, of different pattern. This is a dairying and fodder-crop area in the main and towards the south probably shares the increased rainfall due to the steep scarp of the Greensand.

Physical Area No. 9—the " Islands " of Chedzoy, Weston Zoyland, Middlezoy and Othery are represented on the geological diagram as belonging to the Rhaetic and Keuper Marls group, which is probably correct for the subsoil. The surface is light shelly and gravelly loam of marine origin, (marked on the drift sheets as " Burtle Beds ")—an ancient silt easily worked and fertile. With the Petherton area, these large patches of plough provide the highest potato production in Somerset. On the " Islands," boundaries between holdings are of a nature to use the least possible amount of the valuable land—furrows, hurdles or wire.

When the geological map (Fig. 2) and the map of arable land (see folding-map) are compared, there is a marked difference noticeable between the pattern of ploughlands on the Trias lands of west and north Somerset. The generalised nature of the geological map for the country east of the Poldens (Physical Area 10) does not distinguish the various changes in surface. The Wedmore Isle (Physical Area No. 15) for instance, is largely " Rhaetic " stone, and the upper slopes of the generalised Trias about the Mendip plateau, are in many places composed of Rhaetic material, conglomerates, etc. Further, the Trias beds north of Mendip lie in steep-sided hills and narrow valleys, not so well disposed to cultivation as about the Quantocks. Another important factor is the ancient establishment of the dairying industry, on small-holdings, cut up into small fields, with nearby markets in the two large cities of Bath and Bristol. The ploughlands show the distribution of the general production chiefly of wheat, fodder crops, oats and some potatoes.

The Polden Hills and the Area marked " Lias Clay Hills " are similar in respect to production, but have been separated into two " Production Areas," in order to give roughly the quantity of production for the well-marked physical feature, the Polden Hills.

The extensive Lias beds form a surface of Clays and Marls, with local outcrops of Shales, tracts of white limestone, masked locally in lower regions by Valley Gravel and rainwash deposits. Considerable tracts of Clay-with-Flints also occur, as about Drayton and Curry Rivel.

West of a line roughly from Glastonbury south to Sparkford and Mudford there are considerable tracts of ploughland; to the east of this line the ploughlands are generally small and infrequent.

It is perhaps important that these Central Lias arable regions (Physical Region No. 8) are never far from the wide stretches of alluvial levels, which surround and penetrate between the long downlike hill-folds, and which are commonly of use only in the summer season, as pasture or for hay.

It is a general custom for farmers to hold a certain amount of the " moorland " which may be at some distance from the farmstead, situated on rising ground. The liability to flooding in winter generally prevents ploughing on the Levels, and where agriculture is possible towards the coast it is further prevented in many cases by obligation of tenure designed to protect the rich, long-established pastures.

Taking into account the small size of the average holding in Somerset, the result is that any rising ground near the moors is likely to show a high proportion of ploughland, if the soil is at all suitable, for the provision of winter feed and fattening of stock, or for other cropping which may be profitable.

The most obvious exception, the land to the east of Glastonbury, may be explained partly by the steeper slopes of the Lias below the harder Middle and Upper Lias capping of the hills, and partly by differences of soil material on tracts of shale and limestone and to the washdown from the upper beds.

It may be noted also that the "teart" lands (see page 46) occur on the Lias, and that the only remedy for this condition lies in ploughing, a factor which may be not without influence where the slopes lie conveniently for ploughing. But it must be emphasized that these areas marked as " Lias " are here much more varied in surface than the geological maps available indicate, and a drift survey would be most useful. The tracts of Clay-with-Flint suggest that even the " solid " underlying geological beds are not correctly represented.

The Midford Sand and Marlstone Low Relief Arable Area (Production Region No. 6) can be made highly fertile and is particularly well farmed. Ploughlands are almost continuous on the Midford Sand exposures which occur in the area generalized on the geological diagram as " Inferior Oolite " and widespread on the Middle Lias clays, marls, and sands. The small grassland area to the south marked as " Great Oolite series " on the geological map, consists chiefly of a low-lying marshy "Fuller's Earth" region with washdown and alluvium, and small " Forest Marble " heights.

The Clay-with-Flint Plateau and the Chalk Hills (Physical Area No. 7)

These areas carry a relatively small proportion of ploughland, chiefly on the Clay-with-Flints capping above the scarps. Some of the largest of the few ploughlands extend on to, or lie on, the few exposures of chalk. Little ploughland is evident on the Greensands, as these generally form the steep slopes ; where they are more convenient, ploughlands occur.

The Jurassic Scarplands (The Lower Scarplands 12a. The Fuller's Earth Region 12c. The Bath Region 12d.)

The Scarplands proper from Milborne Port to Frome carry scattered, infrequent ploughlands, chiefly on the Inferior Oolites and Fullers Earth. North of Frome, on the wider exposures, ploughlands increase steadily to the region of Bath, on exposures of Midford Sand, Inferior Oolite, Fuller's Earth, Great Oolite (from which comes Bath stone) Forest Marble and Cornbrash. There are no drift sheets, and the old " solid geology " sheets cannot be trusted in detail.[1]

The large exposure on which ploughland is almost non-existent is the Oxford Clay (12b.) part of which forms the Blackmore Vale district.

In the neighbourhood of Bath, in the parishes of Bath, Batheaston, Bathford, Keynsham and Swainswick, local fertile exposures of Midford Sands and Marls on the lower valley slopes are under cultivation for the production of market-garden crops. The production of the ploughlands over the whole Jurassic belt is uniformly wheat, oats and fodder crops, with small acreage of barley in places (Production Areas 7 and 15, Fig. 14.)

The Alluvial Levels

On the alluvium there is little ploughland, except where it is necessary to renew" withybeds " (see pages 65–70). Locally advantage is taken of higher ground, particularly about the lower slopes of the surrounding hills, and in some places sour pastureland is improved by being broken up and resown after a cleaning crop.

The greater part of the moors is either unsuitable on account of flooding and the soft nature of the surface, or too valuable as pasture and hay country, renewed by deposits of silt, to be broken up under present economic conditions, though there seems to be no reason why many

---

[1] About North Perrot, for instance, there are tracts of Clay-with-Flint, and Marl overlying Clay-with-Flint in regions shown as " Fuller's Earth and Fuller's Earth rock."

of the rich flats, with perhaps improved drainage, should not be as productive as the famed Eastern Fenlands. On the higher alluvium towards the coast, in many places the " ridge and furrow " structure of the fields gives evidence of former wheat lands.

On Compton Moor the peat is ploughed, and until recently continuous corn growing was practised.

PARISHES IN THE PRODUCTION REGIONS

Region 1.

Ashbrittle, Bathealton, Brompton Ralph, Brompton Regis, Brushford, Chipstable, Clatworthy, Culbone, Cutcombe, Dulverton, Elworthy, Exford, Exton, Hawkridge, Huish Champflower, Kittisford, Luxborough, Oare, Raddington, Skilgate, Stawley, Stoke Pero, Thorn St. Margaret, Tolland, Treborough, Upton, Winsford, Withiel Florey, Withypool.

Region 2.

Carhampton, Dunster, Luccombe, Minehead and Minehead Without, Monksilver, Nettlecombe, Old Cleve, Porlock, Sampford Brett, Selworthy, Timberscombe, Watchet, Williton, Withycombe, Wootton.

Region 3.

Angersleigh, Ash Priors, Bickenhall, Bicknoller, Bishops Hull Without, Bishops Lydeard, Bradford, Broadway, Broomfield, Buckland St. Mary, Cheddon Fitzpaine, Churchstanton, Combe Florey, Corfe, Cothelstone, Curland, Crowcombe, Creech St. Michael, Durleigh, Durston, Enmore, Fitzhead, Goathurst, Halse, Heathfield, Kingston, Langford Budville, Lydeard St. Lawrence, Milverton, Norton Fitzwarren, Nynehead, Oake, Orchard Portman, Otterford, Pitminster, Ruishton, Runnington, Sampford Arundel, Staple Fitzpaine, Staplegrove, Stogumber, Stoke St. Mary, Taunton St. J., Taunton St. M., Thorn Falcon, Thurlbear, Trull, W. Bagborough, W. Buckland, W. Hatch, W. Monkton, Wiveliscombe, Wiveliscombe Without, Wellington.

Region 4.

Aisholt, Bridgwater, Cannington, Charlynch, Charlynch det., Chilton Trinity, Doddington, E. Quantoxhead, Fiddington, Holford, Kilton with Lilstock, Kilve and Kilve det., Nether Stowey, Otterhampton, Overstowey, Spaxton, Stockland Bristol, Stogursey, Stringston, Wembdon, W. Quantoxhead.

Region 5.

Bridgwater Without, Chedzoy, Middlezoy, Othery, Weston Zoyland, Lyng, N. Curry, N. Petherton, Stoke St. Gregory, Thurloxton.

Region 6.

Ash, Ashill, Barrington, Beer Crocombe, Chaffcombe, Chillington, Chiselborough, Cricket St. Thomas, Cudworth, Curry Mallet, Dodington, Donyatt, Dowlish Wake, Earnshill, E. Chinnock, Hatch Beauchamp, Haselbury Plucknett, Hinton St. George, Ilminster, Ilminster Without, Ilton, Isle Abbots, Isle Brewers, Kingsbury, Kingstone, Knowle St. Giles, Lopen, Martock, Meriott, Montacute, Norton sub Hamdon, Odcombe, Puckington, Seavington St. Mary and St. Michael, Shepton Beauchamp, S. Petherton, Stocklinch, Stoke sub Hambden, Tintinhull, W. Chinnock, Whitelackington.

Region 7.

Abbas and Templecombe, Ansford, Ashington, Barwick, Beckington, Berkley, Blackford, Bratton Seymour, Bruton, Brympton, Buckland Denham, Burnett, Castle Cary, Chard, Charlton Horethorn, Charlton Musgrove, Chilton Cantelo, Chilthorne Domer, Cloford, Closworth, Combe St. Nicholas, Compton Dando, Compton Pauncefoot, Corton Denham, Crewkerne, Cucklington, E. Coker, E. Cranmore, Elm, Farrington Gurney, Farleigh Hungerford, Farmborough, Foxcote, Hardington, Hardington Mandeville, Hemington, Henstridge, High Littleton, Holton, Horsington, Ilchester, Kilmersdon, Laverton, Lufton, Lullington, Maperton, Marksbury, Marsdon Bigot, Marston Magna, Mells, Midsomer Norton, Milborne Port, Misterton, Mudford, N. Barrow, N. Brewham, N. Cadbury, N. Cheriton, Northover, N. Perrott, Norton Malreward, Norton St. Philip, Nunney, Orchardleigh, Paulton, Pendomer, Penselwood, Pitcombe, Publow, Queen Camel, Queen Charlton, Radstock, Rimpton, Rodden, Rode, Selwood, Shepton Montague, Sock Dennis, Sparkford, Stanton Prior, Stoke Trister, Ston Easton, Stowell, S. Brewham, S. Barrow, S. Cadbury, Sutton Bingham, Sutton Montis, Tellisford, Thorne, Timsbury, Upton Noble, Wambrook, Wanstrow, Wayford, Weston Bampfylde, W. Camel, W. Coker, W. Cranmore, Whatley, Whitchurch, Whitestaunton, Wincanton, Winsham, Witham Friary, Woolverton, Writhlington, Yarlington, Yeovil, Yeovilton, Yeovil Without, W. Crewkerne.

Region 8.

Aller, Babcary, Barton St. David, Butleigh, Charlton Mackrell, Compton Dundon, Curry Rivel, Drayton, E. Lydford, Fivehead, High Ham, Keinton Mandeville, Kingsdon, Kingweston, Langport, Huish Episcopi, Long Load, Long Sutton, Muchelney, Pitney, Podimore, Somerton, Swell, W. Lydford, Wheathill.

Region 9.

Ashcott, Bawdrip, Catcott, Cossington, Edington, Greinton, Moorlinch, Pawlett, Puriton, Shapwich, Sharpham, Stawell, Street, Sutton Mallet, Walton, Woolavington.

Region 10.

Badgworth, Berrow, Brean, Brent Knoll, Burnham, Burnham Without, Highbridge, Chapel Allerton, E. Brent, Godney, Huntspill, Lympsham, Mark, Meare, Weare, Wedmore.

Region 11.

Axbridge, Banwell, Biddisham, Bleadon, Cheddar, Christon, Compton-Bishop, Loxton, Nyland cum Batcombe, Rodney Stoke, St. Cuthbert In, St. Cuthbert Out, Westbury, Winscombe, Wookey, Shipham, St. Andrews.

Region 12.

Alford, Baltonsborough, Batcombe, Croscombe, Dinder, Ditcheat, Doulting, E. Pennard, Evercreech, Glastonbury, Hornblotton, Lamyatt, Lovington, Milton Clevedon, N. Wootton, Pilton, Pylle, Shepton Mallet, W. Bradley, W. Pennard.

Region 13.

Ashwick, Binegar, Blagdon, Burrington, Charterhouse, Chewton Mendip, Chilcompton, Churchill, Compton Martin, Downhead, E. Harptree, Emborough, Holcombe, Leigh upon Mendip, Priddy, Rowberrow, Stoke Lane, Stratton-on-Fosse, Ubley, W. Harptree.

Region 14.

Butcombe, Cameley, Chelwood, Chew Magna, Chew Stoke, Clutton, Congresbury, Hinton Blewett, Litton, Nempnett Thrubwell, N. Widcombe, Puxton, Stanton Drew, Stowey, Winford, Wrington.

Region 15.

Bath, Bathampton, Batheaston, Bathford, Brislington, Camerton, Charlcombe, Claverton, Combe Hay, Corston, Dunkerton, English Combe, Freshford, Hinton Charterhouse, Kelston, Keynsham, Langridge, Monkton Combe, Newton St. Loe, N. Stoke, Priston, St. Catherine, Saltford, S. Stoke, Swanswick, Wellow, Weston, Woolley.

Region 16.

Abbots Leigh, Backwell, Barrow, Bishopsworth, Brockley, Clapton, Clevedon, Dundry, Easton, Flax Bourton, Hutton, Kenn, Kewstoke, Kingston Seymour, Locking, Long Ashton, Nailsea, N. Weston, Portbury, Portishead, Tickenham, Uphill, Walton-in-Gordano, Weston-in-Gordano, Weston-super-Mare, Wick St. Lawrence, Worle, Wraxall, Yatton.

F.   ORCHARDS

The folding-map gives the distribution of orchards in the County as they appear on the Land Utilisation sheets.

The total acreage under orchards given by the returns of the Ministry of Agriculture, 1935, is as follows :—

Apples		Pears		Cherries	Plums	Nuts	Total Acreage
Cider	Other Kinds	Perry	Other Kinds				
15,896	4,080	21	52	14	92	6	20,161

It will be noticed that by far the greater proportion of this area is under cider apple-trees of various kinds, but acreage is only a very rough indication of production, since cider apple-trees are often planted far apart and modern orchard methods with intensive planting and scientific arrangement and management of trees make for greatly increased production per acre. Some of the old orchards contain only a few trees, widely spaced.

Orchards appear on nearly all the chief soil groups of the County, and in regions where there are few or none, the deciding factor is due to local climate, as on the Western Devonian hills, and the Mendips, or to locally impeded drainage, as on the low moors.

Recently planted orchards may be discovered on the Land Utilisation Survey sheets by the absence of the conventional Ordnance Survey orchard symbol under the Land Utilisation Survey distinctive colour (purple ruling), as at Stawell, Glastonbury, and many places on the high alluvium, and in the area north of the Mendips on the several types of country, with a tendency to follow the roads where much new building also appears.

Information as to the management and care of orchards in the County, and suitable types of trees to plant in various districts can be obtained from experts at the Somerset Farm Institute at Cannington, or from the Advisory Report issued by the Institute in 1935.

Cider

The growing of apples for cider is an industry anciently established in the County.

John Billingsley, in his *Survey of Agriculture in Somerset*, published in 1798, gives an account of the cider industry and states that in the Middle District (between the Mendip and Quantock Hills) there was scarcely an orchard that would not let for four or five pounds an acre—an interesting opinion especially as it is further stated in his account that the proper distance apart for the planting of cider trees is 60 feet each way.[1]

Cider was then and until comparatively recent times considered as part of the wages of the agricultural labourer, and the bulk of it was produced on the farms.

A considerable quantity of farm cider is still produced, but an increasing quantity of the cider apples is now sold off the farms to factories which manufacture for a widespread market.

The greater part of the orchards in the County are grassed, and used for grazing, but about the larger towns, particularly in the Bath and South Bristol region, newly planted orchards appear laid out according to modern systems.

Orchard practice varies greatly in different localities, and a complete survey of the orchards in detail is beyond the scope of the present report, but the varied utilisation and importance of strictly local soil changes and a developed local tradition, are illustrated in the following account of three typical districts, and in the brief notes on other districts. No attempt has been made to define the areas on a special map, as the Land Utilisation sheets, which have the parish areas outlined on them can be used for closer study, and it will be realised after reading the notes that only a few districts are clear cut.

Typical Orchard Areas in Somerset
   (1) Wedmore District
   (2) Kingsbury Episcopi District
   (3) Bishops Lydeard District

Wedmore District. Soil type is of the Red or Keuper Marl within the area, surrounded by Lias Clays beyond. The Marl is of a heavy type, retentive of moisture, but not rich in plant foods.

The proportion of orchard land is probably the highest in the County, compared with total agricultural land. The orchards are nearly all attached to small farm-holdings, and often comprise as much as 50 per cent. of the area of the holding. All are grass orchards, mostly grazed by dairy cattle or young stock, occasionally by pigs, but rarely by sheep. Many farmers in the area have a large proportion of their land in the moors around, which flood in winter months. The cattle are often brought into the orchards surrounding the homestead for the winter, and this usually leads to the orchards being " trodden " or the turf badly broken during the wet season. Owners often contend this procedure is helpful to the orchard, and it may be, to some extent, owing to the manure deposited.

The orchards are almost entirely devoted to the growing of cider fruit, a local reputation having been established for the vintage quality of the fruit produced. The cider is manufactured largely on the farms, being consumed locally and in Bristol.

The trees do not make heavy growth, and when full sized are comparatively small. This has encouraged close planting of 5 to 7 yards between the trees, the recommended distance on an average soil being 10 to 12 yards. Replanting of blank places in the orchards has been carried out spasmodically, with very little foresight, and the young trees after planting receive little or no attention.

[1] 30 feet to 40 feet is now considered sufficient.

F

The pruning of the orchards does not receive serious consideration ; a little dead wood is cut out when time permits, but the trees do not make much superfluous wood, and therefore, do not require heavy pruning.

The cropping of the orchards in the area is very irregular, subject to heavy and light crops, due largely to the stunted condition of the trees not favouring a succession of moderate yields.

Insect pests and diseases in the orchards are not abnormal, and are not as a rule troublesome. This may be explained by the hard semi-stunted growth of the trees. Practically no spraying is done in the district.

Kingsbury Episcopi District. This is an orchard area which may be taken as a direct contrast to the Wedmore area.

The soil is of the lighter Lias type, being more or less friable near the surface, with a heavy retentive subsoil. The soil is naturally fertile and aided by generations of careful farming has reached a state of high fertility.

Orchards are plentiful in the district, nearly all being of the standard grass type, and are principally attached to general farm-holdings, although in some cases they are held by smallholders—willow-growers, and the more prosperous workmen.

There is a considerable mixture in the type of fruit grown, with a fair proportion of culinary fruit, principally the variety Bramley's Seedling. A few orchards consist of culinary fruit only, but in most cases trees of Bramley's Seedling are found mixed with cider fruit in the orchards. Most of these Bramley's Seedling trees were planted during the War and immediate post-War period, when demand for cooking fruit was high. The tendency now is to plant cider fruit again.

The orchards are grazed by cattle and pigs, and with sheep to some extent on the mixed farms. Generally the stock are not allowed to tread the orchards badly during the winter, although this is usually decided by the individual farmer, according to his need for pastures.

The raising of young apple-trees has been a practice on a number of farms for generations, and in addition there are two well-stocked nurseries in the parish ; re-planting when necessary has therefore been carried out in nearly all orchards, good local trees being always available for the purpose. One variety of apple has been used exclusively for many years in the raising of young trees, Morgan Sweet, on account of its vigour and the vigour it imparts to other varieties grafted upon it. It was also, at one time, planted extensively to produce early dessert fruit for sending to South Wales.

Owing to the local knowledge of tree-growing and management, based to a large extent on tradition, the young and mature trees receive a certain amount of care and treatment.

Good soil conditions encourage a high rate of growth in young trees and combined with the strong Morgan Sweet stock produce a good-sized tree quickly. Some varieties, which under other conditions make dwarf trees, can, in this district, be brought to a satisfactory size.

The mental outlook of the farmers in the district is alert and self-confident. New ideas are treated with a certain amount of scepticism and are not accepted until their value has been definitely proved. Tradition, based usually on sound practical experience, is the keynote of most procedure, and this tradition has been carefully fostered between father and son.

Most orchards receive a certain amount of pruning when necessary, and unprofitable trees are quickly regrafted to better varieties. The district is the most advanced in the County in the latter respect, and this can largely be attributed to the fact that there are a number of men in the district skilled in this grafting work, and proud of this skill, vying with each other in results, and thus doing excellent work.

The district is renowned through the West of England for the vintage quality of its cider fruit, and cider-makers are anxious to obtain supplies for producing their best blends of cider. In consequence there is always a ready sale for the cider fruit of the area although there are no large-scale cider manufacturers in the district itself. The high quality of the fruit can be directly attributed to the very suitable type of soil for producing vintage quality, and the high quality of the majority of varieties cultivated. This latter point is most interesting as the majority of the true cider varieties grown there were not, until recently, known outside an area of about 5 miles radius. The origin of the varieties is in the first place from chance seedlings, but selections from these were made with care by local experts, and their choice has proved to be one of considerable wisdom. As a result the orchards are stocked almost entirely with such good varieties as Dabinett, Chisel Jersey, Brown Jersey, Taylors, Farmers' Friend, etc., and comparatively few trees of really unprofitable varieties are found.

The outstanding feature of the district is its apple knowledge enshrined in local " lore."

Bishops Lydeard District and North Taunton Vale. Soil type is principally of the Red Sandstone, originating from the surrounding hills, although many variations of depth and texture are found.

The orchards are more scattered than in the two foregoing districts, the farms being larger and a lower proportion of orchards existing on the farms in comparison with the total acreage. The farms are mostly mixed stock farms and the average area of orchard attached to each would be 4–5 acres.

The orchards are all of the standard grass type and are regarded for farming operations as an ordinary pasture. They are usually grazed by sheep, the sheltered position of the orchard often providing a suitable place for lambing and also for any early " bite." Through sheep grazing the herbage of the orchards is usually close and good.

The type of fruit grown is very mixed ; a large proportion of the varieties being of what are termed the " dual purpose " type, meaning that in scarce seasons the fruit is sold for culinary purposes, and in more plentiful seasons for cider. The method of disposal of the fruit is unusual, but as practised throughout the Taunton area. Auction sales are held during August when nearly all the orchards are offered, i.e., the season's fruit is sold as it stands on the trees. The purchasers are local apple-dealers who pick out what they think they can sell for market, and the remainder are picked up when required for cider purposes.

In consequence the farmer has no great knowledge of his individual varieties and their market value, and in selecting varieties for planting gives chief consideration to the cropping abilities of a variety.

On the whole the district grows large trees which are usually given fairly wide spacing, but not always sufficient. Little methodical attention is given to the trees, the usual method being to hire in a local expert to prune the orchard every 7–10 years. Very little regrafting is done, and, should a wrong variety be planted it will remain as long as it lives. The care of young trees is erratic but not generally sufficient to ensure good uninterrupted progress, not sufficient attention being given to protection from stock. No nurseries exist in the vicinity and young trees for planting are obtained from a number of sources.

Owing to the more luxuriant growth of the trees on this deep open soil, pests and diseases often cause considerable damage to the trees. In a few isolated cases, spraying to combat these is carried out.

The cropping of the trees is in most cases usually biennial, not all the trees cropping in the same year. When they bear, the trees usually carry a heavy crop, due to their considerable size.

The general attitude of the farmers towards their orchards is that they are an asset provided they make a good price at the sales, that is, if the trees are healthy, and crop well, but they have little understanding of the trees and their requirements.

Brief Notes on Other Districts

The North. (Long Ashton, Wraxall, Portbury, Clevedon, Nailsea, Backwell and vicinity.)

Grass orchards of mixed fruit-trees, a high percentage being for cider purposes, are typical, growing standard trees which develop to a fair size. Fungus diseases are somewhat prevalent owing to the local rainfall. Market fruit is sent to Bristol, cider fruit nearly all to local factories.

The orchards are reasonably well managed and are grazed by cattle, with a few sheep and pigs.

The North-East. (Keynsham, Frome, Radstock, Bath and vicinity.)

Grass orchards, principally of cider fruit are typical. Standard trees are grown which vary considerably according to soil depth and drainage. Some cider fruit goes to cider factories, but a few local cider-makers, in a small way, deal with a considerable proportion of the crop. Orchard owners who make cider give some attention to their trees, but otherwise orchard management is very erratic. The orchards are grazed principally by cattle, with some sheep.

This is a very scattered orchard district, where orchards have no great importance, and only occur where soil conditions are favourable. They are often only small areas attached to homesteads, principally to supply fruit for the home or for home cider production.

Chew Valley. (Winford, Chew Magna, Chew Stoke, East and West Harptree, Compton Martin, Ubley, etc.)

Grass orchards of mixed fruit, largely for cider, are typical. The trees on the whole develop well, making satisfactory size. Varieties are very mixed with a good many market-fruit trees mixed in each orchard. High rainfall is conducive to fungus diseases. Market fruit is sent to Bristol; cider fruit is manufactured chiefly in small quantities on the farms, and the remainder is sent to cider factories. Interest in the orchards is general, and some attention is given to management. Orchards are grazed chiefly by cattle and some sheep, pigs and poultry.

The district forms a cup in the hills and is a more or less self-contained community with its own ideas on farming, including orcharding.

Northern Coastal. (Kingston Seymour, Yatton, Congresbury, Weston-super-Mare, Bleadon and Lympsham.)

Grass orchards, principally of cider fruit, are typical, well laid out, and in most cases fine old orchards. The trees are of large timber and often immense size, gaining an excellent anchorage in the deep alluvial soil and remaining upright to an advanced old age provided local drainage is good. There is a considerable amount of farm cider-making, the remainder of the fruit going to the cider factory. Care is on the whole good, except in the matter of pruning. Grazing is nearly all by dairy cattle.

There has been a well-run nursery at Sandford (Winscombe), where trees were grown on the true crab stocks, a factor which is probably responsible for a good deal of the exceptional stamina which the trees of the district appear to possess.

Winscombe, Banwell and Wrington. (Winscombe, Banwell, Churchill, Langford, Wrington and vicinity.)

The older orchards are principally for cider but a number of those between 20 and 40 years old are largely for culinary fruit. Trees develop fairly well, especially the younger ones and many fine trees of 20–40 years can be found. Culinary fruit is marketed in Bristol, Cardiff, and sometimes the North. A few farm cider-makers exist but cider fruit goes principally to the manufacturers. Attention to the orchards is very variable ; some are in very good condition and some extremely neglected. Replanting of " blanks " has been well attended to. Grazing is chiefly by cattle, but often by young stock and pigs. The Sandford nursery, which unfortunately no longer exists, was no doubt responsible for the comparative well-being of many middle-aged and older trees.

South of the Mendips. (Compton Bishop, Axbridge, Cheddar, Draycott, Westbury, Wookey, Wells, and vicinity.)

The district is one of very mixed orchard types owing to the divergent views and requirements of growers. Trees on the lower portion of the hillside grow and fruit well. Market fruit is often disposed of to dealers or " higglers " from Bristol and elsewhere, cider fruit being principally used locally. Management is variable, but usually fairly good. Grazing is chiefly by sheep, pigs and poultry.

An outlook unusual for the County is to be found about Cheddar, the smallholders being always ready to adopt new ideas. This has led to many varieties in orchard planning.

The reputed " earliness " of the district is not reflected in the orchards.

Mark and Highbridge Area. (Mark, Highbridge, East Brent, Brent Knoll, Badgworth, Blackford, Huntspill and vicinity.)

The orchards are nearly all old cider orchards, most of which are closely planted with semi-stunted, mature trees, the cropping of which is rarely regular. The majority of the fruit is manufactured into cider locally on the farms. Care and attention generally is not good. Replacements are irregular and pruning almost unknown. The orchards are grazed by cattle and young stock.

This is a community of dairy farmers who give little attention to anything outside their dairying business, and although the land does not respond quickly to better treatment, there is abundant room here for improvement in orchard management.

The Polden Hills. (On the slopes of the Poldens from Pawlett to Street.)

There are a few orchards of market fruit, the majority are for cider. A number of the orchards were originally well planned, especially in the Street area, where there are also some orchards of " bush " and " half standard " trees with culinary fruit. The trees do not develop rapidly, but make hard timber. Culinary fruit (Street area) is sold chiefly to dealers, some direct to Bristol and South Wales, and often to the North ; cider is manufactured on farms to a considerable extent. Care of the orchards is fairly good about Street, but not elsewhere. Orchards are grazed chiefly by cattle and pigs. The Street orchards are held in many cases by local tradesmen and artisans, and their attitude towards them depends largely on the net returns.

The slow development of the trees is due to the proximity of Lias stone to the surface.

East Central. (Glastonbury, West Pennard, Baltonsborough, Butleigh, Barton, West Lydford, Ditcheat, East Pennard and vicinity.)

There is a high proportion of orchard land practically all under cider orchards, with a high percentage of old trees.

The trees crop early and do not attain a great size. Several late-flowering varieties are popular which crop regularly every second year. In the older orchards mosses and lichens are prevalent on the trees owing to their slow growth. Two or three cider factories in the area take the majority of the fruit.

Attention to the orchards is not good in general. Little pruning is done, and replacements are carried out from time to time, but little attention is given to young trees. Grazing is by dairy cattle principally.

Dairy farming is the chief occupation of the district and other farming operations take a decidedly second place. Orcharding was obviously better attended to in the past than at present. Local nurseries at Glastonbury have had a considerable influence in the district, deciding the type and variety of trees grown.

Extreme East. (From Witham Friary to Milborne Port, and from Evercreech to Eastern Boundary.)

The percentage of orchard land is very low except on the more sheltered, lower land. The orchards are very mixed in type, but mostly for cider fruit. Tree development varies with situation but on the whole is slow, producing trees of medium size. Many farms have only sufficient orchard to manufacture cider for home purposes ; where there is a surplus, fruit is sold to manufacturers. Attention to the orchards is very variable, but on the whole they receive some care. Grazing is principally by dairy cattle.

Cadbury District. (North and South Cadbury, Yarlington, Compton Pauncefoot, Blackford, Sutton Montis, Sparkford, Marston Magna, North and South Barrow, etc.)

This is a cider district of great repute in the County, where orchards are developed almost solely for this purpose. The trees develop to moderate size, cropping fairly regularly and well. Good locally selected varieties are principally grown and appear extremely suitable to local conditions. The whole crop is absorbed for cider by local cider-makers. Orchard management is good by comparison with other districts. Grazing is by cattle and young stock.

A distinct type of labourer exists here, keen and interested in apple-trees and looking after them well if given sound instruction.

Somerton Area. (Somerton, Charlton Mackrell, Kingweston, High Ham, Pitney and vicinity.)

In this district, on a thin, poorer type of Lower Lias soil, the orchards are successful if they have sufficient root-hold. The trees make rather under average size and crop biennially. There are some orchards of market fruit in the Charlton Mackrell and Keinton district, where the fruit is marketed in South Wales. Cider fruit is sent to local factories. The orchards are fairly well managed, but trees do not get out of control and need little pruning. Replanting is done spasmodically and a certain amount of orchard knowledge exists about the eastern end of the district. In some parts of the district quarrying has been done extensively and orchards are often planted on quarried land.

Langport and Ilchester. (Around Ilchester, Mudford, Yeovil Marsh, Long Sutton, Long Load, Langport, Aller, Muchelney, Drayton, Curry Rivel and vicinity.)

On the heavy clay of the Lias, the orchards are chiefly for cider, with a few young orchards of market fruit. The trees develop slowly but make large trees eventually and live to a great age. A retentive soil encourages trees which can withstand droughts, and relatively heavy bearing is the rule. Market fruit is sold principally to dealers, and cider fruit to local factories. A few farms make a quantity of cider. Many orchards have been well planned in the past, but management is now less careful. The orchards are grazed by cattle principally.

Some young orchards at Drayton demonstrate that market fruit could be grown successfully on these heavy soils, if properly managed.

Ilminster and South Petherton. (Stoke-under-Ham, Montacute, South Petherton, Tintinhull, Seavington, Barrington, Ilminster district and vicinity.)

There is here a lighter type of soil with mixed orchards of cider and culinary fruit-trees.

Trees develop well, and make good size but fruit irregularly according to the season. The spacing adopted is generally satisfactory. Market fruit is sent to dealers, and cider fruit to cider manufacturers.

Care of the orchards is, on the whole, good, as the farmers take an interest in them and endeavour to get the best from the whole farm. Grazing is by sheep and cattle. The land responds to good farming and permits a quick " turnover " of crops. The farmers are versatile and intelligent in coping with all their problems. That the district is very suitable for the development of dessert fruit cultivation is demonstrated by the successful establishment of one large plantation of this type in recent years, managed with the most up-to-date methods of commercial fruit-farming.

Extreme South. (Yeovil, Crewkerne, and Chard Districts.)

On these lighter soils orchards are more scattered and are chiefly cider orchards. Tree development varies according to the site of the orchard and, considerably, to the varieties chosen. The fruit is sent usually to large cider factories at Crewkerne and Chard. Attention, which is generally fair, depends upon the returns and the orchard yields. Replacements are usually well carried out. Grazing is chiefly by sheep. One or two varieties of fruit, predominating here, were originally planted for market purposes, but owing to low quality are now used for cider.

Parrett Basin. (Bridgwater, Westonzoyland, Huntworth, Moorland, Burrowbridge, Stoke St. Gregory.)

This is a district where orchards are numerous and closely set along the banks of the River Parrett. A good many orchards have been planted for market fruit, especially during the last 30 years. Many younger plantings can be found in the vicinity of Burrowbridge. Trees do not develop quickly for the first 10 years after planting, but following this period, they grow rapidly and attain in many cases a huge size, which is not usually sufficiently allowed for in planning. The varieties of market fruit grown are numerous in comparison with other districts. Cider varieties are also numerous. Market fruit is sent to South Wales and elsewhere by small local dealers and individual farmers, but modern methods are not adopted. Cider fruit is nearly all manufactured in the district by farmers and small makers. The management of young orchards is fair, but older plantings are often very neglected. Grazing is chiefly by cattle and pigs.

A very unusual practice carried out in the Burrowbridge area is to plant orchards in existing willow-beds, the trees developing to take the place of the willows as these lose their vitality.

This district is more disposed to late frost damage to its blossoms than any other owing to the low-lying position and proximity to the river. It is not unusual for a large percentage of the crop to be wiped out in this way.

East of the Quantocks. (North Petherton, Enmore, Spaxton, Cannington, Over and Nether Stowey and vicinity.)

The orchards are mostly well stocked principally with cider-fruit trees, with a few market fruit trees intermixed. The heavier red soil on this side of the hills induces good tree-growth if orchard sites have been well selected. The trees develop freely and crop reasonably well except possibly on the higher parts of the hillside. A few orchards are sold annually in a small orchard sale at Bridgwater. The remainder are dealt with by the farmers, who, in some instances, make a small quantity of cider. Attention to the orchards is, on the whole, fairly good. Grazing is by sheep and young stock. Most holdings have some acreage of orchard attached which is regarded as an asset, if the cropping is satisfactory.

Western Coastal. (Along the coast North of Quantock and Brendon Hills, excluding the district of Stogursey which is Lias Clay.)

The orchards are scattered, mostly in groups around the villages and sheltered valleys, and are relatively unimportant. Westerly and north-westerly gales make exposed positions unsuitable.

The orchards are chiefly of cider fruit with occasional trees of market fruit, or " horde " apples as they are locally known. Tree development varies considerably according to local variation of soil, but it is usually average or below average. The cider fruit is chiefly manufactured by local farm-makers. Care of orchards is varied, but more attention could be paid to the planting and care of young trees. Grazing is chiefly by sheep, resulting in good herbage. The West Somerset farmer usually puts his sheep first and the chief importance of the orchard is often to provide a sheltered lambing-place.

South of Taunton Vale. (From Taunton south to the Blackdown Hills.)

The soil is varied but is mostly a mixture derived from Greensand and Red Sandstone. The orchards vary according to the proportion of these original constituents. Towards the Blackdowns the orchards are not as prosperous. Many types of fruit-trees are grown, a fair proportion of market fruit of varying quality being found in every orchard.

On the whole tree development is good, and many orchards of fine old trees can be found. Many " dual " purpose varieties exist and make the management of the orchards a difficult problem. As with all the Taunton area individual trees do not crop regularly, but the orchard as a whole does not often prove a complete blank.

As in the whole Taunton area, auction sales dispose of the fruit from a large number of orchards. Dealers then handle it, sorting out fruit for their market requirements, the remainder going for cider.

Care of the orchards is satisfactory, but largely dependent upon the price the "orchard" realises at the sales. Pruning and replanting is done periodically. Sheep, grazing cattle and young stock are fed on the grass. The orchards would probably repay more attention, although they are by no means neglected.

Wellington and Milverton Area. (Wellington, Nynehead, Oake, Milverton, Wiveliscombe, etc.)

In the valleys between the hills, the alluvial soils produce some good orchards, chiefly for cider fruit, but with some market fruit intermixed in most. The trees develop to a good size, as a rule cropping well. The varieties are very similar to those grown in the Taunton Vale. A few orchards are sold in the Taunton sales. Other market fruit is packed by growers and local dealers, and the cider fruit goes principally to cider factories.

The orchards receive a reasonable amount of attention and the herbage is nearly always good. Pruning is carried out spasmodically, but is not entirely neglected. Stocking is principally with sheep.

On suitable sites, orchards can be made to pay well in this area.

Extreme West.

The whole district beyond a rough line from Williton to Wiveliscombe is hill country where orchards are only found in sheltered valleys around homesteads. In consequence they are very scattered and of little importance. The orchards are more of the Devon type with shorter stemmed trees, more closely planted than is customary elsewhere in Somerset. The trees do not develop to a great size and in the damper spots are subject to lichens and diseases.

Apart from a few " horde " apples for home use the trees are mostly cider varieties for home production, or for the cider factory. Pruning and replanting does not get much consideration.

Stocking is principally by sheep.

G. POULTRY

Except on a comparatively small number of specialised poultry farms, breeding for day-old chicks, hatching eggs, and stock, or rearing for egg production and stock, poultry keeping in Somerset is a sideline to general and dairy farming.

Egg production is the chief aim, and surplus cockerels and stock are sold for table use in the vicinity of the farms. There is practically no specialisation for the production of table birds.

The chief breeds, besides the home-bred " barn-door " which is widespread in some areas, are Rhode Island Red, White Wyandotte, Light Sussex, White Leghorn, Brown Leghorn and Sussex Game ; by far the most widespread being the Rhode Island Red, which is found, pure or in crosses, all over the County. White Wyandottes are second in importance, though far less numerous.

Distribution appears to depend on the presence of a good local market, and the establishment of breeding-farms, the difficulty being generally that where fowls are run as a sideline with no special attention to management, increase of numbers leads to disease.

Owing to the small acreage required for the few specialised poultry farms of high production and the importance of special training or individual interest with relation to the numbers of poultry carried on general farms, rather than position or soils, poultry farming can be considered of small importance in the utilisation of land in the County. Most farms keep some fowls, for domestic use, and eggs and table birds are sold.

In the region of Wellington and Taunton Vales and the extensions east and west of the Quantocks, there are specialised farms near Taunton, Staplegrove, Wellington, Spaxton, breeding on up-to-date lines with battery-brooders and rearing day-old chicks for egg production and stock birds. Specialised poultry farms are also established near Combe St. Nicholas, Langport, Martock, Ilminster, Wincanton, Cheddar, Portishead, but in the districts about these farms fowls are usually kept in small numbers. The regions about Donyatt, Ilminster (where in the last ten years fowls have increased chiefly on 115 holdings varying from 5 to 40 acres) and Winford (on Mendip) are above the average in numbers of poultry kept.

Feeding throughout the County generally is with proprietory mashes and grain, with wet mash fed particularly in winter. Housing, where anything more than accommodation provided by farm-buildings is used, is usually on the semi-intensive principle, the small farm colony, or colony free range houses, slatted floors, but some districts have fold units with small movable houses and rearing " arks." The semi-intensive system is the most widespread and fold units are sparsely distributed over the higher ground from Exford and Wincanton to Clapton.

Production and shell texture are generally good, but not in winter except on specialised farms. In almost every case where disease is prevalent, the number of birds kept locally is comparatively high and breeding farms are present in the district, though not all breeding-farms are troubled with disease. In two cases where stock are low and disease prevalent, stock have formerly been high.

Compared with 42 counties, the position of Somerset in 1933 as a producer of poultry was as follows :—

Fowls, 9th. Ducks, 4th. Geese, 12th. Turkeys, 6th.

Geese are used to graze the poultry runs on a large number of farms.

H. HOUSES AND GARDENS

No black and white illustration has been made for the Report since house and garden property can best be studied on the one-inch Land Utilisation Survey maps.

Detailed study of the towns is outside the scope of the work, and can be found in numerous special publications. Attention may be drawn, however, to the expansion going on rapidly from the larger towns, and the familiar pattern of " ribbon " development along the main roads, which must be distinguished, however, from the much older growth of habitations along the roads through the lowland moor areas where the embankments, made to raise the roads above the floods, have provided the best sites for cottages for the necessary agricultural labour.

A noticeable feature, following on the provision of good roads, is the spreading of residential property south-west of Bristol as far as the favoured south-western region below Mendip Scarp and the growing popularity of the Western Hill Country, in spite of the high rainfall, for small " retired " residential estates, attracted by the beauty and comparative remoteness of the neighbourhood, and by the sporting facilities offered.

On the one-inch Land Utilisation Survey sheets the progress of recent building development can be studied with fair accuracy, since, while "houses-with-gardens" areas are all marked in purple, recent development is distinguished by the absence of the conventional Ordnance Survey signs under the colour. Modern buildings, and housing estates, usually in red brick, can thus be distinguished from the older habitation sites, and a fair idea of the character of the various localities obtained.

Land Agriculturally Unproductive.

Apart from the sites of towns, the roads and railways, there is remarkably little agriculturally unproductive land in the County. Such areas are marked red on the Land Utilisation Survey sheets, and are generally explained by the Ordnance Survey lettering (quarries, cemeteries, brick and tile works, pitheads, etc.).

North-east of Bridgwater, between the Bridgwater–Bawdrip Road and the Southern Railway, the recently erected British Cellophane Factory site is marked in red, with no lettering, and by Keynsham Hams (Sheet 111) the Fry site is similarly indicated. North of English Combe there is a large new cemetery.

IV. A DETAILED STUDY OF SPECIMEN SOMERSET FARMS

This Survey was conducted by an agricultural expert with an intimate, scientific and practical knowledge of farming in the County, and the friendly help of the various farmers towards a most valuable contribution is greatly appreciated.

Forty-six farms were visited, and a general inquiry was made into the district immediately surrounding each farm. The exact acreages of the farms described have not been quoted as this might have involved a breach of confidence in respect of revealing their identity.

It was impossible, in the time at the disposal of the investigator, to visit every field and record the soil type, since each farm took from 2½ to 4 hours, but in most cases the farmer was able to give a sufficiently accurate account.

On farms where accounts were kept, the actual valuation figures were obtained. A few farms appear to be highly capitalised, but the figures are genuine. In some cases only total capital could be obtained, and in several, where no figure or estimate could be obtained, the figure as given in the Report is estimated from the figures given by the Economics Department of Bristol University.

Except on a very few farms it was not possible to get the actual operations necessary to effect a tilth for any particular crop, as on all soils, except the very light ones, weather conditions play such a large part in cultivation.

"Crop yields" refer to average yields for each farm, as yields from field to field vary so much according to weather in a particular season.

The farm studies are arranged according to the physical regions of the County.

THE WESTERN HILLS AREA. (Physical Regions 1a, 1c, 1d.)

The "Old Devonian." West of Porlock Vale.

Soils. Typical Old Devonian soils are poor. They are usually free and easily worked, but stones and gradients make cultivation difficult in many fields. There is good natural drainage but the soil is inclined to be sour. Manures required are chiefly phosphates and organic matter. Club-root is fairly common unless the lime content is kept up.

Stock. The chief use of stock is for breeding, a few cattle are fattened, and small quantities of butter and cream are produced for market in Minehead. *Sheep* : Chiefly Exmoor breeding flocks, with a few Devon Closewools. *Pigs* : Small numbers of various breeds are kept, chiefly crosses. The average is one or two sows per farm.

Power. Horse.

Land Values. Farms in this area are rented at 20/– to 24/– per acre. "Off-farms" without a farmhouse, usually rented by men farming in the lowlands, may be only 7/6 to 10/– per acre.

Growing Season. On the specimen farm at about 900 feet stock grass is available about the third week in May. Oats are sown as soon after March 25th as possible. Harvest commences in mid-August in an average season.

Specimen Farm.

Area 75–100 acres. Held on yearly tenancy.
Soil. Typical Old Devonian.
Working Capital. About £10 per acre, 82 per cent. in livestock.

Labour Employed. One man and one boy. Seasonal requirements are met by interchange of labour amongst neighbours.

Crops. The rotation followed is oats, roots, oat with " seeds," seed hay, grass (3–6 years according to quality of sward). All are consumed on the farm.

Preparation of the Land. Ley to corn. Ploughed, dragged twice, harrowed twice, rolled. Drainage is natural and part of the farm free and easy working, but stones and gradients make cultivation difficult in some fields.

Manuring. Oats after ley—nil. Roots after oats—dung ; 10 cwt. slag ; 5 cwt. compound root manure per acre.

Grassland. The farm has about 26 acres permanent grass, 14 acres of which is very poor, consisting of bent, bracken, brambles, etc., 12 acres are good, yielding about 20 cwts. of hay per acre. Temporary pastures yield 30–40 cwts. of hay in the first year, and the stock-carrying capacity afterwards is at least four times that of the permanent pasture. The farm has grazing rights on Porlock Common, used for sheep and a few ponies. The number of stock put on this common is limited to the number which can be wintered on the farm.

Livestock. Cattle are Devons or of Devon type. Some milk is sold, and young stock reared. *Sheep*: A breeding flock of Exmoors is kept. *Pigs*: None. *Poultry*: A few "barndoor" fowls are kept. Surplus eggs are sold and fat chickens in summer.

EXFORD REGION.

Soils. The soil in this region is of the Devonian type; it is easily worked, but is inclined to be sour and has a very high lime requirement. Apart from lime, manures required are chiefly phosphates, with organic matter on arable land.

Stock. This is a rearing district, with some dairying for a local summer market. Cattle are chiefly Devons and Devon type. *Sheep*: Chiefly Exmoors, a few crossed with Devon Closewool, but little crossing is done. *Pigs*: Very few pigs kept, one or two sows per farm, chiefly Wessex Saddleback.

Land Values. Farms in this area are rented at or about 10/– per acre. Many of the Exmoor farms have grazing rights on the moor. Stocking is generally limited to stock wintered.

Growing Season. On the specimen farm, at about 1,000–1,400 feet, stock grass is available about the beginning of May. Oats are sown about mid-April, and harvest commences normally in the last week in August.

Specimen Farm.

Area 500–600 acres. Yearly tenancy.

Soil. Typical, easy-working Upper Devonian. Very little variation from field to field.

Working Capital. About £4 per acre, 80 per cent. in livestock.

Labour Employed. Two men ; extra seasonal labour costs about £15 per annum.

Crops. Rotation : Roots (folded) ; oats ; roots (folded) ; rape and grass seeds ; seed hay ; grass up to 6 years according to sward. All consumed on the farm. Club-root is sometimes present in swedes and turnips.

Preparation of the Land. Ley to oats. Plough, harrowed twice, spring harrow twice ; seed drilled and harrowed once, rolled once. Drainage is natural and the soil free and easy-working.

Manuring. Ley to oats—nil ; ley to roots or swedes ; dung ; 8 cwt. slag and super (about 6 slag to 2 super) ; roots folded and no manure for following corn crop.

Average Yield. Oats—30 bushels per acre. Swedes—18 tons.

The farm is typical of the district as regards cropping and stock (except for dairying) but is rather above the average as regards yields and stock-carrying capacity.

Grassland. The grassland on this farm is rather above the average for the district, having a large proportion of rye-grass and wild white clover. There is about 100 acres of permanent pasture and meadow. Average hay yield is about 20 cwt. per acre. The grassland responds well to slag.

Livestock. Devon Cattle are kept and the calves reared and fattened. *Sheep*: An Exmoor breeding flock is maintained, a few crossed with Devon Closewool. Breeders are sold in August and September. *Pigs*: One breeding sow only—a Wessex Saddleback. *Poultry*: About 50 Rhode Island Reds and Game. Surplus eggs are sold.

DULVERTON AREA.

Soil. Typical Upper Devonian. Easy working, inclined to be sour but good natural drainage. Responds to phosphates. Club-root is occasionally present.

Stock. A rearing district; a few cattle are fattened and a considerable quantity of milk is now being produced from perhaps a third of the farms. Cattle chiefly Devon and Devon type. *Sheep*: Exmoor, and crosses of Devon Closewool and Dorset Downs. *Pigs*: An average of one breeding sow per farm. Crossbreds with Large White becoming popular.

Land Values. Farms in the area are rented at 17/6 to 20/- per acre.

Growing Season. Oats sown mid-March to mid-April and harvested about mid-August. Stock grass is available about May 1st.

Specimen Farm.

Area 150–200 acres. Yearly tenancy.

Soil. Typical Devonian. Little variation from field to field.

Working Capital is about £7 10s. per acre; some 76 per cent. being in livestock.

Labour Employed. Two men and one boy; extra seasonal labour costs about £10–£15 per annum.

Crops. Rotation practised: oats, roots, oats or barley with seeds, "seeds" hay or grazed, grass grazed (two years). Crops are consumed on the farm.

Preparation of the Ground. Ley to oats; plough, cultivate, harrow three times, drill seed, harrow once, heavy roller once. Drainage is natural and soil free and easy working. Horse power is used, but a tractor hired occasionally.

Manuring. Ley to oats, 10 cwt. of lime where roots are to follow, no manures otherwise. Mangels—dung; 5 cwt. mangel manure and wood ashes. Swedes—dung; 4 cwt. dissolved bone and super, or turnip manure.

This farm is about the average for the district and is typical with regard to stock and cropping.

Grassland. About half the farm is in permanent pasture, which cuts for hay about 25 cwt. per acre. The pastures which are good and above the average for the district, respond to slag and are limed occasionally.

Stock. Devon cattle are kept. The calves are reared and part sold as stores, part fattened. *Sheep*: A crossbred flock is maintained, of Exmoor ewes crossed with Devon Closewool. Half the flock is crossed with Devon Closewool and half with Dorset Down. Fat lambs and hoggets are produced. *Pigs*: None. *Poultry*: About 50 head of "barndoor" breed.

THE PORLOCK VALE.

Soils. The soils of the vale vary in composition, but are in general easy to work, well drained. About Porlock the soil is heavier and more marly towards the shore, becoming lighter and more stony towards the village. The soils are slightly acid, but liming is not generally practised. The locality is specially favourable for malting barley and roots. Phosphates and organic matter as the chief manurial requirements. Patches of Raan in swedes are fairly common.

Stock. Fat lambs and hoggets and fat cattle are produced. *Sheep* : Exmoors, Closewools, Dorset Downs, Hampshire Downs, South Downs, " Downs " used for crossing purposes.

Land Values. Some farms in this area are rented at 50/- to 60/- per acre. The high reputation of the malting barley increases local values.

Growing Season. Oats are sown any time after March 20th and cut in the first or second week of August. Stock grass is available about April 20th.

Specimen Farm.

Area between 80–120 acres. Freehold.

Soil. Not a very marked difference, but the soil is in part heavier and more marly, in part lighter and more stony. Working capital is about £10 per acre, about 70 per cent. being in livestock.

Labour Employed. Three men are permanently employed and extra labour as required at harvest and haymaking.

Crops. Rotation practised : Barley, roots, oats and " seeds," clover hay. Barley is sold off the farm, oats partly sold and the greater part fed on farm.

Preparation of the Ground. Ley to Barley—plough, cultivate twice, drag twice, drill seed, harrow once, roll once. The soil has natural drainage and is free and easy working.

Manuring. Barley—4 cwt. per acre Fison's Barley Manure. Roots—dung, 5 cwt. per acre dissolved bone ; without dung—3 cwt. slag, 3 cwt. compound.

Grassland. All the grassland is permanent pasture, the hay yield being 30–35 cwt. per acre.

Livestock. Crossbred cows for milk and Devon-type steers for grazing, are carried. *Sheep* : Exmoor ewes and Dorset Down are crossed and the ewes crossed with Hampshire Downs. Devon Closewool ewes crossed with Dorset Downs. The ewes are bought about July, for fat lamb and fat hogget production. *Pigs* : None. *Poultry* : About 40 " barndoor " breed are kept and the surplus eggs sold.

THE MINEHEAD–WATCHET AREA.

Soils. The soils in the area are varied, consisting broadly of Lias Clays, Marls, Sandstone soils and Alluvium, as in the Wellington and Taunton Vales where examples of each type have been recorded for the report. The greater part of the area is responsive to lime as it is slightly acid. The Sandstone soils are easily worked and well drained, the Lias Clays and Marls are inclined to be difficult, depending upon weather conditions. Low-lying arable and pasture fields are drained by covered stone drains, and the marshes by open drains. Manurial requirement chiefly phosphates, with potash for certain crops (e.g., mangolds).

Stock. Cattle are grazed, fat lambs produced, " hogging " is fairly common and milk is sold from many farms. *Sheep* : Exmoor Horn and Devon Ewe with Dorset Down. *Pigs* : are bred for stores, or for the bacon trade. Large Black, Wessex Saddleback and Large White are the chief breeds, Wessex Saddleback the most common.

Power. There are a few tractors in use in the district.

Land Values. Farms in this area are rented from 20/- to 37/- per acre.

Growing Season. Barley is sown as soon as possible after mid-February and harvested in mid-August. Stock grass is available by mid-April.

Specimen Farm.

Area between 300–350 acres. Yearly tenancy.

Soil. Lias Clay, alluvial meadows, Upper Keuper Sandstone. Working Capital, about £10 per acre.

Labour Employed. Ten men and 1 woman with extra seasonal labour costing about £60 per annum.

Crops. Rotation. On the Lias there is no fixed cropping ; on the Sandstones a four-course rotation is followed. Barley and wheat are sold off the farm, the other crops consumed.

Preparation of the Land. The Lias fields are difficult to cultivate except under suitable weather conditions. Practically all the fields were originally drained and are still fairly efficient. The fields on Sandstone have good natural drainage and are easily worked.

Manuring. Swedes. Farmyard manure. 5 cwt. turnip manure per acre.

Yields. Average barley yield is about 40 bushels per acre. Swedes and kale are sown together and folded off. The yield is usually good but no definite figures were obtained.

Grassland. About 172 acres are in permanent pasture, the hay yield varying from 20 to 27 cwt. per acre. Basic slag and farmyard manure are used on the grassland which is very good, of the rye-grass-clover type. Except for the alluvial meadows, the grassland was arable until comparatively recent years and if a field shows signs of deterioration it is ploughed, cropped two years and regrassed.

Livestock. A dairy herd of Friesians is kept and calves are bought to rear ; Shorthorn and Devon cattle are bought for grazing. *Sheep :* Dorset Horn Ewes crossed with South Down produce fat lambs for the Easter trade. *Pigs :* Wessex Saddleback sows crossed with Large White, for the store trade. *Poultry :* Negligible.

THE VALES OF WELLINGTON AND TAUNTON DEANE, THE FAULT CORRIDOR AND SURROUNDING SLOPES.

This is an area of varied and sharply contrasting soils. Representative farms have been chosen on six classes of soil material, Upper (Keuper) Red Marl, Upper Sandstone, Pebble Beds and Conglomerates, Lower Sandstones and Breccias, Valley Gravel and Rainwash, Lower Marl. Upper (Keuper) Red Marl, is a dark red, glistening heavy marl, sticky and difficult to work in bad weather conditions, considered to be " three-horse " land. This requires careful drainage for good results and is generally drained by stone and pipe drains to ditches and streams. It is not a sour soil and benefits by phosphates and potash for certain crops ; favourable particularly for wheat and beans. Crop diseases are not prevalent.

Specimen Farm I.

Area between 400–450 acres. Freehold.

The *Soil* is very variable, some fields having outcrops of two or three types, and consists of (1) a sticky loam with many flints, with yellow clay beneath ; (2) a sticky red marl, stony in places and with traces of blue clay ; (3) a very sticky loam with blue clay beneath.

Working Capital about £9 per acre. 83 per cent. in livestock.

Labour Employed. Ten men and 2 boys, with extra seasonal labour to the value of about £15.

Crops. All the crops typical of the area are grown (see page 74) but no system of rotation is followed. Wheat and barley are sold, the remainder of the crops consumed on the farm.

Preparation of the Land. Both horses and tractors are used. The majority of the fields are under-drained (i.e. have covered drains) and cultivation depends on the weather conditions. For swedes, the ground is ploughed once or twice, twice dragged, harrowed and rolled.

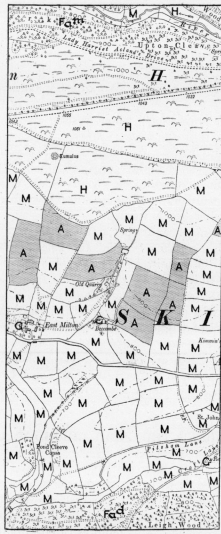

Based upon the Ordnance Survey Map, with the sanction of the Controller of H.M. Stationery Office.

FIG. 15.—The Western Hills Area (Devonian).

This map illustrates the sharp distinction between the unimproved land, which is shown by the symbols of rough pasture and furze ; and the improved land, on which ploughed fields are placed at a high elevation on a south-facing slope. It shows the fairly small fields which are here separated by stone-faced banks, topped with beech, using considerable space but nevertheless affording shelter to stock which is very valuable in these high regions. To the north and south of the section woods are seen to cover north-facing slopes : where woods are not present these slopes are usually under bracken and rough pasture.

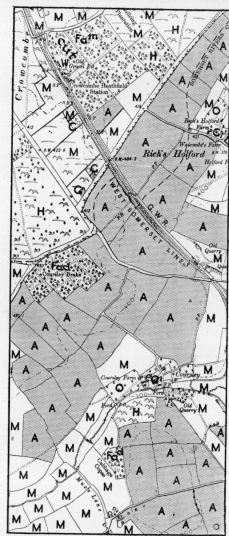

Based upon the Ordnance Survey Map, with the sanction of the Controller of H.M. Stationery Office.

FIG. 16.—The Fault Corridor.

This map provides a good illustration of the complexity of soil conditions in the area. The group of ploughed fields north of the railway is chiefly on Valley Gravel ; the five larger fields south of the railway are on Upper (Keuper) Sandstone ; the smaller fields south of these lie on Pebble Beds and Conglomerate. The heath to the west lies on Lower Marl, the woods north of the railway on Valley Gravel. New houses and gardens are shown developing along the edge of the former heathland and on the land nearby some fields have recently been improved from heath to grassland, on soils derived from Alluvium and Pebble Bed.

These maps and those of a similar character which follow are all reduced from the Field Survey Maps and are on a scale of 4 inches to 1 mile. Each represents a characteristic section of the region concerned. Throughout the fields or other divisions of land are marked in accordance with the Land Utilisation Survey's scheme of symbols : A—Arable ; M—Meadow and Permanent Grass ; H—Heathland, Commons and Rough Grazing ; F—Forest and Woodland ; G—Gardens ; O—Orchards ; W—Land Agriculturally unproductive. In addition arable land has been stippled unless crops have been named.

Manuring. Wheat is top-dressed with nitrogen. Mangolds, farmyard manure and 2 to 3 cwt., concentrated complete fertiliser, 1 cwt. nitrate of chalk. Swedes, farmyard manure and 2 to 3 cwt. concentrated complete fertiliser.

Crop Yields are fair in an average season but fluctuate considerably. Wheat, about 8 sacks per acre. Swedes, 15 to 25 tons per acre.

The Growing Season. As much corn as possible is sown in autumn and winter. Spring corn is sown in March if soil condition allows. Oat harvest is commenced about the 25th of July, wheat and beans about August 1st. Stock grass is available about May 1st.

Grassland. There are about 250 acres of permanent pasture. Hay yields vary between 25–30 cwt. per acre. The land responds to slag. Farmyard manure is used and sheep are run over from folds as much as possible in such a manner as will give each field a turn. The lower fields are good and well grazed, but some of the higher fields are rather rough and weedy.

Stock. A pedigree Devon herd is maintained for production of stock bulls and grazing cattle. *Sheep :* Chiefly Dorset Downs crossed with South Down or Ryeland, for fat lamb production. *Pigs :* Wessex Saddleback crossed with Large White for production of pork. *Poultry :* A few " barndoor " for house use.

Livestock in the locality. *Crossbred cattle :* Shorthorn and Devon, are reared chiefly for milk production. *Sheep :* Chiefly Dorset Down crossed with South Down for fat lamb production. *Pigs :* Wessex Saddleback, Large Black and Large White, chiefly Large White crossed for bacon production and the store trade. *Poultry :* Rhode Island Reds and White Wyandottes appear to predominate, for commercial egg-production, but certain farms breed their own stock and sell surplus hatching eggs. Birds are housed in slatted-floor houses and managed on the semi-intensive system. Production is about 50 per cent. throughout the year, with fair shell texture, but disease has been prevalent.

Horses and tractors are used for power.

Land Values. Farms in this area are rented at about 30/- per acre.

Specimen Farm II. (Vicinity of Bishop's Lydeard.)

Area between 200–300 acres.

Soil. Chiefly Red (Keuper) Marl.

Working Capital about £9 per acre, 84 per cent. in livestock.

Labour Employed. Four men and 2 boys, extra seasonal labour to the value of about £25 per annum.

Crops. The rotation practised is wheat, roots or beans, barley with " seeds," seed hay. The wheat is sold off the farm, and beans, straw and roots are consumed.

Preparation of the Soil. Practically all the fields are pipe-drained, and the soil is difficult to work. For winter wheat the ground is ploughed once, dragged once, drilled and harrowed. For swedes, ploughed, dragged twice, rolled twice, ploughed again, again double dragged and rolled, again ploughed, harrowed, rolled, and the seed drilled.

Manuring. For wheat, after ley, beans or roots, a top dressing of nitrogen is used when necessary. For swedes, a light dressing of farmyard manure and about 3 cwt. concentrated complete fertiliser. *Average yields :* Wheat yields are about 40 bushels per acre ; swedes are a doubtful crop in a dry year, and " seeds " are also rather difficult to establish.

Growing Season. Wheat harvest commences about August 1st. Stock grass is available about the last week in April.

Grassland. 156 acres are in permanent pasture, the average hay yield being about 25 cwt. per acre. The pastures are deficient in lime and respond well to slag. On the whole the grassland is good, composed chiefly of rye-grass and clover, but some fields contain a fair amount of creeping bent which tends to increase unless attention is paid to cultivation and manuring.

Livestock.   The farm rears Devon and Devon-cross cattle which are sold as stores at 2–2½ years old.   *Sheep :* Dorset Horn Ewes are crossed with South Downs for fat lamb production for the spring trade.   Ewe lambs are bought in May.   *Pigs :* Large Black sows are crossed with Large White and the pigs sold as " slips."   *Poultry :* A few " barndoors " are kept.

The Locality.   Farms in this area are rented at from 40/– to 60/– per acre, the latter figure referring to small farms.

Livestock in the Area.   This is a dairying, rearing and fattening area.   Fat lambs are general ; dairy cattle are chiefly Shorthorns, while Devons are reared for fattening.   *Sheep* are generally pure Dorset Downs, or Dorset Downs crossed with South Down.   Both horses and tractors are used for cultivation.

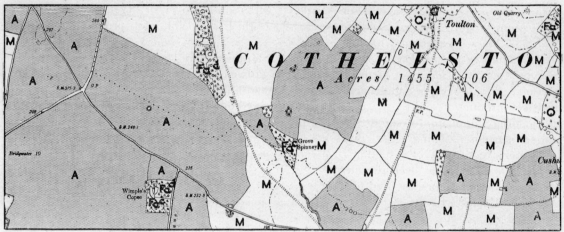

Based upon the Ordnance Survey Map, with the sanction of the Controller of H.M. Stationery Office.

FIG. 17.—The Vale of Taunton Deane.

This map illustrates the contrast in field pattern between the land on the Upper (Keuper) Sandstone (the large fields to the west) and on the Red (Keuper) Marl, (the small fields to the east).   The Sandstone soils are light, well drained and easy to work and are therefore cultivated in large tracts wherever possible. The Marls, stickier and heavier to cultivate, require to be drained and have a much smaller proportion under the plough and the fields are chiefly under grass and are far smaller in size.   The number of small ponds in the fields is noteworthy.   In the north-east the section includes part of the lower slopes of the Quantock Hills.

UPPER SANDSTONE (Nynehead Area).

The soils do not vary greatly ; in general a free-working sandy loam on Sandstone, easy to cultivate, with a natural drainage except locally in hollows where pipe-drainage may be necessary.   The soil is inclined to be acid and requires lime at intervals, and complete manures for satisfactory crops ; especially favourable for growing of barley and roots. " Finger and toe " and clover-sickness are sometimes prevalent.   Fields are very large and arranged for convenience of working.

Stock in the Locality.   Shorthorns are kept for milk production ; Shorthorns, Devons and Aberdeen Angus crosses for fattening.   Dairying, rearing and fattening are the policy of most farms.   *Sheep :* Down crosses are kept as " flying flocks " for production of fat lambs and hoggets. *Pigs :* Chiefly Large Whites, are fattened. *Poultry* in the immediate locality are sparse. Both mechanical and horse power is used for cultivation.

Land Values. Farms in the area are rented at about 35/– per acre.

Growing Season. Barley is sown in March if possible. Harvest commences about the first week in August. Stock grass is available about the first week in April.

Specimen Farm III. (Nynehead Vicinity).

Area between 350 and 400 acres. Yearly tenancy.

Soil. A free-working sandy loam on Sandstone, with little variation and natural drainage, except in hollows where pipes are laid.

Working Capital about £19 per acre.

Labour Employed. Nine men with extra seasonal labour at a cost of some £80 per annum.

Crops. There is no fixed rotation as on the light soil frequent manuring is necessary, but the following rotations are typical of the policy aimed at :—

1. Barley. 2. Barley with " seeds." 3. Clover hay. 4. Barley. 5. Roots.

1. Barley—catch crop of vetches, etc. 2. Roots. 3. Barley with " seeds." 4. Clover hay. Barley is sold as malting barley, the other crops consumed.

Preparation of the Soil. The soil is easy to cultivate. *Manuring :* For Swedes, farmyard manure and complete manures (3 cwt. I.C.I. + 1 cwt. nitrate of soda). About half a ton of lime per acre is applied to arable land every seven years.

Average Yields. The average barley yield is about 11 sacks per acre.

Grassland. There is about 190 acres of permanent pasture, all of which is cut in turn, yielding about 28–30 cwt. per acre. Every fourth year the pastures are dressed with phosphates (super and S.B.F.) and potash salts (3 cwt. of super, 2 cwt. of S.B.F. and 1 of K_2O). Much of the grassland was in poor condition four years ago but with the manuring as above and heavy stocking it is rapidly improving and is now in very good condition.

Livestock. Shorthorns and Devons are kept for calf-rearing, and Shorthorns, Devons and Angus are grazed and yard fattened, chiefly the latter. *Sheep :* Ewes are bought in May, chiefly Dorset Horns and Dorset Downs crossed with South Down for production of fat lambs. *Pigs :* None. *Poultry :* a few " barndoors."

PEBBLE BEDS AND CONGLOMERATE (Preston-Bowyer Area).

The soils are somewhat similar to those in the Upper Sandstone areas—a light, sandy loam, free working and with a natural drainage. The soil is not sour, but arable land needs liming at intervals, manurial requirements being chiefly phosphates and organic matter ; favourable for barley and beet. Clover sickness is fairly prevalent. Stock is as for the Sandstone area described above (page 98). Most farms have a very mixed cattle policy, including dairying, rearing and fattening.

Sheep and Pigs. As for the Sandstone area.

Poultry. The predominant breeds are White Wyandottes and Rhode Island Red. Breeding and commercial egg production is carried out locally, surplus cockerels only being sold for table poultry as a side-line. Housing is chiefly semi-intensive, with small arks for rearing. Feeding is usually dry mash and grain, with one farm feeding only wet mash and grain. Production and shell texture is good (winter production was poor in 1936). Disease has been prevalent for the past four years, leading to re-organization of the system on some farms. Poultry form a considerable item in the farming system of a number of farms, some of which specialise in this branch.

Cultivation is chiefly by horse power, but some tractors are in use.

Land Values. Farms in this area are rented at about 40/– per acre.

The Growing Season. Winter wheat is sown in November if possible, barley in February and March ; stock grass is available about mid-April.

Specimen Farm IV.   (Preston Bowyer Vicinity).

Area. Between 250 and 300 acres. Freehold.

Soil. A light sandy loam on Sandstone and Conglomerate without much variation.

Working Capital is about £10 10s. per acre.

Labour Employed about twelve men and one woman ; with little extra seasonal labour required.

Crops. The following rotations are practised according to the position of the fields :—

(*a*)   1st year—Barley.
              Rape and Rye and Winter Barley for spring folding.
       2nd year—Mangolds
       3rd year—Barley.
              Trefoil and Italian rye-grass for spring folding.
       4th year—Sugar beet.
       5th year—Barley with " seeds," folded in the spring.
       6th year—Clover hay (mown twice) folded.

(*b*)   1st year—Barley.
              Trifolium or vetches, folded in the spring.
       2nd year—Swedes and kale or turnips, folded.
       3rd year—Barley.
       4th year—Barley with " seeds."
       5th year—Clover hay (cut twice), folded.

Barley for malting and beet are sold, the rest consumed.

Preparation of the Land. The land is all easy to work.

Manuring. For malting barley after clover, 1 cwt. sulphate of ammonia. For malting barley after roots fed off, no manure. For malting barley after beet, tops removed, no manure. For sugar beet, $2\frac{1}{2}$ cwt. sulphate of ammonia, $2\frac{1}{2}$ cwt. super, 2 kainit and farmyard manure.

Average Yield of barley is 11 sacks per acre ; of wheat, 11 sacks per acre ; of beet, 12 to 14 tons ; of mangolds, 35 to 40 tons.

Grassland. About 90 acres are in permanent pasture. Certain fields are mown every year and dunged every other year. The average hay yield is about 30 cwt. per acre. One or two low-lying meadows are irrigated. No artificial manures are used, but the grassland is of good type, well grazed and productive.

Livestock. Red Polls are kept for milk sale, the heifers being reared for herd replenishment and barren cows fattened. *Sheep :* A pedigree flock of Dorset Downs is maintained for rearing rams. The surplus ewes are fattened. *Pigs :* Large White sows are kept and the litters sold as stores. *Poultry :* A few " barndoors " kept for farm use.

LOWER SANDSTONE AND BRECCIA (Staplegrove Vicinity).

Soils. In these foothill areas the soils naturally vary considerably, Red Marls on Clay, Gravels, Shales and Shillets. The arable land is in general easy to work and naturally drained. Soil is slightly sour. General manurial requirement, phosphates and organic matter.

Stock and stocking policy is much the same as for the Sandstone and Conglomerate areas already dealt with.

Poultry is a feature of the locality. Pedigree breeding is carried out by two farms, one specialising in Rhode Island Reds and the other in Buff Rhodes. Housing is chiefly on the semi-intensive principle : feeding on scientific principles of dry and wet mash and grain. A few turkeys are kept. Rhode Island Reds and first crosses are kept by general farmers for egg production. Production and shell texture are good and disease not prevalent.

Land Values. Farms in this area are rented at 50/- to 60/- per acre.

Growing Season. Spring corn is sown as soon as possible after mid-February. Harvest commences about the first week in August. Stock grass is available about mid-April.

Specimen Farm V.

Area between 50 and 100 acres. Leasehold.

Soil varies somewhat but is chiefly an easily worked Red Marl with Blue Clay underlying in some places, Gravel in others, and a Shale of shillet also occurs in a few places. Tilth is obtained with very little trouble.

Working Capital is about £9 10s. per acre, about 77 per cent. being in livestock.

Labour employed. Two boys with extra seasonal labour at a cost of about £20 a year.

Crops. There is only one arable field on the farm, which is cultivated according to no particular rotation. Wheat and a small quantity of peas are sold, the remaining crops consumed. Nitrogen is used in preparation for wheat.

Grassland. All is permanent pasture, the average hay cut being 25–28 cwt. per acre. Farmyard manure only is used. The grassland is very good on the whole, well drained, and cattle are out practically all the year round. Some fields are rather weedy and would be improved by ploughing up. Depletion of plant food has been retarded to some extent by restriction clauses in the lease as to the type of stock to be kept, the size of the dairy herd (12 cows) and the amount of grass cut for hay.

Livestock. Shorthorns are kept for milking, Devon crossbreds reared for fattening. Crossbred sheep produce fat lambs and fat cull ewes.

VALLEY GRAVEL AND RAINWASH (East Lydeard Vicinity).

The soils in the vicinity consist of Red Marl deposits with Gravel probably underlying, Alluvial Silt and Gravel. There is considerable variation. The soils are, however, adaptable and easy to work, and not sour. Crop diseases are not prevalent. Rearing, fattening and some dairying is practised. Dorset Down ewes with Dorset Down or South Down rams produce lambs for fattening.

Pigs are reared—Wessex Saddleback, Large White and Large Black—chiefly for the bacon trade.

Poultry for this area is included in the previous district.

Both horses and tractors are used for cultivation.

Land Values. Farms in this area are rented at about 40/- per acre.

Growing Season. Barley is sown as soon as possible after mid-February and harvest begins about the last week in July. Stock grass is available about the second week in April.

Specimen Farm VI.

The farm was chosen as showing arable land or land marked on the drift sheet (No. 279) as " valley gravel and rainwash " in the vicinity of East Lydeard.

The area is between 250 and 300 acres. Freehold.

Soil. Chiefly Red Marl with Gravel to the north. The meadows appear to be of mixed alluvial type with Gravel underlying it.

Working Capital about £12 per acre, 81 per cent. of which is in livestock.

Labour Employed. Four men and 1 boy, with extra seasonal labour at a cost of about £50 per annum.

Crops. No rotation is practised. Wheat and barley are sold, the remainder consumed.

Preparation of the Ground. There are pipe drains in many fields; cultivation, both by horse and tractor, varies according to the situation of the field, but presents no particular difficulty, in contrast to the Red Marls lying at higher levels.

Manuring. Mangolds: farmyard manure and complete manure—C.C.F., No. 2. Swedes not usually dunged—C.C.F., No. 6. Average crop yields not available.

Grassland. This is chiefly permanent pasture yielding about 30 cwt. per acre when cut. The grassland is of good type and well grazed, the meadows carrying stock in winter without "poaching" badly. Some of the newer pastures north of the farm are not very productive and are being broken up in turn and reseeded.

Livestock. This is a rearing and grazing farm; some store cattle are sold. The cows are crossbred from a Devon bull. *Sheep* are as previously noted for Taunton Vale area. *Pigs :* about 20 sows are kept, Large Black, Wessex Saddleback and Large White, for rearing bacon pigs. *Poultry* for farm use only.

LOWER MARL (Stogumber Vicinity).

The exposure of Lower Marl is not extensive. The soil is very deep, red, rather light, sour but with good natural drainage and can be worked in almost any weather. Club root is very common.

Stock is kept locally for various purposes, some dairying, fattening and production of store cattle. The chief breeds are Devons and Shorthorns, the latter most common. *Sheep:* for fat lambs, for hogging and stores, are bred, the chief breeds being Dorset Down crossed with South Down, Dorset Down, Hampshire; and Exmoor crossed with Dorset Down. *Pigs* are sold chiefly as weaners or stores, with a few fattened, the chief breed being Wessex Saddleback crossed with Long White. *Poultry* are kept by general farmers, one farm specializing in commercial egg production, with a breeding plant. Chief breeds as general in the Vale are Rhode Island Reds and White Wyandottes. Disease has been prevalent.

Both horses and tractors are used.

Land Values. Farms in this area are rented at about 25/- per acre.

Growing Season. Spring corn is sown at the end of February if possible. Harvest commences in the first week of August. Stock grass is available about May 1st.

Specimen Farm VII.

Area. Between 250 and 300 acres. Freehold.

Soil. The soil is fairly uniform all over the farm—a very deep red soil, rather light, which appears to be a mixture of red Marl, Sandstone and Gravel.

Working Capital is about £6 10s. per acre.

Labour. One man is permanently employed and there is practically no seasonal labour employed.

Crops. The rotation followed is : wheat, roots or beans, barley or oats with " seeds," seeds hay. Wheat is sold and barley if satisfactory, the remainder is consumed.

Preparation of the Soil. The soil can be worked in almost any weather and cultivation is easy.

Manuring. Wheat after clover, 1 cwt. of nitrogen top dressing.

Swedes, farmyard manure + 8–10 cwt. basic slag.

Average Yield. Wheat yield is about 7 sacks per acre ; swedes about 18–20 tons.

Grassland. About 160 acres is in permanent pasture, very few acres of which are cut for hay, which is obtained chiefly from " seed " hay. The grassland varies considerably in value, the low-lying meadows, some of which are irrigated, being of good type and productive. The new pastures which have been laid down during the past 6–8 years are also very good, but there is a considerable amount of old pasture which is rough and unpalatable, and which could be improved only by breaking-up and re-seeding.

Livestock. Dairy Shorthorns are kept for production of milk which is sold. Shorthorn-Devon are bred for the " store " trade. *Sheep :* Dorset Down type ewes are kept, crossed with South Down for fat lamb, or with Dorset Down for hogging and upkeep of flock. *Pigs :* Wessex Saddleback sows crossed with Large White, litters sold as weaners, or for pork. *Poultry :* A few " barndoors " only.

NORTH-EASTERN SLOPES (Spaxton Vicinity).

Soils. Chiefly Upper Devonian (as for the Western Upland area, but at generally lower altitudes). Red (Keuper) Marl, some Conglomerate and Alluvium. The soils are in general sour, but the ease of working varies with the type as previously described in other regions. No special draining is required except on the the alluvial flats. The soils are very adaptable and no diseases are prevalent amongst crops.

Stock. Smallholders are practically all dairymen producing milk. Cattle are chiefly Shorthorn–Devon cross. Calves are reared for fatttening. Sheep and pig policies, and breeds, are as described earlier for other regions of the Taunton Vale.

Both mechanical and horse power is used.

Land Values. Farms in this area are rented at about 30/- per acre.

Growing Season. Spring oats are sown at the end of February and early in March. Harvest commences in the first week in August. Stock grass is available about mid-April in early fields.

Specimen Farm.

Area between 350 and 400 acres. Freehold.

Soil is chiefly Upper Devonian with some Red Marl to the east and west. In the valley below the farmhouse the soil is a Conglomerate with many pebbles.

Working Capital, about £15 per acre.

Labour Employed. Six men, with extra seasonal labour at a cost of about £50 yearly.

Crops. The following rotation is followed, but not strictly owing to peas being grown and some arable being now in grass : wheat ; barley ; roots ; oats or dredge with " seeds " ; seeds hay ; grazed. Wheat and barley are sold, the remainder consumed on the farm.

Preparation of the Land. The fields have natural drainage. The Devonian is easily worked, the Red Marl more difficult. Preparation for swedes—winter plough, cultivated, ploughed (a third time if necessary), light-harrowed and seed drilled.

Manuring. For second corn crop, 3 cwt. 35 per cent. super, 1 cwt. sulphate of ammonia. Swedes, farmyard manure (heavy), 4 cwt. kainit, 6 cwt. super, $1\frac{1}{2}$ cwt. sulphate of ammonia.

Grassland. There is about 200 acres of permanent pasture as well as temporary grass. Hay yield from permanent pasture is about 30 cwt. from about 50 acres cut. Temporary pastures (up to 12 years) have a larger stock-carrying capacity than the permanent pasture. Grass responds well to slag and N.A. phosphate.

Livestock. A dairy herd of Shorthorn–Devon cross is maintained and milk sold. Calves are reared for grazing and winter fattening. Shorthorn heifers are bought. *Sheep :* Breeding ewes are reared. Dorset Down ewes bred with Dorset Down or South Down for fat lambs from South Down cross. Dorset Downs are hogged. *Poultry :* Rhode Island Reds for egg production are kept.

THE COASTAL LIAS CLAYS (Stockland Vicinity).

The area is a small one. The soil is mostly uniformly heavy with Lias Clay underlying, not sour, requiring chiefly phosphates, " three-horse " land, difficult to work. Drainage is by pipes on the arable, with open ditches on grass. It is particularly favourable for wheat and beans, and no crop diseases are prevalent.

This is a dairy and rearing district. Fattening of cattle is confined to the marsh. Fat lambs are produced, about half for the spring trade and the remainder for the summer. *Sheep :* Dorset Horn and Dorset Down bred with Dorset Down or South Down, also Exmoor and Cheviot crossed with Dorset Down. *Pigs :* Sold chiefly as stores, chief breeds being Wessex Saddle, Large Black and Large White.

Land Values. Farms in the area are rented at about 25/- per acre.

Growing Season. Oats and beans are sown early in October, wheat up to mid-November. Harvest commences at the end of July. Stock grass is available in mid-April,—on the marsh land in the first week in May.

Specimen Farm.

Area between 400–450 acres. Yearly tenancy.

Soil. There is very little variation, all heavy soil with yellow clay underlying.

Working Capital is about £10 4s. per acre.

Labour Employed. Five men and 1 boy with seasonal labour at a cost of about £20 per annum.

Crops. The following rotation is followed, but not strictly adhered to—wheat; oats; beans; wheat with seeds ; seed hay ; second seed hay ; fallow. Wheat is sold off the farm, the remaining crops are consumed.

Preparation of the Ground. Arable land is pipe drained. For wheat, after two years ley, the land is bastard-fallowed ; the original practice was dead fallow after 1-year ley.

Manuring. Wheat after fallow, no manure, but mustard is sometimes ploughed down. Mangolds, heavy farmyard manure and superphosphate, 6–8 cwt. per acre and 1 cwt. nitrogenous manure.

Grassland is all permanent pasture. The meadows cut 25–30 cwt. of hay. Two tons could be cut but they are stocked late with " couples " and are cut early. The grazing land is good and capable of "finishing" Devon heifers but not steers. Slag is used on mowing meadows, but no manure on the grazing marshes, which are not allowed to be mown. On the whole the grassland is of good type and productive, but some of the higher pasture fields carry a poor, weedy herbage and would greatly benefit from phosphates.

Stock. Shorthorns are carried for milk ; Shorthorns crossed with Devon produce calves reared for grazing ; 20 Irish heifers are calved yearly. Devon, and Devon cross stock is bought for grazing. *Sheep :* A " flying flock " of Dorset Horn crossed with Dorset Down, and Exmoor crossed with Dorset Down, both crossed again with South Down, produces fat lamb. The Dorset Horn–Dorset Down cross are bought in June–July, the Exmoor and Dorset Down in September. *Pigs :* About 12 breeding pigs are kept, Wessex Saddle crossed with Large White. The litters are sold as large stores at six months. *Poultry :* About 300 hens are kept for egg production. Rhode Island Reds crossed with Light Sussex. Rhode Island Reds are crossed with Game for table birds.

THE " CLAY-WITH-FLINT " PLATEAU AND THE CHALK HILLS.
(Vicinity of Cricket St. Thomas and Churchstanton.)

Soils. The surface of the country consists of hills and valleys, the hills in places capped with more or less weathered Clay-with-Flints, Greensand, Chalk, Marlstone, etc. The soils vary, the two specimen farms being chosen to show results on the Clay-with-Flint areas where most of the arable land appears in the Land Utilisation Survey sheets. In the Cricket St. Thomas region the greater part of the soils are not easy to work but cannot be classed amongst the most difficult. Pipe draining is found only on low fields adjoining the streams. The soils are not sour, and require chiefly phosphates in the form of " super." In the higher, Churchstanton region, where typical " Clay-with-Flint " occurs, soils are rather poor and " hungry," liberal use of manures, phosphates and organic, being required to get good crops. The grassland is acid, but the arable seems to be neutral owing probably to previous liming and aeration. The soils are light to medium and easy to work, though certain fields are " tricky " if weather conditions are unfavourable. The area generally is not specially favourable for any particular crop, and no crop diseases are prevalent.

Stock. Milk, store sheep, " weaners," and some bacon pigs are produced. *Cattle* are chiefly Shorthorns, Devons, or crossbred. *Sheep:* Down crosses predominate, kept as breeding flocks. *Pigs :* Wessex Saddleback and Large White are kept to produce " weaners," " stores " and some fat pigs and baconers.

Land Values. In the Cricket St. Thomas area farms are rented at from 25/- to 30/- per acre. In the Churchstanton area farms are rented at about 20/- per acre.

Growing Season. Cricket St. Thomas : Winter wheat and oats are sown in October and November, spring corn in March when possible. Winter oats are cut about mid-July. Stock grass is available about the third week in April. *Churchstanton :* Sowing times are the same as above, harvest commences about mid-August. Stock grass is available about the second week in May.

Specimen Farms. (1) Cricket St. Thomas Vicinity.

Area is between 800–900 acres. The unit really consists of three farms run in such a manner that if necessary all could be let as separate holdings. Freehold.

Soil. No true Clay-with-Flints though part of the area is indicated as " Clay-with-Flints " on the drift sheet, No. 295. The soil varies from a medium loam with many flints to a heavy loam with few flints. At some points the underlying stratum is chalk and at others it is limestone. The arable fields are at about 700 feet elevation.

Working Capital is between £8 and £9 per acre, about 58 per cent. in livestock (this low percentage is probably explained by the special circumstances mentioned above.)

Labour Employed. Fifteen men and 4 women, extra seasonal labour negligible.

Crops. No particular rotation is followed. The arable land is in corn, roots, or some kind of sheep feed. No clover crop is taken ; wheat is sold, the remainder is consumed on the farm.

Preparation of the Soil. There is natural drainage. Most fields are fairly easy to work though one is " tricky " in bad weather conditions.

Manuring. For roots, farmyard manure and compound manures and nitrogen. Corn following roots requires no manure.

Average Yields. Wheat and oats average about 10 sacks per acre ; mangolds, 30–35 tons per acre ; swedes, 25–30 tons per acre.

Grassland. About 800 acres is in permanent pasture. The hay yield averages about 20 cwt. per acre. The land responds to superphosphate, is also dressed with farmyard manure when possible, and holds out fairly well in summer.

Livestock. Pedigree and graded Shorthorns are reared for milk production. *Sheep :* a self-supporting flock of crossbred ewes with Sussex ram is maintained for " store " sheep. *Pigs :* Middle White and Large White are reared and sold as " stores." *Poultry :* a few Rhode Island Reds crossed with Light Sussex are kept for eggs.

(2) Churchstanton Vicinity.

Area between 200–250 acres. Freehold.

Soil. These vary from light to heavy loam, overlying Clay on rock, with Flints very numerous in all fields.

Working Capital is about £8 8s. per acre.

Labour Employed. Two men are employed regularly, and extra seasonal labour at a cost of about £40 per annum.

Crops. The following rotation is followed, more or less, though not strictly adhered to :— wheat or oats ; roots or fallow ; wheat with " seeds " ; clover, hay. The clover is allowed to stay down two years if good enough. Wheat is sold.

Preparation of the ground. The ground is easy to work, though certain fields are " tricky " if weather conditions are unfavourable. All fields have natural drainage.

Manuring. For mangolds and swedes—farmyard manure and superphosphate and sulphate of ammonia. Wheat is top-dressed with nitrogen.

Average Yields. Wheat yields, 7–9 sacks per acre ; oats, 11 to 14 sacks per acre.

Grassland. About 100 acres is in permanent grassland, including rough pasture. Certain fields are mown every year, yielding about 20 cwt. per acre. The mowing fields get farmyard manure and phosphates every third year, the pastures only superphosphate at long intervals. Some of the grassland carries a very sweet herbage and is well grazed but much of it is very rough indeed, with bracken, brambles, etc., and very rough herbage.

Livestock. A crossbred herd of Devon and Shorthorn is kept for milk production. Young stock is reared for herd replenishment or to be sold as stores. There are no sheep kept. *Pigs :* Large White and crossbreds are reared for bacon and pork. *Fowls :* a few " barndoors " only.

THE LIAS CLAY ARABLE AND PASTURE HILLS. THE RHAETIC PLATEAU AND THE POLDEN HILLS.

This region is one of the least satisfactory generalisations on the Physical Region map (Fig. 3). Apart from the extensive alluvial and downwash deposits indicated by broken line and marked in the Geological Map, the areas marked as Lias and Trias vary considerably in surface texture—not all the Lias is Clay ; some of the Trias is Red Marl or Marl downwash, some is a sticky Marl with many stones and rock at varying depths ; Gravels, Flints and outcrops of yellow Clay.

What has been called the " Rhaetic Plateau," is more or less uniform, a rather sticky Marl with many stones and rock (White Lias Limestone, etc.) at varying depths, but below the scarp, ploughgrounds occur on Red Marl, downwash and moor soils.

North of Compton Dundon and on Somerton Moor large areas of ploughed land appear on peat. An even larger extent used to be ploughed, but of recent years flooding has been more serious. Clay-with-Flints occurs about Drayton and probably elsewhere on the Upper Clays.

On the south slopes of the Polden Hills ploughgrounds are chiefly on Red Marls. Soils in the High Ham Plateau region are not sour, but rather " hungry," and good crops are dependent on a liberal supply of farmyard manure.

Along the Langport–Aller–Othery road the soils vary in condition, some being sour and some not. Arable land receives complete manuring, but the grassland receives none, and seems not to respond where manure has been tried. Open drains and rhines drain the grassland.

About Somerton, Curry Rivel and Drayton the general opinion appears to be that the soils are not sour, that no manuring is necessary on low-lying pastures, but that on the higher land and the arable, phosphates, supplemented by nitrogen and farmyard manure are needed. The soils are very heavy and difficult to cultivate unless weather conditions are favourable. Under-draining is present in the greater part of the fields, with open ditches and rhines in the " Drainage Board " areas.

About Street soils are not sour and require chiefly phosphates.

About Shapwick there is heavy " three-horse " land, the majority of fields being pipe-drained. The soil is not sour but requires phosphates.

The same general description as above serves for the Greinton–Moorlinch area, except that a few fields are sandy and easy to work.

Stock and Farm Policy. Shorthorn cattle for milk production are common to all the district ; young stock is reared and there is some fattening on moor pastures. Sheep are kept for fat lambs in some areas, and pigs bred for stores, etc. Both horse and mechanical power is used for cultivation.

Land Values. In the neighbourhood of Street farms are rented at about 40/– per acre. The farms are generally small, with detached moor pastures. On the plateau farms are rented at from 20/– to 25/– per acre. About Curry Rivel and Drayton farms are rented at from 20/– to 50/– per acre, the higher figure referring to small farms with a high proportion of good lowland pasture, chiefly milk farms. About Aller the figure is difficult to obtain as there are few well-defined farms, the majority consisting of a farmhouse with a few fields, the remainder of the land consisting of scattered fields rented from various owners. In the Shapwick area farms are rented at from 24/– to 25/– per acre. On the south slopes of Polden, about Greinton on the Trias Marls, farms are rented at about 40/– per acre. As elsewhere in Somerset, the size of farms is an important factor in determining rent, the smaller farms bearing a higher proportion of " overhead " charges for capital sunk in buildings, etc.

Growing Season. The following times for sowing, harvest and early stock grass, were obtained :—

Street.—Winter corn sown before November if possible ; spring corn late February or early March. Harvest begins at the end of July. Stock grass is available at about the end of April.

Drayton.—Winter wheat, oats and beans sown before mid-November if possible ; very little spring corn is sown. Harvest begins about August. Stock grass available in mid-April.

Low Ham.—Wheat is sown before Christmas ; winter oats in October and November. There is no spring corn. Oat harvest begins on July 1st. Stock grass available May 1st.

Aller.—Winter oats are sown as soon as possible after mid-August.

Stock grass available May 1st or earlier in a dry year. (The moor pastures are not available until the effects of winter flooding are gone.)

Shapwick.—Sowing as for Street. Winter oats cut 1st and 2nd week in July. Wheat cut 3rd and 4th week in July. Stock grass avilable about May 1st.

Greinton. As for Shapwick, but stock grass available second week in April (this apparently refers to pastures above the level of floods).

Specimen Farms.   (1) High Ham Vicinity.

Area between 350 and 400 acres. Freehold.

Soil. The soil is a sticky Marl with many stones and rock at varying depths, often quite near the surface. All drainage is natural. The soil is suited to wheat, beans and mangolds, but not to barley, beet or potatoes. No disease is prevalent.

Working Capital is about £9 16s. per acre.

Labour Employed. Five men. No seasonal labour.

Crops. The rotation practised is more or less as follows, but is varied to suit particular conditions: wheat, beans, wheat or oats, mangolds, wheat with "seeds," clover hay. Wheat and beans are sold off the farm.

Preparation of the Land. The arable land is very stony and rather shallow in places. In an average season the soil is not particularly difficult to work, but can be very awkward if not weathered.

Manuring. For mangolds and swedes farmyard manure + 3 cwt. per acre of I.C.I. No manure is used for beans or oats. Wheat is top-dressed with nitrogen.

Average Yields. Wheat yields about 9 sacks per acre; oats about 14–15 sacks; beans about 8–9 sacks.

Grassland. About 250 acres is in permanent grass, certain fields of which are cut every year, giving an average hay yield of about 30 cwt. The mowing-fields are manured with super-phosphate every third year and also dressed heavily with sheep. No manures are used on the grazing fields. Much of the grassland on the home farm is very thin and "burns" badly in summer, carrying a sweet herbage but not very productive and suitable only for sheep. The lower fields are good, but weedy and capable of improvement. Land held on Aller Moor is very important for summer grass, and the "seeds" are important as a hay crop.

Livestock. Shorthorn cows, most of which were bought in, are maintained for milk production and are crossed with a Devon bull for stock to be reared and fattened. A flock, chiefly of Dorset Downs is kept for the production of store sheep and summer fat lambs. The ewe lambs are reared. No pigs are kept and only a few Rhode Island Reds for egg production.

(2) Vicinity of Aller.

Area, between 400–500 acres. Freehold. The low-lying grass fields on the edge of the moor are a dark alluvial soil with Yellow Clay underneath. The arable fields and higher pastures vary considerably, but are chiefly a very sticky Red Marl with outcrops of Yellow Clay, or Gravel and Flints.

Working Capital is about £8 14s. per acre.

Labour Employed. Eight men. Practically no extra seasonal labour is required.

Crops. The rotation followed is, wheat, beans, wheat, roots, wheat or oats with "seeds," clover hay. Wheat and part of the bean crop are sold. Part of the arable land is under-drained. Most of the fields are fairly easy to work in favourable weather, but can be very awkward under unfavourable conditions.

Manuring. Wheat after clover or beans receives no manures; for mangolds the soil receives heavy farm-yard manure + 5 cwt. per acre c.c.f.

Average Yields. Wheat averages about 9 sacks per acre.

Grassland. All the grass is permanent with no temporary leys. About 80–90 acres are cut every year, yielding up to 40 cwt. per acre. Some fields are flooded for short periods in the winter. No artificial manures are used, and where they have been tried no effect has been visible on the grassland, which is of good type and productive, suitable for either dairying or grazing, but if not managed with care the lower grasslands soon become full of tussock grass and rushes.

Livestock. Shorthorn cows are kept for milk and cheese made in summer. *Sheep :* cross-bred Down ewes are crossed with Ryeland, Dorset Down or South Down for production of fat lambs for the late spring and summer trade. Hogget ewes are bought in July and August. *Pigs :* Crossbred stores are bought for whey fattening. *Poultry :* day-old chicks are bought and reared for egg production.

(3) Vicinity of Drayton.

Area, between 450–600 acres. Yearly tenancy.

Soil. All heavy Clay, either blue or yellow, with considerable areas of Clay-with-Flints in the higher fields.

Working Capital, about £10 per acre.

Labour Employed. Ten men, with seasonal labour to the value of about £50 per annum.

Crops. Arable crops consist of wheat, oats, roots, beans, clover and vetches. No fixed rotation is followed. Wheat and beans are sold. The oats are consumed with the remaining crops.

Preparation of the ground. The soil is very heavy and difficult to cultivate unless weather conditions are favourable. Practically all fields are under-drained, but many of these drains are now out of order and the land is suffering in consequence. Part of the farm is in a Drainage District (Langport). Horse power is used with a tractor hired occasionally.

Manuring. Wheat receives no manure, mangolds farmyard manure only. Fertility is maintained by stocking, the " cake " bill being very heavy.

Average Yields. Wheat and beans about 10 sacks per acre, oats about 14 sacks per acre.

Grassland. All grassland is permanent and the same fields are mown each year, the average hay yield being 25–30 cwt. per acre. No artificial manures are used, fertility being maintained by heavy cake feeding. The grassland is of good type, well grazed and productive. A large area within the Drainage District is flooded during the winter, but in a normal season is not under water for long periods. The under-drains in many fields are gradually becoming ineffective, thus affecting stocking dates. Although no difference is apparent to the eye, the pastures vary considerably, many being teart (see pages 44 and 46) and can be stocked only by cattle that are in really good condition. Young and lean cattle scour badly on these pastures.

Livestock. Chiefly Devon cattle are grown for summer and winter fattening. *Sheep :* Dorset Down and Dorset Horn crossbred ewes are crossed with South Down rams for fat lamb production. Some ewes are reared on the farm, but the greater number is bought in September. *Pigs :* Wessex Saddleback and Large Black sows are crossed with a large white boar for production of " store " pigs. *Poultry :* A few " barndoors " are kept for home use.

(4) Vicinity of Street Polden Slope.

Area, between 250 and 300 acres. Part freehold, part yearly tenancy.

Soil. The soil in the higher, south-facing fields is chiefly a medium Loam, red in colour, underlain by Red Marl. The level fields on the low ground vary somewhat but are chiefly of a peaty nature, with Alluvium overlying the Peat in certain fields and parts of others. The soil is not sour and is pipe-drained only in a few of the meadows.

Working Capital. About £10 10s. per acre.

Labour Employed. Five men and 2 boys, with extra seasonal labour at a cost of about £100 per annum.

Crops. No rotation is followed. Arable crops consist of potatoes, roots, beans, wheat and oats. Wheat is sold, and the remaining crops consumed.

Preparation of the Soil. The arable contains a fair amount of sand and is fairly easy to work. Both horse and mechanical power are used.

Manuring. No manures are used except farmyard manure and sheep. About 5 cwt. per acre of superphosphate is used for potatoes and roots.

Average Yields. The average wheat yield is about 8 sacks per acre, oats about 15 sacks, potatoes, 7–8 tons. Owing probably to heavy stocking the land is rich and corn is liable to be " laid," a condition possibly aggravated by lack of phosphates.

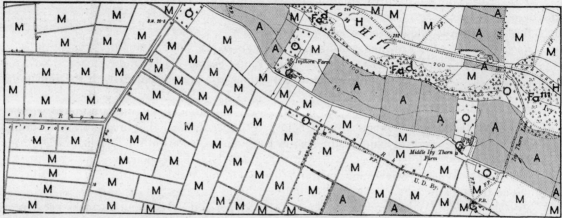

Based upon the Ordnance Survey Map, with the sanction of the Controller of H.M. Stationery Office.

FIG. 18.—The Polden Hills and The Moors.

This map shows the south scarp of Polden Hills with arable fields on the Red Marl slopes. Two ploughed peat fields can be seen on the moor itself—an unusual feature except on this moor. The road-ways known as " droves " that can be observed crossing the moor and giving access to the fields, are usually little better than strips of the surrounding pastures. The various moor fields are owned or rented by farmers who live and have their barns and other buildings on the high ground, the farm sometimes being some distance from the scattered " moor " fields belonging to it. This map and Fig. 19 illustrate two of the many field patterns to be seen on the " moors." While shape and size of fields vary considerably, certain characteristics are common. The ground is remarkably level ; the fields are square or oblong wherever possible, a feature due to the planned development of these specially drained areas, the allotments being based on surveys. In both illustrations, main and secondary drainage channels can be seen, the former known as " rhynes," the latter completely surrounding the rectangular fields, and acting also as fences. These are usually the only boundaries and to preserve their usefulness in summer as well as to water stock the water is artificially " penned " or dammed up by sluices.

Grassland. All is permanent grass, fields being cut in turn and yielding about 30 cwt. per acre. Only farmyard manure is used every other year. The grassland is in good condition, well grazed and free from weeds.

Stock. Shorthorns are kept for milk production and young stock reared for herd replenishment. *Sheep :* Dorset Downs are reared for production of fat lamb and store sheep. About 40 two-tooth ewes are bought yearly. *Pigs :* Large Black sows are crossed with a Large White boar for production of " stores." *Poultry :* A few Rhode Island Reds are kept for house use only.

(5) The " Compton Moor " Arable.

On the Land Utilisation Map a considerable area of ploughland appears on the Moor north of Dundon Hill. This stretch of arable is Peat and until comparatively recent years continuous corn-growing was practised—wheat and winter oats. These crops did well if not flooded too long in winter, or lifted by frost in spring, wheat yielding 9–10 sacks, oats 14–15 sacks per acre. Spring corn does not do well as a general rule, but mangolds and swedes are grown to some extent. Farmyard manure is the chief fertiliser used, but a little phosphate is used by some farmers.

Rents are about £2 per acre.

Much of the land is now being laid down to grass, owing to low corn prices, and also to the fact that flooding is more serious than it was a few years ago.

(6) Shapwick Vicinity.

Area, between 200–250 acres. Yearly tenancy.

Soil. The soil is of heavy clay texture generally, but varies a great deal in depth. Stony outcrops are frequent and in many cases solid rock occurs only a few inches below the surface. The soils are are not sour.

Working Capital required is about £9 14s. per acre.

Labour Employed. Three men are kept and extra seasonal labour is required at a cost of about £30 per annum.

Crops. The following rotation is practised with occasional bare fallow :—Beans or roots ; wheat ; oats with " seeds," seed hay or grazed ; wheat. Wheat is sold and part of the oats and beans.

Preparation of the Soil. Practically all the fields are under-drained. The soil is hard-working " three-horse " land.

Manuring. For mangolds and beans farmyard manure only ; wheat after beans, and oats after wheat, receive no manures.

Average yields. Wheat yield is about 8–9 sacks per acre ; oats, 10–12 sacks ; beans 9 10 sacks.

Grassland. All pasture is permanent and includes 30 acres on King's Sedgemoor, used for young stock and dry cows in summer. All the upper pastures are mown in turn, the average hay yield being about 20 cwt. per acre. The grassland responds to superphosphate. There are a few acres scheduled as rough pasture which are being broken up and reseeded. Apart from these the grassland is of fairly good type, but appears as if phosphates could with advantage be used more freely.

Stock. Crossbred cattle, chiefly Shorthorn, are kept for milk production, the young stock being reared for herd replenishment or sale. *Sheep :* a Dorset Down type flock is kept for producing " store " sheep for the Michaelmas trade. *Pigs :* Weaners are bought and sold as stores, a few being fattened.

(7) Greinton Vicinity. South Polden.

The area is formed by the Trias deposits which lie against the Polden Scarp and rise above the low alluvial and Peat moorland of King's Sedgemoor.

Area, between 250 and 300 acres. Yearly tenancy.

Soil is practically all a sticky Red Marl with occasional veins of Blue Clay, except on a north slope which is a greyish, heavy soil with gritty Blue Clay about 6 to 9 inches from the surface. The soil is not sour, and requires chiefly phosphates.

Working Capital is about £9 12s. per acre, some 70 per cent. in livestock.

Labour Employed. Five men ; practically no seasonal labour.

Crops. The following rotation is followed as a rule, but not strictly adhered to :—Wheat ; beans ; wheat ; roots or oats ; wheat ; wheat with " seeds " ; seed hay. Wheat and part of the bean crop are sold.

Preparation of the Land. The fields in the King's Sedgemoor area are drained by rhines and ditches and some of the higher fields are under-drained. Cultivation of the land is difficult, as it is heavy " three-horse " land.

Manuring. For mangolds, heavy farmyard manure only ; wheat after mangolds, and beans after mangolds, a top-dressing of nitrogen is required ; wheat after wheat, complete manure.

Average Yield of wheat 8–9 sacks per acre, of mangolds probably 35 tons per acre.

Grassland. About 200 acres is in permanent pasture, the average hay yield being about 27–28 cwt. per acre. The pasture, which responds to phosphates, is of very good type, well grazed and winter green except for two or three fields north of the farm on the upper slopes, which need ploughing up and reseeding. The fields near King's Sedgemoor drain are inclined to be coarse and to revert to tussock grass, rushes, etc., if not well managed.

Livestock. Shorthorn cows are kept for milk production and the heifers reared for herd replenishment. *Sheep :* Crossbred Down ewes are bought in August for fat lamb production. *Pigs :* Long Whites are bought as weaners and sold as large stores. *Poultry :* for house use only.

THE " MARINE DEPOSIT " ISLANDS, AND MOOR PASTURES ON WESTON LEVEL (BURROWBRIDGE).

The Westonzoyland arable field is farmed in conjunction with adjoining farms. Much of it is owner-occupied, other parts being let on yearly tenancy, rents varying from £3 to £5 per acre. The soil is a deep, sandy loam, easily worked but rather " hungry." No special drainage is required. Barley and potatoes are the chief crops with small areas of wheat, roots and peas. Farmyard manure is the chief fertiliser, with small amounts of phosphates, and sulphate of ammonia. Some of the land is well farmed, but much of it is badly farmed—ill-fertilised and full of couch. Power is obtained from both horses and tractors. Wheat yields are from 8–10 sacks per acre ; barley, 9–10 sacks ; potatoes, 5–6 tons per acre. The specimen farm lies south-west of Middlezoy on the moor. The fields are scattered.

Area, between 150 and 250 acres. Freehold.

Soil. All Alluvial Loam overlying Peat and Clay. The soil is easy to work and not sour.

Working Capital is about £13 18s. per acre, 78 per cent. being in livestock.

Labour Employed. Three men, practically no seasonal labour being required.

Land Values. Farms in the area are rented at from 50/- and 55/- per acre, with accommodation land up to 80/- per acre. There is a small amount of land under plough, but no rotation is followed. Wheat is sold.

The higher fields are pipe-drained, the lower fields have open surface drains, all drains running to rhines and ditches. The soil is not sour and is easy to work.

Manuring. No manure is used for wheat ; for mangolds, farmyard manure only. Yields are not available

Grassland. All the pasture is permanent, certain fields being mown each year and yielding on the average 30 cwt. per acre. No artificials are used, but the mowing-fields are dressed every third year with farmyard manure. The majority of the fields are well grazed and carry a good herbage, although some fields are rather poor and look as if phosphate would be beneficial. Unless well managed this grassland quickly becomes covered with rushes.

The Growing Season.   Wheat is sown in December if possible and harvest commences about the first week in August.   Stock grass is available about May 1st.

Livestock.   Devons and Shorthorns are kept for summer and winter fattening.   Sometimes about 100 lambs are bought in September and wintered and sold fat in May.   *Pigs :* Wessex Saddleback crossed with Large White are bought and fattened.

THE LIAS CLAY PASTURE REGION.

This is a typical heavy clay region.   Soils are in general very heavy yellow or blue-grey Clays, not sour, and responding to phosphates.   Some of the farms are rather wet and appear

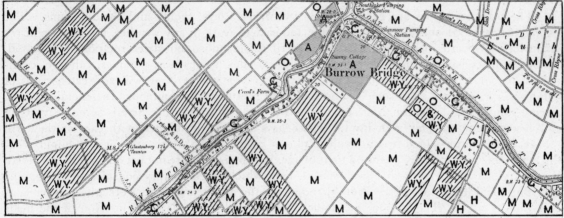

Based upon the Ordnance Survey Map, with the sanction of the Controller of H.M. Stationery Office.

Fig. 19.—The Moors.

This map shows the willow beds (see pp. 65–70) and illustrates the drainage problem which must be dealt with in the low moor regions.   It will be seen that the rivers Tone and Parrett are followed on the north sides by embankments, while to the south a narrow strip of cottages and gardens with some small orchards appears beside a road—the dwellings of " withy-bed " owners, or labourers and farmers.   The overflowing of the rivers originally raised the banks by depositing silt ; the process through generations has been improved upon by various engineers ; but the problem remains that the surrounding moors are not raised much, if at all, above the beds of the rivers, and therefore water from the moors must be pumped over the protective banks into the river.   A pumping station is seen near the confluence in the north. In this section the letters WY and the ruled lines indicate withy beds.   The 6-inch Sheet was revised in 1902–3, the land utilisation information is for 1935, so that from the comparatively small extent of the osier plantations shown by O.S. symbols it is evident that there has been a considerable extension of planting, though elsewhere plantations have been removed.

to need re-draining, the condition appearing to be gradually becoming worse.   The area is practically all under grass.   Shorthorns are carried for milk production and herd replenishment, there are practically no sheep, and pigs are bought as stores and fattened (Large Whites crossed).

Land Values.   Farms in the region are rented at 35/- to 40/- per acre.   Stock grass is available about May 1st.

Specimen Farm (Vicinity of Wraxall).

Area, between 150–200 acres.   Freehold.

Working Capital.   About £17 18s. per acre, 74 per cent. in livestock.

H

Labour employed. Five men with extra seasonal labour at a cost of about £20 per annum.

Grassland. The whole farm is in permanent grass, each field being mown in turn, with an average yield of 25–30 cwt. of hay per acre. No manure is used except farmyard manure. The grassland is in good condition and well grazed. The fields on blue-grey Clay are the worst, being wet and weedy, owing probably to the failure of a proportion of the drains.

Livestock. Shorthorns are kept for milk and summer cheese-making. *Pigs :* Large White crosses are bought as stores and whey-fattened for bacon. *Poultry* is kept for domestic use only.

THE MIDFORD SAND AND MARLSTONE LOW RELIEF ARABLE AREA.

This is an area of complicated soils, difficult to describe accurately, since no drift sheets or soil surveys are available, and the existing solid Geology sheets are difficult to interpret in places.[1]

The main soil types are Light and Heavy Marls, Clays, Sands and Sandy loams. The Sands and Sandy loams are very adaptable and easy to work in any weather, but require heavy manuring, farmyard manure and complete artificials, and so no strict rotation is followed. Arable crops consist of wheat, clover, mangolds, swedes, sugar-beet, potatoes, cabbage, cauliflower, parsnips, carrots, French beans and peas ; some maize is grown, and catch-crops of trifolium, rye, vetches. On some of the soils club root is fairly common. In general the soils are not sour. The loams on Marlstone vary from light to heavy and there is some heavy Clay and heavy loam on Clay-with-Flint. These have often to be treated with care or they will " bake " badly after which it is difficult to obtain a tilth. The Marls are not so " hungry " as the Sands, but require more attention to drainage. Crop diseases are not prevalent. In the North Perrot area there is Clay-with-Flints subsoil, over which the soils vary considerably. Some is very flinty and liable to " bake," but on the whole the arable is easy to work, the heavier land being under grass. The soil on the arable is rather acid, and a large proportion of the fields are pipe-and-stone drained. There is a slight tendency to club root. Both horses and tractors are used.

Livestock. Shorthorn cattle for production of milk and cheese are general throughout the whole region, some farms rearing their own stock and others buying as required. Crossbreds, Devon type, and Angus crosses (about South Petherton, for yard fattening) are fattened and young stock reared.   Both standing and "flying" flocks are maintained, the former for production of stores and fat lambs, the latter for fat lambs, the chief breeds being Dorset Down and Dorset Horn. *Pigs :* Chiefly Large White, Wessex Saddleback crosses are bred for fattening, for bacon, or for stores.

Land Values are generally high, rents about South Petherton ranging from 50/- to 60/- per acre ; about Ilminster from 40/- to 60/- (the latter figure referring to small farms) ; about North Perrot, from 30/- to 40/- per acre.

The Growing Season. Winter wheat is sown according to the season in November or January. October is generally considered too early, but wheat is sometimes sown ; spring corn in February, March or April. Oats and barley sown in February if possible. Stock grass is generally available at the end of April or beginning of May ; one farmer on marlstone and Lias gave the date as late as May 12th, and the earliest time given was the second week in April.

Specimen Farms (1) South Petherton Vicinity.

Area, between 200–250 acres. Freehold.

[1] A large area north of South Perrott is mapped as " Fuller's Earth and Fuller's Earth Rock " ; the immediate subsoil in places is Clay-with-Flints, and in view of the Greensand areas mapped to the south, the area may be incorrectly mapped.

Soil. The Geological sheet gives the position of the farm as partly on Midford Sand and partly on Marlstone, but the soil is described as being practically all a deep, Sandy loam.

Working Capital. About £13 6s. per acre.

Labour Employed. Fourteen to sixteen men, with practically no occasional labour.

Crops. No strict rotation is followed. Crops consist of wheat, clover, mangolds, swedes, sugar-beet, potatoes, cabbage, parsnips, carrots, French beans and peas. Sugar-beet, wheat, potatoes, etc., are sold off the farm.

Preparation of the Ground. For sugar-beet after clover hay, complete artificials are used ; for potatoes, after beet and swedes, complete artificials ; for swedes after fallow and corn crops, farmyard manure only. Practically all the fields are under-drained and are easy to work.

Average Yields. Wheat yields are about 12–14 sacks per acre ; sugar-beet yield averages 15–16 tons ; potatoes 10–12 tons per acre.

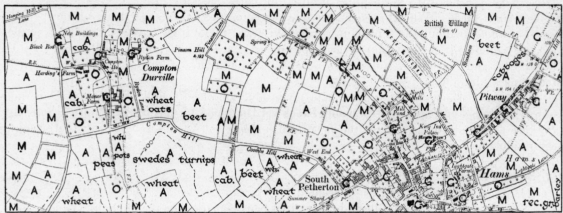

Based upon the Ordnance Survey Map, with the sanction of the Controller of H.M. Stationery Office.

FIG. 20.—The Midford Sand and Marls Region.

This map illustrates conditions in Production Region 6, the Midford Sand and Marl area, where "quick-turnover" farming prevails. It shows the high proportion of orchard land and the relatively small fields, with a fairly high proportion of crops grown for human consumption. This section must be considered as a "specimen" rather than "typical," since even in this small area there is considerable variation and the sands, marls and clays occur in patches.

Grassland. All the grassland is in permanent pasture, certain fields being cut for hay each year and yielding about 30 cwt. per acre. There is no system of manuring and practically none is used except that the grazing fields occasionally receive phosphates. Grassland is of good type and well managed.

Livestock. Shorthorns are kept for milk and cheese is made all the year round ; young stock is reared on the farm. Shorthorns are crossed with Angus for yard-feeding. *Sheep :* Dorset Down wethers are bought in August and fattened on arable crops. *Pigs :* Wessex Saddle-back pigs are bred and fattened for bacon.

(2) Region of South Petherton.

Area, between 400–600 acres. Yearly tenancy.

Soil. Three farms were examined, each being partly on Midford Sand and partly on Marlstone and Clay. Soils in different fields varied from sharp Sand, and deep Sandy loam, to a heavy loam with patches of Clay and a heavy Clay.[1] The soils are not sour.

[1] The area is one of the richest and most productive in Somerset, as well as one of the most complex drift regions.

Working Capital. About £10 per acre, 74 per cent. in livestock.

Labour Employed. Seventeen men, with practically no extra seasonal labour.

Crops. There is no fixed rotation, but the two examples following are typical of what is aimed at :—

(1) Wheat ; ley ; potatoes ; parsnips ; carrots ; swedes ; potatoes.

(2) Wheat ; ley or spring corn ; beet ; potatoes ; parsnips or wheat.

Preparation of the ground. The majority of the fields are pipe-drained and easy working, but a few fields on heavy Clay or heavy loam with patches of Clay, are difficult. Both horses and tractors are used.

Manures. For potatoes after sugar-beet, the tops are fed off by sheep, followed by a light dressing of farmyard manure, and, per acre, 4 cwt. superphosphate, $1\frac{1}{2}$ sulphate of ammonia, $\frac{3}{4}$ m/potash, $\frac{3}{4}$ S/potash. No manures are used for corn.

Average Yields. Wheat, 12 sacks per acre ; potatoes, 10 tons ; sugar-beet, 14 tons per acre.

Grassland. About 180 acres is in permanent grass, the average hay yield being 27–30 cwts. On the lighter soils and on Alluvial loam pastures are excellent type and well grazed. On the heavy Clay and Marls they suffer from water-logging and lack of fertiliser, many of the fields requiring re-draining.

Livestock. Dairy Shorthorns are kept for production of both milk and cheese. An Angus bull is used on some cows and the young stock yard-fattened for farmyard manure. *Sheep* and *Pigs* are as already described for the first farm. *Poultry :* A few sex-linked fowls are kept for egg production.

(3) South Petherton Area.

Area, between 200–300 acres. Freehold.

Soil. The farm is on Middle and Lower Lias beds as marked on the old Solid Geology sheet. The soil varies considerably. The meadows are on heavy Lias Clay loams. The greater part of the arable is a medium loam of considerable depth on Middle Lias, a few arable fields bordering an area marked as Midford Sand, are a deep Sandy loam. Nearby the farm an area is marked on the Geological sheet as " brick earth." The soils are not sour.

Working Capital. About £13 14s. per acre, 75 per cent. in livestock.

Labour Employed. About 17 men, with very little extra labour.

Crops. No rotation is regularly followed, and the arable crops are as previously described on the two former farms. About 45 acres are under orchard and " nursery," chiefly for production of dessert and cooking apples. The orchards stand partly on Lower Lias, partly on Marlstone, according to the geological sheet. Wheat, oats, sugar-beet, potatoes, etc., are sold ; the greater part of the straw and hay is consumed on the farm.

Preparation of the Soil. Nearly all the fields are drained by pipes in good working order. Generally speaking the land is easy to cultivate if worked at the right time, but is sufficiently heavy to " bake " badly if weather conditions are adverse. A tractor helps in overcoming this by speeding up operations during fine spells.

Manuring. The chief manure used is farmyard manure with artificials, usually complete, for potatoes and sugar-beet.

Average Yields. Wheat, 13–14 sacks per acre ; oats, 20 sacks ; sugar-beet, 13–14 tons ; potatoes, 7–8 tons per acre.

Grassland. About 150 acres is in permanent grassland, certain fields being cut every year, and others at intervals. The average hay yield is 35 cwt. per acre. The grassland is maintained with farmyard manure or sheep folding, supplemented by artificials at intervals. All the grass-land is of good type and productive except some heavy fields on the Maristone which "burn" rather badly in summer, especially if grazed too tightly in late spring and early summer.

Livestock. Cattle are as typical of the district. A flock of Dorset Downs is maintained, half being crossed with Sussex ram for fat lambs. *Pigs:* as typical of the district.

(4) Ilminster Region.

Area. 300–400 acres. Yearly tenancy. The farm stands on ground which is marked on the solid Geology sheet as partly Marlstone, partly Midford Sand and partly Lower Lias.

Soil is practically all light loam on what is probably Middle Lias Sand, except for a strip to the south-west about 200 yards wide which is stony and sticky, many of the stones bearing fossil patterns. On the Drift sheet No. 311 just clear of the farm to the south-west, an area of Upper Lias Clay appears, on to which the farm apparently extends. The soils generally are slighty acid and club root is fairly common.

Working Capital is about £17 per acre, 83 per cent. being in livestock.

Labour Employed. Thirteen men are employed regularly, and extra seasonal labour is required at a cost of about £150 per annum.

Crops. As usual in the area, no fixed rotation is followed and all the crops, as already listed for the district, including some maize, are grown, with catch-crops of trifolium, rye, vetches, parsnips and cauliflower. The productivity of the light soils in the district is well illustrated by the policy on this farm of quick turnover with heavy manuring. Swedes and oats are consumed, the remainder of crops sold.

Preparation of the Soil. All the grassland is pipe-drained, but the arable land is not drained, being generally a Sandy loam, easy to cultivate. Both horses and a tractor are employed.

Manuring. For sugar-beet, 2 cwt. sulphate of ammonia, 3 cwt. superphosphate, 2 cwt. muriate of potash ; for potatoes, 2 cwt. sulphate of potash instead of muriate of potash, with the above manures. For swedes, farmyard manure ; for oats and wheat, no manures.

Average Yields. Wheat yields about 9 sacks per acre ; potatoes about 12 tons; sugar-beet about 15 tons per acre. Catch-crops, swedes and beet-tops are eaten by folded sheep.

Grassland. All grassland is permanent, about 100 acres being park land and the remainder pasture (118 acres). The park is never cut, about 50 acres being grazed by sheep and the rest by cattle. About 30 acres of the pasture is never cut, the remainder being cut yearly, the average hay yield being about 27 cwt. per acre. No artificials are used on the grass, but the mowing fields get farmyard manure every third or fourth year. The grassland, except for a part of the park, is almost level and on a deep Sandy loam. The herbage is of good quality and well grazed, and does not appear to be lacking phosphate though none is put down.

Livestock. A pedigree Shorthorn herd is maintained. Milk is sold in winter and cheese made in summer. Young stock are reared for the herd and the bulls sold. *Sheep:* A standing flock of Dorset Horns is kept and wether lambs fattened. Ewes are drafted out as breeders after the third lamb crop. *Pigs:* Crossbred sows are crossed with Large White for bacon pigs and stores.

(5) Ilminster Region.

Area, between 350–400 acres. Yearly tenancy.

Soils. The soils on this farm are of heavier type. The farm stands apparently on Lower Lias, Marlstone, and Midford Sand, and the soils vary accordingly, from a heavy loam over Clay, a heavy loam over Marlstone, to very light Sand which is many feet deep.

Working Capital is about £17 per acre.

Labour Employed. Fifteen men, 2 boys and a woman are employed regularly, and there is very little extra labour required.

Crops. There is no fixed rotation, the arable crops being as stated for the district, with clover every seventh year. Wheat and beet are sold.

Manuring. For mangolds and beet, farmyard manure and compound manure ; no other artificials are used.

Average Yields. Wheat yields about 10 sacks per acre; beet yields about 13 tons per acre.

Grassland. The grassland is all permanent, certain fields being kept for mowing and others always grazed. Farmyard manure is used on the mowing fields. No artificials are used, fertility being maintained by heavy feeding of " cake " on the pastures. The grassland is of good type and well grazed. Drainage is efficient but some of the older drains are showing signs of choking.

Livestock. Shorthorns are kept for milk and cheese ; Devons for grazing. Both breeding and " flying " flocks of Dorset Down and Dorset Horn sheep are kept. *Pigs :* Wessex Saddleback and Large Whites are kept for the store trade and for bacon pigs.

(6) North Perrot Vicinity.

Area between 150–200 acres. Yearly tenancy.

Soil. The farm is on an area marked on the old Geological sheet as Fuller's Earth and Fuller's Earth rock. A drift survey would probably revise this. The soil varies considerably, but broadly speaking the fields south of the farm (across the railway) are medium to heavy loams overlying Clay-with-Flints. Fields north of the farm are rather a queer type of soil varying from light to medium sandy loams overlying Clay-with-flints and very stony. There is a slight tendency to club root.

Working Capital is about £12 12s. per acre.

Labour Employed. Five men are employed permanently and no extra labour is required.

Crops. No particular rotation is followed. The crops consist of wheat, oats, mangolds, swedes, kale, trifolium, vetches and clover (for sheep). Wheat is sold and oats when the price makes it worth while.

Preparation of the Ground. Nearly all the fields are under-drained, but many of these are out of order. The arable fields can be described as easy working, although flinty, and they will " bake " badly if ploughed wet.

Manuring. For mangolds, farmyard manure + complete artificials + nitrogen top-dressing ; swedes, follow green crops folded, and received no manure ; wheat, after mangolds, receives no manure ; kale receives farmyard manure + slag and potash salts.

Average Yields. Wheat yields 11–12 sacks per acre ; oats, 15 sacks per acre.

Grassland. About 168 acres are under permanent grass. Certain fields are cut for hay each year, yielding about 30 cwt. per acre. The mowing fields receive slag periodically, but at rather long intervals. The grassland appears to be fairly well managed, is well grazed and carries a good type of herbage except for two or three fields on heavy loam overlying Clay-with-Flint south of the railway, which are very poor. Many wet patches exist due to failure of drains.

Livestock. The usual Shorthorns are kept for milk production. *Sheep :* A " flying " flock of Dorset Down ewes crossed with Sussex is kept for fat lamb production. Ewes are bought in July or August and lambed whilst sound. *Pigs :* large stores, crossbred Large White type are bought and fattened for bacon. *Poultry :* A few " barndoor " hens and about 50 Khaki Campbell ducks are kept.

THE LOWER SCARPLANDS.

The specimen farms have been chosen on Forest Marble, Fuller's Earth, Bradford Clay, Cornbrash, and Inferior Oolite. On the Clay, Fuller's Earth, and above the Forest Marble, soils are in general sticky and heavy to work, slightly acid, requiring phosphates and nitrogen. Most of the arable land, which is infrequent, requires under-draining. The Inferior Oolite soils are easy to work and require all-round manuring, but are not acid.

Stock. Shorthorn cows are kept generally for milk for sale or cheese-making or both. Some farms rear their own stock and others buy all the cows required. Stock in the district is generally wintered out. There are comparatively few *Sheep*. In the Somerton district a few Hampshire Downs are kept for fat lambs, and on the inferior Oolite about Milborne Port there are breeding flocks of Dorset Downs and Dorset Horns. *Pigs* are chiefly Large White, Large Black, and some Wessex Saddleback, for bacon production or " stores."

Power is obtained from both horses and tractors, but chiefly horses.

Land Values. These vary chiefly according to the size of farms. There is little arable. In the vicinity of Laverton farms are rented at from 25/- to 30/- per acre (Forest Marble, Fuller's Earth and Bradford Clay) ; in the vicinity of Henstridge farms are rented at from 20/-, and 31/- to 50/- per acre, the considerable variation being due to both size of farms and the considerable variation of soils on the Oolites and Clays, with the added disadvantages of position on steep country, etc. The high rents in general refer to small dairy farms on heavy country (Clays and Marls) well situated as regards slope ; some areas have rock (Forest Marble and Fuller's Earth) close to the surface. About Milborne Port farms are rented at 27/- to 55/- per acre, as there is here also great variation between the light loams on the Oolites and the Heavy Clays.

Growing Season. Spring corn is sown before mid-March if possible. Wheat is sown at the end of September or early in October. Harvest begins in the first week, or about the middle of August. Stock grass is available in mid-April or the beginning of May.

Specimen Farms. (1) Vicinity of Laverton.

Area, between 250–350 acres. Yearly tenancy.

Soil. The farm is on Forest Marble, Bradford Clay and Fuller's Earth, according to the Geological sheet. The soil varies at the surface, but is chiefly heavy with Clay at no great depth, except for two or three fields which have considerable areas of Stonebrash. The soil is slightly acid.

Working Capital is about £11 per acre.

Labour Employed. Four men are employed regularly, and seasonal labour at a cost of about £30 per annum.

Crops. A rotation is not strictly followed, a few acres being fallowed every year. The following is typical of what is aimed at : wheat ; beans or roots ; oats or barley with " seeds " ; seed hay. Wheat is sold and the remainder of crops consumed on the farm.

Preparation of the Ground. All fields are pipe-drained and the arable is difficult to handle being heavy and with Clay at no great depth.

Manuring. For mangolds, farmyard manure is used + 5–6 cwt. per acre of mangold manure + 1 cwt. nitrate of soda ; for swedes, farmyard manure only. No manure is used for corn.

Average Yields. The average wheat yield is 7–8 sacks per acre ; the oat yield is 12–14 sacks; the mangold yield is 30 tons per acre.

Grassland. Nearly all the pasture is permanent, the average hay yield being about 25 cwt. per acre. The herbage, which responds to slag and super, is of rather poor type and weedy, many of the fields appearing to need renovating. The grass cannot be stocked in winter as it " poaches " badly.

Livestock. Shorthorns are kept chiefly for milk sale, but some cheese of Cheddar type is made. The young stock is reared. *Sheep :* There are very few, chiefly Hampshire Downs for fat lamb and " hogging." *Pigs :* Chiefly Large White and a few Large Blacks are kept for production of fat pigs and stores.

(2) Henstridge Vicinity.

Area, between 200–250 acres. Yearly tenancy.

Soil. The farm stands apparently on Fuller's Earth and Forest Marble. The majority of fields are heavy with a brownish-yellow Clay about 8 to 12 inches from the surface ; the " Forest Marble " fields are heavy and very stony with solid, fossiliferous rock at no great depth.

Working Capital is about £10 8s. per acre.

Labour Employed. Four men are permanently employed and practically no extra labour is required. There is no arable land. Some of the fields have apparently been drained in the past, but the drains are now functioning imperfectly.

Manuring. Only farmyard manure is used on the pastures, which appear to be suffering from phosphate deficiency.

Grassland. All is permanent, with about 35 acres of rough pasture, and all fields are cut in turn yielding about 25 cwt. per acre. The greater part of the grassland is of a rather poor and weedy type although it is apparently very productive. Many fields require draining.

Livestock. A dairy herd of Shorthorn type is kept for milk production, the young stock being reared for herd replenishment. There are no sheep. Three Large White sows are kept and pigs raised as stores.

(3) Henstridge Vicinity (Forest Marble).

Area, between 400–450 acres. Yearly tenancy.

Soil. The arable land is heavy with a Yellow Clay subsoil and patches of Shaly Forest Marble Stone. The grassland is similar with solid rock near the surface in many places.

Working Capital is about £12 per acre.

Labour Employed. Eight men are employed with practically no extra labour.

Crops. The following rotation is practised : wheat ; oats with seeds ; clover hay for two years. Wheat and a proportion of straw are sold.

Preparation of the Soil. Practically all the fields are under-drained, the drains being in fair working order. The soil is difficult to work unless the weather conditions are good.

Manuring. For wheat after clover no manure is used, or only superphosphate. For roots, farmyard manure + 5 cwt. per acre of compound manure.

Average Yields. Wheat yields about 8 sacks per acre ; oats about 12 sacks.

Grassland. All the grassland is permanent, fields being cut in turn, yielding about 25 cwt. of hay per acre. The grassland is manured with farmyard manure, basic slag and sulphate of ammonia. The grassland is of good type, well grazed, and productive except where rock is near the surface.

Livestock. A self-supporting dairy herd of Shorthorns is maintained. No *Sheep* are kept. Large Black and Large White sows are crossed with a Large White boar for production of bacon pigs.

(4) Vicinity of Milborne Port (on Inferior Oolite).

Area, between 250–300 acres. Yearly tenancy.

Soil. The soil is a light loam on Inferior Oolite which varies considerably in depth, being in some places very deep and free from stones, in others, very stony or with solid rock at or near the surface. The soil is not sour.

Working Capital is about £8 12s. per acre, 68 per cent. being in livestock.

Labour Employed. Five men are employed and seasonal labour at a cost of about £20 per annum.

Crops. The rotation practised is generally as follows, but is not strictly adhered to : wheat ; roots ; oats with " seeds " ; clover hay, cut and the aftermath folded. Wheat is sold.

Preparation of the Soil. The soil is free-working, has a natural drainage, and is easy to cultivate except where stones and rock occur.

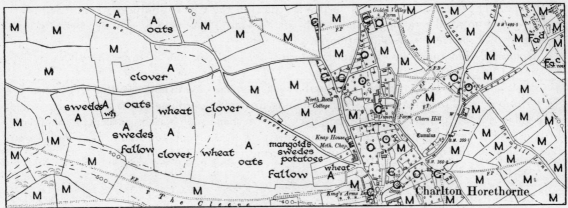

Based upon the Ordnance Survey Map, with the sanction of the Controller of H.M. Stationery Office.

FIG. 21.—The Lower Scarplands.

This map illustrates the tendency in this area to make use of the comparatively small outcrops of suitable soil material for arable land. The group of arable fields to the west of the village are all on an exposure of inferior Oolite, whose soils are easy to work. The remaining area, devoted to much smaller grass fields, is on Forest Marble, where the land is heavier and more difficult to work. The small orchards are all grass ones.

Manuring. For roots, farmyard manure only is used ; corn is grown without manures on root ground that has been folded.

Average Yields. The average wheat yield is 7–8 sacks per acre ; oats, 15–16 sacks per acre.

Grassland. About 220 acres of grassland is permanent, every field being cut in turn, yielding on an average, 25 per cwt. per acre. No artificial manures are used, ricks being made in the fields and fed on the ground. The grassland is in good condition with a very sweet and clovery herbage. It is well drained and does not " paunch " so cattle are out all the year round. Certain parts " burn " badly in summer owing to the thinness of the soil.

THE OXFORD CLAY VALES.

Soils. The soils are chiefly heavy Clays, sour and requiring phosphates. There is little arable land. A large number of fields are pipe- or stone-drained, many needing redraining.

Stock are chiefly Shorthorn cattle for milk production and sale, and cheese-making. Some young stock is reared but not enough for herd replacements. *Sheep* : There are very few sheep, chiefly Down-type hoggets bought for fattening. Wessex Saddleback, Large Black and Large White *Pigs* are bought as stores for fattening on these farms. Few are bred.

Land Values. Farms are rented at from 40/– to 60/– per acre.

The Growing Season. Stock grass is available about May 1st.

Specimen Farm.

Area, between 250–300 acres. Freehold.

Soil. About 40 acres are in woodland. The soil is all heavy Clay except for an arable field which is a deep sand on the level portion and very stony, and rather heavy on the slopes (Cornbrash).

Working Capital is about £21 per acre, 84 per cent. being in livestock. (Excluding Forest portion.)

Labour Employed. Six men and 2 boys are employed, with very little extra labour.

Crops. The one arable field, which is not typical of the Clays, produces wheat, oats, roots and clover, in no fixed rotation. Wheat and oats are sold. The field is easy to work although stones and rock interfere with cultivation in some parts.

Manuring. For mangolds, farmyard manure + 3 cwt. per acre of superphosphate, 2 cwt. of Kainit, 1 cwt. nitrate of chalk. For wheat, C.C.F. No. 4, 1 cwt. per acre.

Average Yields. The wheat yield is about 8 sacks per acre ; oat yield about 12 sacks per acre.

Grassland. All the grassland, which responds to slag, is permanent, the average hay yield being about 25 cwt. per acre. It carries a very poor herbage with a large percentage of weeds, but is capable of great improvement if attention is paid to drainage and manuring. At present many drains are out of order and the land is suffering from excess of water.

Livestock. Cattle, sheep and pigs are as typical for the district.

THE BATH REGION.

The region is merely a convenient generalisation, since the soils, slopes, and altitudes vary considerably. The farms are chosen to show conditions on the Bath stone heights, and in the vale to the west of Bath. The Bath stone soil is fairly adaptable, easily worked with natural drainage, and not sour, but a " hungry " type needing phosphates and organic manures.

Stock grass is available in the Wellow area about the second week in May. The altitudes on Bathstone are high and this possibly reflects a slight local climatic difference. About Kelston stock grass is available about the 17th–20th April.

Soils on the lower lands are very variable, Clays and Sands, with outcrops of Stonebrash and Freestone. Phosphates are required on the Clays, which are difficult to work, and complete manures with organics on the Sands.

Wheat, oats and beans are grown. The whole district is chiefly occupied with dairying, with Shorthorn cattle chiefly, but sheep are kept for fat lamb production in some places, chiefly Dorset Downs, Exmoors, Crossbreds and Kerry Hills. There are few pigs, chiefly Large Whites, mostly sold as stores.

Land Values. In the vicinity of Wellow farms rent at about 25/– per acre ; in the vicinity of Kelston, from 35/– to 50/– per acre. Locally about Bath there is land which lets for market-gardening at high rents, and on the steep heights there is much low-value pastures.

Specimen Farm (on Great Oolite).

Area, between 50–100 acres. Freehold.

Soil. There is not much variation. All the soil is a light, free-working stony loam overlying Bathstone, or what is called locally " bastard " Bathstone, being very much split up and not suitable for quarrying.

Working Capital is about £13 10s. per acre.

Labour Employed. The farm is worked by father and son.

Crops. The rotation followed is : wheat ; oats with " seeds " ; seed hay ; roots or wheat ; catch-crops are worked in when possible. The soil has a natural drainage and can be worked almost irrespective of weather.

Manuring. Farmyard manure only is used.

Average Yields. The average wheat yield is 6–7 sacks per acre ; oats, 12 sacks per acre.

Grassland. All grassland is permanent, mown and grazed in turn, yielding about 25–27 cwt. per acre. Farmyard manure only is used. The herbage is rather weedy and " benty," but sweet and well grazed. Absence of sheep, which have been replaced by dairy cows, has not been good for the grass which appears to need phosphates.

Livestock. Shorthorns are kept for milk sale, and Large White pigs sold as weaners.

Specimen Farm (Vicinity of Kelston).

Area, between 250–300 acres. Yearly tenancy.

Soil. The farm stands on Lower Lias Clay, and Alluvium. The meadows by the river are a deep alluvial soil, the remainder of the farm is Clay with an outcrop of rock on the higher ground by the river. There is a narrow Rhaetic exposure.

Working Capital is about £10 12s. per acre.

Labour Employed. Seven men are employed permanently and no extra labour required.

Crops. No strict rotation is followed ; mangolds, wheat and oats are grown, and beans and bare fallow are sometimes introduced. The wheat is sold.

Preparation of the Ground. The majority of the fields have pipe or stone drains still in fair working order. The arable land is rather heavy and difficult to cultivate as it is stony in places and " bakes " badly in dry weather.

Manures. For mangolds, farmyard manure + complete artificials, about 5 cwt. per acre of mangold manure ; wheat and oats are not manured.

Average Yields. The average wheat yield is 8–10 sacks per acre ; oats, 12 sacks per acre.

Grassland. About 260 acres is in permanent grass, certain fields being mown every year, others being mown at irregular intervals and some never mown. The average hay crop is about 35 cwt. per acre. The fields regularly mown get farmyard manure every year, and no artificials are used.

The grassland is well managed and is of good type with well-mixed herbage. The fields adjoining the alluvial meadows are overlying Limestone and Freestone, and the soil is very shallow so the herbage " burns " quickly in dry weather.

Livestock. A self-supporting dairy herd of Shorthorns is maintained for milk sale. A " flying " flock of Devon Down or Crossbred Down ewes is crossed with Ryeland for production of lambs fattened on grass. The ewes are bought in October and lambed two or three seasons if sound. *Pigs :* A few Crossbreds are bought and fattened.

THE NORTH SOMERSET HILL AND VALLEY REGION.

The chief occupation of the region is dairying, with " flying " flocks of Downs and Kerrys for fat lamb and fat ewe production. Pigs of the usual breeds are sold as stores or fattened. The soils vary considerably in texture and slope, but there are large areas of Red

Marls and Lias Clays. Much of the field-draining was done forty years ago, and is now out of repair.

Land Values. Farms are rented at from 30/- to 40/- per acre.

Specimen Farm. (Chelwood Vicinity).

Area, between 300–400 acres. Yearly tenancy.

Soil. The soil varies considerably, many fields having two or three different types. Generally it is heavy Clay with much loose Limestone, but there are large areas of Marly texture and banks of practically pure Red Sand. The farm apparently stands on Lower Lias, Rhaetic and Red (Keuper) Marl, and in parts on an area marked as " Penarth Beds."

Working Capital is about £8 14s. per acre.

Labour Employed. Five men and a boy are permanently employed, with extra labour to the value of about £25 per annum.

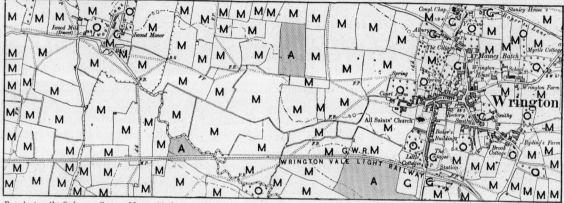

Based upon the Ordnance Survey Map, with the sanction of the Controller of H.M. Stationery Office.

FIG. 22.—The North Somerset Region.

This map lies in the area immediately north of the Mendips where the Red (Keuper) Marls are heavy and drainage is often difficult. In consequence comparatively little land is under the plough, the majority being in small grass fields.

Crops. There is little arable. Crops consist of wheat, mangolds and kale, not grown in regular rotation. The wheat is sold. No spring corn is sown owing to difficulty of cultivation and trouble with charlock, poppy, etc. Cultivation is very difficult and the weather plays an important part. Yields also are difficult to estimate, as these vary very considerably according to the season.

Manuring. Wheat receives 1 cwt. per acre of sulphate of ammonia. Other crops farmyard manure only.

Grassland. All pasture is permanent, some fields being mown each year, the average hay yield being about 25 cwt. per acre. Farmyard manure is used on the mowing fields, the grazing fields being manured occasionally with phosphates. The grassland is of good type and well grazed although some fields are very wet and appear as if draining would effect a great improvement. Stock grass is available about May 1st.

Livestock. Shorthorns and Guernseys are kept for milk sale, and the young stock reared for herd replenishment. *Sheep :* A " flying " flock of Kerry Down crosses and Kerrys is maintained. Ewes are bought in September and couples in March.

Specimen Farm (Blagdon Vale Area).

Area, between 200–250 acres. Yearly tenancy.

Soil. The farm stands on Red (Keuper) Marl and partly stream Alluvium. The soil is chiefly a heavy loam on Red Marl. There is a strip of Peat by the brook with Red Marl beneath.

Working Capital is about £11 14s. per acre.

Labour Employed. Five men are employed with extra labour at a cost of about £30 per annum.

Crops. The rotation, varied a little according to the season is : wheat ; oat with " seeds " ; clover hay (two years) ; wheat ; roots. The wheat is sold.

Preparation of the Ground. One or two fields are drained by pipes, but the majority have open furrows and ridges at wide intervals. The arable land is rather on the heavy side, but generally speaking is not difficult to cultivate. The ground is not sour.

Manuring. For mangolds and for kale, farmyard manure + 10 cwt. of compound manure ; for wheat, about 4 cwt. of compound manure per acre top-dressed in spring. Oats receive no manure.

Average Yield. The average yield of wheat is 12 sacks per acre ; oats, 20 sacks ; mangolds, 56–60 tons per acre.

Grassland. About 180 acres is in permanent grass, certain fields being mown every year, yielding about 35 cwt. of hay per acre. The mowing fields get farmyard manure every other year, but the grazing fields get little or none. All the grassland lies rather wet and is in need of draining. Some fields are in good condition as regards herbage and are well grazed, but there is a considerable area which is very wet and full of rushes (along the course of the brook), and which would improve with drainage.

Livestock. Besides the usual Shorthorns for milk sale, a " flying " flock of Crossbred Downs, crossed with South Downs, is usually maintained (Border Leicester have been tried) the ewes and lambs being grazed during the summer. The ewes are bought in August and September. *Pigs :* Wessex Saddleback and Large White sows breed pigs for bacon and pork.

THE MENDIP AREA.

Two farms were chosen, one on the high Plateau Limestone of Mendip, and one in the Cheddar Vale region, using the rich flats, the lower slopes, and high pasture.

The high Mendip farm is roughly typical of the larger Mendip farms. The smaller farms are chiefly dairy cattle and rearing farms, and more productive. One or two newcomers are trying the plough again, but their chances of success are not considered good by experienced Mendip farmers.

Stock. Shorthorn type cattle are kept for milk sale. Usually sufficient young stock is reared for herd replenishment. *Sheep :* A few Devon crosses are kept for production of " stores." *Pigs :* Chiefly Large Whites are kept, the small farmers selling weaners, the large farmers fattening pigs for bacon.

Specimen Farm (Charterhouse Vicinity).

Area, between 600–700 acres. The greater part is freehold, part yearly tenancy.

Soil. All a light, easy-working loam on Carboniferous Limestone. The soil is sour.

Working Capital. About £4 per acre.

Land Values. Farms in the locality are rented at from 10/- to 30/- per acre. The smaller farms, with little rough land and with good buildings make up to, and in some cases, over 30/– per acre.

Workmen Employed.   None.

There is no cropping done, but the land is all free working with natural drainage. All-round manuring is essential if the land is to be farmed. The whole farm is in permanent grass which is available for stock about May 1st. Certain fields are mown every year, yielding from 20 to 30 cwt. per acre according to the season. Farmyard manure is used on the mowing fields. The fields are large and carry a very poor and " benty " herbage, but will produce a considerable quantity of grass during the summer. Fields that are not mown are very rough. One field is being cut for lawn turves.

Livestock.   Crossbred cattle of Shorthorn type are kept and some milk is sold. Some young stock is reared and yearlings are bought for herd replenishment and sold with calf. *Sheep:* Exmoors, Cheviots and Crossbred Down ewes are crossed with Ryeland or Hampshire Down

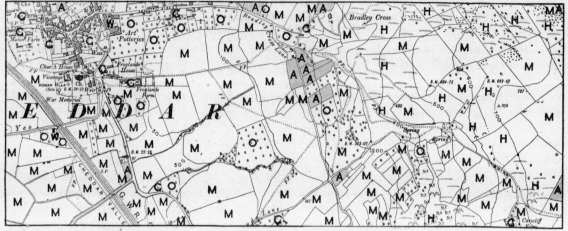

Based upon the Ordnance Survey Map, with the sanction of the Controller of H.M. Stationery Office.

FIG. 23.—The Mendip and the Cheddar Areas.

This map illustrates the utilisation of the south-west facing Mendip scarp. In the eastern half the land climbs steeply to the Mendip plateau, where the regular, rectangular-shaped fields are considerably larger than those appearing on this map. The poor character of this limestone country is indicated by the outcrops of bare rock and the extent of the land shown as rough pasture. On the lower slopes of the hills are the small cultivated strips, market-garden land devoted to strawberries, violets and other " early " crops, and to orchards. In the south-west, beyond the railway, appear the first drainage channels of the rich Cheddar Moor.

rams. A Southdown ram is used for early lamb grazed on land about Cheddar. Lambs from the Ryeland and Hampshire Down rams are sold as stores.

CHEDDAR VICINITY.

Practically the whole of the arable land round Cheddar is devoted to strawberries,[1] and early spring flowers such as anemones, violets, etc., and is in the hands of smallholders and working men who do the cultivation in their spare time. The farms are all made up of scattered fields embracing a variety of soil types from high Mendip to rich Alluvial. The low-lying land

[1] A very full account of the strawberry cultivation can be found in *An Economic Enquiry into the Production of Straw-berries*, by C. V. Dawe, M.Com., and H. T. Horsman, B.Sc., etc. University of Bristol, *Bulletin* No. 8 (1932).

is in grass, the Mendip slopes in special garden crops. The district is an early one ; stock grass is available about mid-April. Very little manure is used on the rich grassland, and if managed well it does not appear to need any. On the arable at the foot of the hills phosphates and farm-yard manure are needed. In the higher fields between the moor and Mendip slopes there are some pipe-drains.

Land Values. The " moorland " (pastures of the alluvial level) rents at about £3 per acre ; secondary land rents at about £2 per acre, with £1 per acre for poorer land adjoining the hills. Mendip land above the vale rents at about 4/– to 5/– per acre. Rents on the small-holdings vary to an extraordinary extent, owing to the special nature of the cultivation of the area. Approximately 111 acres, held by 65 smallholders growing strawberries and other market-garden crops, and early flowers, rents on the average at between £5 and £6 per acre, the highest rents being at the rate of between £11 and £12 per acre, and over half the growers renting at between £3 10s. and £7 10s. per acre.

Specimen Farm (Cheddar Vicinity).

The farm consists of several home fields, detached moorland fields, and some rough pasture on Mendip slopes.

Area is between 200–300 acres, part held on yearly tenancy and part freehold.

Soil. About 100 acres are held on Mendip. Some of the fields consist of heavy alluvial soils of great depth ; some at slightly higher levels are very heavy loams, rather shallow and overlying Gravel.

Working Capital. About £8 16s. per acre.

Labour Employed. Three men with extra labour at a cost of about £10 per annum.

Grassland. The whole farm is in permanent grass, certain fields being mown each year, the average yield being 30 cwt. per acre. No artificials are used ; farmyard manure is used on the grass, but chiefly on the fields owned by the occupier.

The low-lying fields are in good condition and well grazed. They cannot be stocked in winter, but are very productive in summer and do not suffer from drought. Not being clay, there is hardly any tendency to " bake " or crack in dry weather. The higher fields carry a very good herbage, but are not so productive. They are dry and are stocked during winter.

The Mendip land is used for young cattle in late spring and early summer—as long as there is water available. Sheep and lambs are run there practically all summer.

Livestock. A dairy herd of Shorthorns is maintained for milk sale, some of the young stock being reared. *Sheep :* Down crosses crossed with Ryeland and Border Leicester crossed with Suffolk are kept for the production of " stores." Ewes are bought in September and kept as long as they are sound.

THE WEDMORE ISLE.

Farms in and about the Isle are made up of scattered fields, part being on the heights and part on the rich alluvial meadows. This distribution is due to the difference in soil types and the effect of the low-lying pastures upon stock which makes change essential in order to keep the cattle healthy. The soil types are much more varied than can be shown on the Geological map. The heights are formed on a wide Rhaetic exposure, marked " Wedmore Stone," with Sand in places, on the old Geological sheet ; to the east is Red Marl, and to the west Lower Lias Clay.

Stock is chiefly Shorthorn cattle for milk sale, and Down type " flying " flocks for summer fat lamb and a few hoggets.

Land Values. Farms in the area are rented at from 50/– to 70/– per acre.

Growing Season. Stock grass is available about the second week in April.

Specimen Farm.

Area, between 50–100 acres. Part freehold, and part yearly tenancy. The distribution of the fields is scattered, typical of the farms on Wedmore, some being three miles apart.

Soils. Some fields lie on Red (Keuper) Marl ; an arable field is on medium-heavy Clay loam (Lias) and pastures nearby are chiefly a light loam over pure Sand and Sandstone (Rhaetic). Near Wedmore, fields consist of heavy Clay loam and orchards near Latcham are on Red (Keuper) Marl.

Working Capital is about £10 8s. per acre, about 70 per cent. being in livestock.

Labour Employed. The farm is worked by the owner and 1 boy.

Crops. Roots and potatoes only are grown, both consumed on the farm. Fields on the Clay about Wedmore are pipe-drained ; the moor fields on Tilham Heath and Latcham Moor are in Drainage Districts.

Manuring. Farmyard manure only is used.

Grassland. All grassland is permanent. The average hay yield is about 25 cwt. per acre. No artificial manures are used and the grassland is in very fair condition and well grazed, but carries a large proportion of weeds, especially buttercups.

Livestock. Shorthorn cows are kept for milk sale and a few cattle fattened on grass.

THE GORDANO AREA (About Portishead and Clapton).

Soils vary from Clay loams, Peat and Alluvium to light Red Sandstone loam, some slightly acid. The arable is mostly a sharp Sand, easy to work, on which all-round manuring including organic is necessary. The low-lying fields on heavier soils are pipe-drained. Potatoes do fairly well on the sands.

Stock. Shorthorns are kept for milk sale and both Shorthorns and Devons fattened ; little rearing is done and most of the cows are bought. *Sheep :* Chiefly Welsh Cross ewes (Kerry and Clun are crossed with Ryeland or Down rams for fat lamb production. *Pigs :* There are few pigs, chiefly Large White crosses sold as stores or fattened.

Land Values. Farms in the area are rented at from 34/– to 60/– per acre, depending on size and the great variation from poor, light Sandstone and Limestone soils to heavy Clay loams, or alluvial grassland.

Growing Season. Wheat is sown before November if possible, harvest commencing August 1st. Stock grass is available about mid-April.

Specimen Farm. (1) Clapton Vicinity.

Area, between 450–550 acres. Yearly tenancy.

Soil. The majority of the fields are a light Red Sandstone loam of a very sharp texture, the low-lying pastures being heavy Clay loams or Peat.

Working Capital is about £16 per acre.

Labour Employed is 12 men, with little extra labour required.

Crops. There is no fixed rotation ; arable crops are wheat, potatoes, mangolds, swedes, kale and vetches. Wheat and potatoes are sold.

Preparation of the Ground. Nearly all fields are pipe-drained on the flat pasture and arable fields, the latter being free-working. The steep fields are not drained.

Manuring. For potatoes, farmyard manure + 5–8 cwt. of fish manure per acre ; for mangolds, farmyard manure + nitrogen if necessary.

Grassland. About 440 acres are in permanent grassland, certain fields being cut practically every year, the average yield about 30 cwt. per acre. Some of the low-lying pastures are of good type, well grazed and productive, but there is a large area of hill pasture which is of poor quality and could be scheduled as rough grazing. There are also several acres of marshland which carry a very poor type of herbage and can be stocked only in summer. Basic slag gives good results on the good pastures and also on the rough, peaty fields, but on the poor Sandstone hill pastures the effect of slag is apparent only from the preference which the stock show for the slagged parts. This is probably due to all-round soil poverty.

Livestock. Shorthorns are kept for milk production and barren cows fattened. *Sheep :* A " flying " flock of Crossbred Welsh ewes are crossed with Suffolk rams for fat lamb production. The ewes are bought in September. *Pigs :* A pedigree herd of Large White pigs is maintained for sale, bacon and pork.

(2) The Old Red Sandstone (Gordano Coast).

Area, between 250–300 acres. Yearly tenancy.

Soil. The soil is practically all a light, Sandy loam, varying in depth and very stony. In general it is not acid, but it has been heavily limed in the past and some fields are now showing signs of acidity.

Growing Season. Wheat is sown in October if possible ; oats in February. Harvest commences at the end of July. Stock grass is available about the first week in May.

Working Capital is about £8 10s. per acre.

Labour Employed. Two men are permanently employed and extra seasonal labour at a cost of about £60 per annum.

Crops. The following rotation is followed : Oats ; roots and fallow ; wheat with " seeds " ; seed hay. Grass is sometimes left two years. Wheat and part of the oats are sold.

Preparation of the Ground. Cultivation is easy except for the large number of stones in places and rock a few inches down. Drainage is natural.

Manuring. For mangolds, farmyard manure + 6 cwt. mangold manure per acre ; for swedes, 6–7 cwt. per acre of swede manure ; for wheat, 5 cwt. per acre of corn manure.

Average Yields. Yields vary considerably, being adversely affected by a dry season. Wheat is nearly always a light crop, with oats very good in normal or wet years.

Grassland. About 100 acres is in permanent grassland and about 80 acres in rough pasture. The fields which are mown regularly yield 20–25 cwt. of hay per acre. Grassland responds to phosphate and sheep and cattle are fed on the grass with hay, swedes, etc. ; no artificials are used. Much of the pasture land is very poor indeed, and appears badly in need of plough, phosphates and seed.

Livestock. Livestock is as described for the previous farm.

NORTH SOMERSET LEVELS (Wick St. Lawrence Vicinity).

Except for a coastal outcrop of Limestone, and a few patches of Lias Clay, the district is high Alluvium.

The chief stock consists of Shorthorns for milk sale, and insufficient stock is reared to keep up the herds. There is some summer grazing of old cows, Devons and Aberdeen-Angus crosses. *Sheep :* " Flying " flocks of Cheviot, Kerry Hills, and Downs crossed with Dorset Down or South Down are kept. A few crossbred pigs are kept.

Land Values. Farms in the area are rented at from 60/- to 70/- per acre.

Grassland. Stock grass is available about mid-April. Large farms are at considerably lower rents, to 30/– per acre.

Specimen Farm.

Area, is between 400–500 acres. Leasehold.

Soil. The low-lying fields are heavy alluvial soil. In places there is a Clay subsoil, and an arable field lies probably on a patch of Lias. There is some cliffland on Limestone, where the soils are thin, overlying rock.

Working Capital is about £6 2s. per acre. 83 per cent. being in livestock.

Labour Employed. Five men are employed permanently, and 1 extra hand for six months.

Crops. There is very little ground under plough. No rotation is followed. Wheat, beans and fodder crops are grown and wheat sold. The majority of fields are pipe-drained, but these are deep and placed at wide intervals and many have ceased to function. The majority of the low-lying fields are also laid out on a ridge-and-furrow system. The arable fields are heavy and difficult to cultivate, with wet patches due to failure of drains.

Manuring. Manuring consists of farmyard manure and slag.

Grassland. All grassland is permanent, the average hay yield from the fields mown every year being 30 to 40 cwt. per acre. About 200 acres are low-lying and in fair condition, except for wet patches due to insufficient drainage. No artificials are used. The herbage on cliff-land " burns " badly in summer, but is very sweet and well grazed.

Livestock. Shorthorn cows are kept for milk and cheese production, stock being reared for the herd. Exmoor and Cheviot ewes are crossed with Dorset Down rams for fat lamb production, ewes being bought in September and one crop of lambs taken. *Pigs :* Crossbred sows are crossed with a Large White boar and the pigs fattened.

CENTRAL LEVELS (Huntspill Drainage District).

Soil. Heavy Alluvium.

The farm chosen is a typical dairy farm, all in grass.

Area, between 50–100 acres. Freehold.

Land Values. Farms rent at about 70/– per acre.

Working Capital. On the specimen farm working capital is about £15 per acre.

Labour Employed. One man and 2 boys.

Crops. The small amount of arable land in the area (not on the farm) is heavy and hard to work, being neglected and badly farmed in many cases.

Manures. The grass responds well to superphosphate and slag and farmyard manure is essential on the mowing fields. All fields are surface-drained with ridge-and-furrow, ditches and rhines.

Grassland is all permanent, certain fields being mown every year and yielding 25–30 cwt. per acre of hay, receiving farmyard manure at least every third year. The pastures get no manure. The land does not " bake " or crack in summer and stands drought well, having good, well-grazed herbage.

Stock on the farm are all Shorthorns for milk sale. Some rearing is done in the district, but not enough for herd replenishment. The farm has no sheep or pigs, but " flying " flocks, chiefly Exmoor, are kept locally for fat lambs in summer, and fat ewes. Onc crop of lambs only is taken. *Pigs* are few, chiefly Large White.

V. THE MAKING OF THE FIELD PATTERN OF SOMERSET

By

S. C. MORLAND, M.A., C.C.

The history of land cultivation in Somerset from its early beginnings in the Neolithic or Bronze Age, until the coming of the Saxons, is a subject interesting in itself, but that need not concern us here. The break between the older and newer civilisations appears to have been long enough for the land to have gone out of cultivation, in all but the western part of the County at all events. The Saxons had captured Bath after the battle of Dyrham in 577, pursued the Welsh to the Parrett in 658, and were settled round Exeter and Crediton before 675. The systematic settlement of Somerset dates therefore from the second half of the seventh century.

The factors that in course of time determined the position, size and character of each village, were the water supply, the nature of the land, the type of settler, and occasionally the policy of the ruler. The Geological map illustrates the first point by showing the string of villages on the Cornbrash, where water is plentiful, while the adjacent Oxford Clay has no village and few scattered farms, and the Forest Marble very few villages. On the Lower Lias series are many adequate springs and wells supplying large villages, but also areas such as Neroche Forest between Taunton and Ilminster, and the country north of Dundry Hill, where water was scarce and where woodland long remained. Areas of Keuper Marl round North Curry, along the south edge of the Polden Ridge, and round Wells, have small villages or hamlets, which may be an effect of a water supply inadequate for larger villages. Along either side of the Mendips and the west and south of the Quantocks a line of villages marks the level of the springs, while similarly a fringe of hamlets and farms round Pennard Hill marks the line where the Lower Lias Clays throw out the water soaking through the sandy Middle Lias above.

For cultivation the Saxons avoided the hill-tops tilled in the Iron Age, and land that was water-logged ; within the area of each village they required pasture and meadow for their plough-oxen, for which rough ground and damp ground were suitable. Much land that was naturally forest, particularly on the Lower Lias beds, was cleared and ploughed at a very early date, probably as early as the more open lands on the Sandstones, Marls, Inferior Oolite, Forest Marble and Cornbrash.

We have no direct knowledge of the type of settler in our different villages, but something can be inferred from the conditions four centuries later, at the time of the Domesday Survey. Villages on the ancient demesne of the Crown, such as Somerton, where the villeins had 40 ploughs and the King 5, and in consequence the villeins had very little work to do each week for their lord, probably were settlements of free men. Shapwick is a good example of a monastic manor, where a large village with the manor-house and demesne land was the centre of a group of six smaller villages held in Saxon times by thegns doing military service for the Abbot. Here the Abbot's villeins were subject to more labour service than the King's villeins at Somerton, and the thegn's villeins in the smaller villages were in a worse position still. Taking a general view of the County, the larger the village the better the position of the villeins ; in many small manors of recent growth all the land was in demesne.

The well-recognised difference of character between the villages east and west of the Parrett and Neroche Forest may have been due to the increasing weakness of the Welsh as the Saxons

131

advanced westward. Possibly there were fewer settlements made by bands of victorious warriors because a smaller army was adequate. Whatever the causes, three general types of settlement can be distinguished in West Somerset : villages and hamlets with common fields, manors with a few cottages, and scattered homesteads attached to a manor. Williton and Porlock are typical of the first class—the Saxon villages, and King's Brompton and Winsford of the third class, which may have been Welsh settlements undisturbed except for the very little labour service rendered to their Saxon lords. The second class includes many early and late settlements, similar to those in other parts of the County, but in the west the proportion of the land they cover is great.

How far the settlement was planned in general or in detail by the ruler, is purely a matter of conjecture ; we know that Ine founded Taunton before the year 722, when his queen burnt it, and that he founded, or more probably re-established, Glastonbury Abbey. But what is really more significant, we find that a group of large villages directly dependent on the King covers the strategic centre of Somerset, where the Fosse Way crosses the marsh at Ilchester and Petherton bridge, and the track-ways cross it at Langport and Somerton. Somerton, Curry Rivel and South Petherton, with Martock, Long Sutton, Kingsbury and Kingsdon, form the nucleus of Somerset. In the east of the County the royal villages of Frome and Bruton cover important fords, and Milborne Port an important track-way. Bedminster and a group of large free villages guard the mouth of the Avon on the south, as does Westbury on the north. Kingston Seymour and Congresbury, near the mouth of the Kenn ; Cheddar near the limit of navigation on the Axe ; Burnham, Huntspill, Cannington and North Petherton round the tidal Parrett, all large villages with comparatively free villeins in 1086, seem to indicate at some stage or other in the settlement, some elements of planning.

At the time of the Domesday Survey there were approximately 4,000 plough-teams in Somerset. From particulars given in the surveys of the Glastonbury Abbey estates, these ploughs would have tilled about 120 acres each in two-field villages, or 80 acres each year. If we allow for the fact that much enclosed land, particularly extensive in West Somerset, was probably ploughed every year, the area of arable should have been about 450,000 acres, or nearly half the area of the County. A great deal of land had been brought into cultivation in the eastern part of the County that lay outside the open fields of the original settlement, and allowing for the extent of hill and marsh, the land was fairly fully cultivated in 1086.

The Bath, Wells and Glastonbury records, and the maps attached to the Enclosure Awards, show that the two-field system was normal in Somerset. The three-field system existed in seven large hamlets in Martock Parish, in South Petherton, Barrington and Stoke-sub-Hamdon. Outside that area I have only found it at Pitney and Keinton Mandeville. Four fields were occasionally used, possibly owing to two fields being sub-divided ; Somerton is a good example. In many places all traces of a two- or three-field system disappeared early, if either system had ever been worked, but large fields remained of quite irregular size. Such were Chedzoy in 1574, Kingsbury Episcopi (3–5 Jas. I.) and Westonzoyland and Othery at the time of the Enclosure awards. Some quite small hamlets, such as Wookey Hole, and East Street in West Pennard, had two fields, but many others, such as Pibsbury in Long Sutton and Week in Curry Rivel, had one open field.

The Pembroke surveys in the sixteenth century show that in some two-field villages, two-thirds of the demesne land was cropped every year ; this suggests that the system was not altogether inelastic, and that alternate years of corn and fallow were going out of fashion.

West of the Parrett and Neroche Forest, we know that Bossington and Porlock were open-field villages, and the six-inch map shows by the lines of the hedgerows that many other villages had open fields, but that these were small compared with East Somerset. I have found no trace of the three-field system in West Somerset, and of the two-field system only at Lilstock. Arable land in a common field presupposes a number of peasants whose strips were intermingled ; naturally the fields of many of the small manors in West Somerset were enclosed, because the number of tenants was too small for open-field agriculture. Further, the demesne land of some manors and the land of the scattered cottages on the hills lay, more or less, in a ring fence. In Celtic Wales and Scotland it was often the custom to plough and manure the " infield," round the hamlet, every year, and to plough part of the outfield, the waste, for a few years in succession until it was exhausted, when another piece would be ploughed up. Very much the same was being done at West Bagborough in 1314.

The boroughs differed from the villages in that the burgesses grew no corn, but held meadow, pasture and garden land with their tenements. This is illustrated by the fact that Axbridge, Langport and Ilchester parishes contain no possible arable land ; at Taunton the borough with its market was the centre of a large manor, but burgesses held no corn-land.[1] At Bath the Abbey had a barton with two open fields in demesne.

Historians may continue to argue as to whether the Black Death was or was not a turning-point in the course of social development in agricultural England. Probably from the time of the first Saxon settlement, the process of subdividing family holdings had gone on alongside the more desirable process of clearing and cultivating the woods and wastes that still remained between the settlements. From the Norman Conquest onwards, comparative peace brought about the clearer recognition of the rights of lords and tenants to hunt or pasture beasts on the remaining woods and commons ; the population continued to increase, but relatively little new land was brought into use.

A comparison of the manors included in the Glastonbury surveys of Abbots Michael of Ambresbury (1235–52) and Roger Ford (1252–61), the Porlock survey of 1306, and the Beauchamp surveys of 1287, with the same manors as recorded in Domesday Book, clearly illustrates the growth of population. The fact that the total area the tenants cultivated had not greatly increased is not so obvious, because the Domesday Book division of the hidage as between the land in demesne and the tenants' land was arbitrary. (At Mells, for example, were 10 hides and two ploughs in demesne, and the villeins held $3\frac{1}{2}$ hides and 3 ploughs. 180 years later there were 430 acres in demesne requiring 3 ploughs, and the tenants had $3\frac{5}{8}$ hides. At Batcombe were $9\frac{3}{4}$ hides and 2 ploughs in demesne, and the villeins held half a hide and 3 ploughs ; at the later date the villeins held $2\frac{3}{4}$ hides, which compares with the ploughs rather than the hidage.) The particulars collected are set out in the following table, which must leave many points unexplained, and shows for this group of manors that the number of tenants had increased by 106 per cent. in less than 200 years, with little or no increase in the area of their land, if the hides in the thirteenth century are compared with the ploughs in 1086.

These surveys also show considerable increase in the values of the manors of Brentmarsh and Sowi, owing to the use of marshland for pasture and meadow, and of Glastonbury, owing to this and to the clearance of land between West Pennard and Woodland Street for ploughing. If the Black Death, as is possible, robbed many manors of half their serfs, it is easy to understand that the level of wages rose, and that serfs who could do so escaped to other manors to work for wages. The benefit to the serfs of the reduction in population was shared by the lords, who could use the land left on their hands and develop new methods of cultivation.

Somerset from the fourteenth to the eighteenth centuries was of the greatest importance

[1] Fulke Bourchier Lord Fitzwarren held, among other things (d. 19 Edw. IV) " nine messuages, eight gardens, ten acres of meadow, and 20 acres of pasture, in Pyntenay and Taunton, of the Bishop of Winchester in free Burgage."—*Collinson*, p. 271.

DOMESDAY SURVEY

Manor	Villeins	Bordars	Cottars etc.	Serfs	Hides held	Ploughs owned
Porlock	6	3	—	6	$1\frac{1}{2}$	—
Mells	8	7	5	2	$3\frac{1}{2}$	3
Baltonsborough	5	9	3	4	$\frac{3}{4}$	2
Batcombe	4	14	—	6	$\frac{1}{2}$	3
Brentmarsh	50	47	—	5	11	16
Butleigh	11	7	—	7	$2\frac{1}{2}$	6
Ditcheat	13	18	3	2	2	7
Dundon	5	10	—	4	$1\frac{7}{8}$	3
High Ham	22	21	—	5	$3\frac{3}{8}$	8
Marksbury	6	5	—	5	3	3
East Pennard	17	9	10	4	7	6
Sowi	27	13	12	2	7	14

NOTE.—The Manor of Brentmarsh included Brent Knoll, East Brent, Lympsham and Berrow, and the Manor of Sowi included Westonzoyland, Middlezoy and Othery.

SECOND SURVEY

Manor	Date	Free Tenants	Villeins	Cottars With Land	Cottars Without Land	Hides held
Porlock	1306	2	24	—	32	$1\frac{1}{2}$
Mells	1252–61	6	7	35	11	$3\frac{3}{8}$
Baltonsborough	1252–61	2	29	—	6	$2\frac{3}{4}$
Batcombe	1252–61	—	14	21	—	$2\frac{3}{4}$
Brentmarsh	1252–61	32	137	99	—	18
Butleigh	1235–52	4	24	18	4	$6\frac{1}{2}$
Ditcheat	1235–52	8	18	35	6	6
Dundon	1287	9	26	—	—	$3\frac{1}{2}$
High Ham	1235–52	1	24	20	—	6
Marksbury	1252–61	—	16	14	—	4
East Pennard	1235–52	—	25	27	—	$5\frac{1}{8}$
Sowi	1235–52	5	72	45	—	$9\frac{3}{8}$

in the woollen industry in England. Frome, Pensford, Shepton Mallet, Croscombe, Taunton, and Ilminster, were the principal manufacturing centres. Although sheep-farming also grew in importance in parts of Somerset, this County was not one of those in which " putting down houses of husbandry for sheep-runs " was a cause of serious complaint. In Domesday Book flocks of sheep are recorded in most manors, the distribution being rather more heavy east of the Parrett, and the flocks largest on the Lias Limestone round Somerton, on the Mendips, and on the Oolite hills round Bath and Henstridge. In 1421 the lady of the manor of Porlock had a flock of 400 sheep reduced by murrain and the demands of her larder to under 200 in four years. In the time of Henry VIII the tenants had grazing rights for over 2,500 sheep on the moors and commons of this manor. A century later it was stated to be the custom here to drive the sheep to enclosed lands for the night and graze them by day only on the moor, to avoid their wandering into the forest of Exmoor, where they might be and were impounded. Billingsley, writing in 1791, complains that many Somerset farmers did not understand the value of folding sheep at that time. Sheep-farming was one of the many factors that made the enclosure of open arable profitable : the centres of the wool industry mentioned above, are all in areas of comparatively early enclosure.

On Exmoor and the Brendon Hills (not including the old " Forest ") where large flocks of sheep were grazed, three types of arable enclosure can sometimes be distinguished. In the valleys and near the larger villages, narrow fields with parallel and slightly curving hedges show where the common fields lay, and that these were often enclosed piecemeal by their owners or tenants. Much of the land on the hills, belonging to the little hamlets and isolated farms, was divided into strips a furlong wide and three or four furlongs in length, and these strips into three or four almost square fields. The land of many of the tiny manors, and the demesne land of the larger manors, was divided to suit the convenience of a ring-fence farm, though many cases of fields equally divided into two may indicate that, as at Porlock (temp., Henry VIII) demesne closes were let to two tenants. In West Somerset much land that was enclosed from the waste for use as pasture can be distinguished by its irregular boundaries.

Many villages in Taunton Dean had open fields at one time, but no trace of the two- or three-field system can now be found ; isolated farms dot the country from Ashbrittle to Milverton ; hamlets between Wiveliscombe and Bagborough, and between Taunton and Bishop's Lydeard ; and between Taunton, Pitminster and Wellington, hamlets and farms, many of them dating from the thirteenth century and later. By the end of the Middle Ages almost the whole of the cultivated land in Taunton Dean was enclosed. In the Customs of the Bishop of Winchester's great manor, a distinction was made between " bondland," held with a cottage and subject to feudal services, and " overland," let for a rent without a cottage and not subject to services. At Donyatt in the Pembroke Survey of 1574, the " overland " lay in closes, when most of the arable in the village appears to have still been in common field.

The open arable fields in the parts of Somerset where the villages used the two- or three-fields system, were gradually reduced in area by individuals fencing acre strips or groups of strips. Many villages gradually enclosed the whole of their open fields in this way ; sometimes, as at Draycott in Rodney Stoke, each strip seems to have been separately fenced ; sometimes, although the fields to-day are larger, the pattern of the open fields remains, as at Cucklington and Street ; often in smaller villages a large landowner was able to make larger fields suitable to modern agricultural methods, so that the old boundaries are now obliterated. The open fields that survived until the eighteenth century were enclosed by a series of Acts of Parliament ; the area was still large in the villages on the Lias ridge that stretches from Alford through Keinton Mandeville, Somerton and Long Sutton to Drayton and Curry Rivel, on the Poldens, in Martock and South Petherton, in Weare and Wedmore, and in a few other parishes in the County, such as Weston-super-Mare, Portishead, Ditcheat, Lilstock, Queen Camel, Milborne Port, Cheddar and North Perrott. The straight lines drawn by surveyors contrast on these lands with the curving lines of the furlongs in the earlier enclosures. Even to-day there are in some places small parcels of land divided into strips by stones and baulks of earth, last vestiges of the open-fields still unenclosed : the well-known fields at Westonzoyland and Middlezoy were enclosed by Act of Parliament early in the nineteenth century and the land re-divided into larger parcels, but few farmers there have wasted good land on a hedge to divide their corn from their neighbour's peas and potatoes.

Much of the work of clearing forest lands was done by the Saxons at the time of their first settlement. Further progress had been made before the Norman Conquest, and we have seen above that the Abbots of Glastonbury added to their lands in the thirteenth century by further clearing. Similar work was done by the Priors of Witham and Stavordale on the wooded Oxford Clay in East Somerset. The extreme irregularity of many of the fields enclosed from woodland shows that they were not intended to be ploughed. Much was too heavy and wet for any crop but grass, and Billingsley writes of Neroche Forest that the unenclosed portion was so damp as to cause foot-rot in sheep. The Cucklington and Stoke Trister surveys of 1574 show that by that date much of this clay land was already in use as pasture. The second use to which woodland was put was for sport : in Domesday Book a park is recorded at Donyatt, and at this time there were five royal forests—Exmoor and Mendip, which were probably not wooded, and Selwood, Petherton and Neroche which certainly were. Before the end of the Middle Ages the Abbot of Glastonbury had four deer-parks, the Bishop of Bath and Wells at least three, and there were many others in private hands. Timber in parks, being preserved from villagers in search of wood, became a source of profit ; deer required grass as well as shelter ; grass could be used for cattle more profitably than for deer, and gradually many parks became rich pastures. Enclosure Acts were applied to Exmoor Forest, Petherton Park, and a few woods where villagers had common rights, such as the North Wood in Baltonsborough in 1720.

The great marshlands—Sedgemoor, Brentmarsh (through which the Brue flows) and the North Marsh, had little value in early times, although on the slightly drier land along the banks of the Lower Parrett and behind the sandhills by the shore, were villages with a surprisingly large number of ploughs, working land that now is drained by ditches. We have little actual record of drainage done here in the Middle Ages, and most of the little that I have found comes from the Glastonbury surveys. From these we learn that South Moor, between Glastonbury and Butleigh, had once been a swampy alder thicket, but was dry and open enough to hunt on by the end of the fifteenth century,[1] and that the double ditch draining the moor north of Glastonbury was in existence a few years later, and Ashton Rhine, on Godney Moor, rather earlier. The conveyance of goods by water on the Axe to Bleadney, and on the Brue as far upstream as Baltonsborough, necessitated some care of waterways, but the maintenance of fishing weirs caused flooding. The recently published diary (1709–26) of Dr. Claver Morris, of Wells, describes meetings of the Commissioners of Sewers and their expeditions to view watercourses. The Court of Sewers levied a rate on the land benefiting from the erection of a " clei," (or clyce, to control the flow of water from one watercourse to another), the " throwing " of a rhine, or the widening of the watercourse under a bridge, and performed many of the functions of the modern Drainage Boards. The present drainage system was almost completed with the enclosure of the common moors by Acts of Parliament in the eighteenth and early nineteenth centuries, adding many thousand acres of pasture, and on King's Sedgemoor much useful arable land. Between Glastonbury and Burnham, the turbary land—peat-bog thick with alder, oak and birch, is gradually being worked out by cutting the turf, leaving valueless swamp, but a little of the land from which the turf has been removed is now coming back into agricultural use owing to the improved drainage of the past few years. A scheme is now under consideration for improving the drainage of the moors, to reduce flooding and to remove water from the land more quickly when flooding occurs (see above, page 26).

The Enclosure Acts also dealt with the remaining common pasture lands. On the Mendips 25,000 acres were enclosed ; for many years much corn was grown on these hills, but to-day rough grass and ruined farm-buildings reflect the change in the price of wheat. Lansdown,

---

[1] As a result of the mill the Abbots had built at Beckery, the improved watercourse between Baltonsborough and Glastonbury brought down enough mud to cover these moors to a depth of 4 feet in 600 years between Glastonbury and Street.

Broadfield Down, the Quantocks and the Exmoor commons,[1] and the Blackdowns were transferred to private ownership without, in many cases, any great change in the character of the pastures. When Exmoor Forest was enclosed, the royal allotment of 10,000 acres was sold in 1818 to John Knight, a Shropshire ironmaster, who added a further 5,000 acres to this estate by buying the allotments of other landowners. He and his son, Sir Frederick Knight, carried through the greatest piece of land improvement in Somerset in modern times, converting many thousand acres of hill bog, after failure with mixed arable farming, into improved grassland and rape pasture for sheep. Their experiments were costly; the return on their capital was small; but the improvement of the land has been permanent.[2]

The change from the corn-growing Somerset of Norman times to the green County we know to-day, was both gradual and continuous. In Norman times, when cheese was made from ewes' milk, enough meadow was required to provide hay for the plough-oxen. A comparison between the particulars given of some Glastonbury manors in Domesday Book and in the thirteenth-century surveys shows that the area of meadow was increasing. In Domesday Book, at Baltonsborough were 16 beasts and 30 acres of meadow; in the thirteenth century were pasture for 70 cows and 108 acres of meadow in demesne. A dispute about a moor near Godney, where good hay could be mown, was settled in Abbot Michael of Ambresbury's favour. In Glastonbury, which included West Pennard, the amount of meadow is entered as 60 acres in Domesday Book, as 170 acres in Roger Ford's survey (1252–61), and as 290 acres, excluding West Pennard and the " Vineyards," in Richard Bere's survey (1493–1524). The " Vineyards," in the sixteenth century, were five closes of pasture, " full of sweetness." At Porlock several closes of demesne land, pasture in the sixteenth century, lay in the open arable field in 1306; this was a result of sheep rather than of cattle farming. In the seventeenth century Cheddar cheese was manufactured, and by 1791, when Billingsley surveyed Somerset agriculture, the country north of the Mendips grew very little corn (and that badly), but was given over to grazing on the sea-marshes, hay round Bristol and Bath, and dairying elsewhere.

A few other changes in agriculture may be noted. Orchards are little mentioned in the Middle Ages—less than 2 acres in sixteenth century Porlock; the Glastonbury tenants drank ale. By 1791 they were productive from Taunton Dean to Bath, and Billingsley doubted whether the effects of too much cider were any better for the farmers than for the labourers. Some of the best orchards in the Lias Limestone district are on land that has been quarried and re-levelled (see above, page 86).

Flax and hemp were important crops until the nineteenth century on good land between Wincanton, Yeovil and Crewkerne, and in Taunton Dean. Teazels, required in quantity for finishing woollens, were extensively cultivated, when Billingsley wrote, between Wrington and Harptree.

In conclusion a note about tenures. Customary tenures, often for three lives and subject in some cases to heriot, were still common at the beginning of the nineteenth century; the " overland " in West Somerset, and other more newly enclosed land, was, from early times, let for a money rent; demesne land from the fifteenth century onward was often let for a term of years, and it was on demesne land that progressive farming became possible.

---

[1] Belonging to the parishes of Porlock, Stoke Pero, Exford, Winsford, Hawkridge, and others. " Exmoor " is used locally for a greater area than covered by the old " Forest."
[2] Orwin, C. S., *The Reclamation of Exmoor Forest*, 1929.

APPENDIX I

STATISTICAL SUMMARY

The Land Utilisation of Somerset according to the Official Statistics of the Ministry of Agriculture and Fisheries

All areas in acres.

Year	Total Area [1]	Area under Crops and Grasses	Arable Land	Permanent Grass — For Hay	Not for Hay	Rough Grazing
1866		735,604	276,916	458,688		
1867		772,095	285,629	486,466		
1868	1,047,220	777,822	284,508	493,314		
1869		795,519	277,353	518,166		
1870		792,702	293,992	498,710		
1871		802,059	296,880	505,179		
1872		804,659	296,868	507,791		
1873		817,438	295,152	522,286		
1874		825,628	288,974	536,654		
1875		834,121	290,436	208,109	335,576	
1876		839,731	289,228	187,977	362,526	
1877		841,512	286,208	555,304		
1878		849,091	282,735	566,356		
1879		850,746	272,170	578,576		
1880		854,664	262,958	591,706		
1881	1,049,815	856,317	258,159	598,158		
1882		860,244	254,229	606,015		
1883		862,090	247,382	614,708		
1884		864,307	241,512	623,233		
1885		867,469	241,512	211,245	414,712	
1886		869,710	235,627	226,588	407,495	
1887		868,361	232,170	228,215	407,976	
1888		867,488	230,127	248,368	388,983	
1889		868,987	282,667	251,680	388,640	
1890		868,721	224,784	240,025	403,912	
1891		868,940	221,529	227,808	419,603	
1892		865,084	215,992	222,588	426,504	
1893	1,042,488	862,499	211,312	192,481	458,706	
1894		863,089	212,353	247,778	402,958	45,334
1895		860,649	207,214	232,809	420,626	48,341
1896		856,091	204,057	225,549	426,485	49,284
1897	1,039,711	857,530	209,618	242,169	405,743	49,761
1898		856,631	205,561	236,729	414,341	50,383
1899		856,287	203,526	226,399	426,362	50,475
1900	1,037,231	854,538	199,879	234,469	420,190	51,004
1901		854,219	196,141	220,902	437,176	51,192
1902	1,035,038	854,362	195,340	242,099	416,923	51,031
1903		854,248	191,322	242,057	420,869	52,097
1904		854,105	185,721	243,300	425,084	52,933
1905		854,408	182,007	237,553	434,848	53,768
1906	1,035,145	854,495	179,526	247,836	427,133	53,892
1907		854,931	178,967	255,552	420,412	54,031
1908		854,015	175,655	256,360	422,000	53,917
1909		853,808	176,342	252,292	425,174	53,456
1910		853,380	171,579	255,438	426,363	54,503
1911		852,793	170,451	258,470	423,872	55,795
1912	1,034,770	850,451	172,416	269,115	408,920	58,967
1913		848,911	164,324	266,472	418,115	57,982
1914		848,541	162,398	252,236	433,907	58,349
1915		846,256	158,218	247,150	440,888	49,306
1916	1,034,776	848,520	158,523	260,694	429,303	48,952
1917		850,034	162,487	257,125	430,422	47,460
1918	1,034,766	844,757	194,622	246,644	403,491	53,362
1919		834,023	196,642	234,528	402,853	58,117
1920		815,286	188,318	247,765	379,203	53,664
1921		805,149	178,821	222,915	403,413	97,233
1922		799,426	168,188	246,074	385,164	95,745
1923	1,034,720	800,680	179,007	242,011	379,662	84,251
1924		801,328	173,095	248,598	379,635	85,631
1925		799,599	165,613	236,704	397,282	87,915
1926		799,788	164,575	239,787	395,426	88,610
1927		799,956	158,285	238,285	403,386	90,113
1928		798,859	153,048	249,601	396,210	92,266
1929	1,034,695	797,760	147,801	262,136	387,823	93,005
1930		796,340	144,096	272,270	379,974	93,392
1931	1,034,036	793,541	140,160	257,313	396,068	94,794
1932		791,113	134,580	243,833	412,700	97,063
1933		789,646	131,875	249,502	408,269	97,013
1934	1,031,148	787,648	131,269	264,136	392,243	98,298
1935		786,645	147,161	252,851	386,633	97,701
1936		782,002	129,707	247,996	404,299	98,468

[1] Including water up to 1898 inclusive.

SUMMARY OF THE LAND UTILISATION SURVEY
From Official Statistics.

	Acres	% of County
Forest and Woodland[1]	48,330	4·7
Arable	129,707	12·5
Permanent Grass	652,295	63·3
Heath and Rough Grazing	98,468	9·6
Orchards	19,516	1·9
Unaccounted for	82,832	8·0

[1] 1924 Census, with the addition of subsequent plantings by the Forestry Commission.

APPENDIX II
LIST OF SURVEYORS OF FIELD SHEETS
List of Abbreviations

S.	- School.		Dup.	-	Duplicate by.
C.S.	- Council School.		f.	-	Finished by.
C. of E.	- Church of England School.		c.	-	Checked by.

1 S.E. & 2 S.W.—Portishead C. of E., '31.

2 N.W. & N.E.—Portishead C.S., '31.

2 S.E. —Pill Boys' and Girls' SS., '33.

3 S.W., 4 S.W., S.E., 6 N.E., 9 N.E., 10 N.W., 16 N.W. & N.E.—Department of Geography, University of Bristol, '33.

4 N.W., N.E. & S.E.—Clevedon C. of E., '31.

5 N.W.—Clapton Junior C. of E., '31, Dup. Wraxall S., '31.

5 N.E.—Wraxall C. of E., '31.

5 S.W.—Nailsea S., '31, f. Somerset Rural Community Council, '34.

5 S.E. —Somerset Rural Community Council, '34.

6 N.W.—Long Ashton S., '31.

6 S.W. & 12 N.W.—Bishopsworth S., '31.

6 S.E. —Whitchurch C.S.,'31.

7 N.W. & S.W.—Keynsham C.S., '31.

7 N.E. & S.E.—Weston (Bath) C. of E. and Corston C. of E., '31.

8 N.W., S.W. & S.E.—Batheaston C. of E., '31.

9 S.E. —S. H. Reynolds, '35.

10 N.E.—Yatton C.S., '31, Dup. Yatton C. of E., '31.

10 S.E. & 18 N.E.—Sidcot S., '35.

11 N.W., S.W. & S.E.—Wrington C. of E., '32.

11 N.E. —Winford C. of E., '32.

11 S.E. —Dup. Butcombe C. of E., '32.

12 N.E. & S.E.—Stanton Drew C.S., '33.

12 S.W.—Chew Magna C. of E., f. F. J. Male, '31.

13 N.W.—Compton Dando C. of E., '31.

13 N.E.—Corston C. of E., '32.

13 S.W.—Farmborough C. of E., and Killamarsh S., '31.

14 N.W., N.E., S.W. & S.E.—Combe Down S.S., '31.

14 S.W. —Dup. South Stoke C. of E., '32.

16 S.W. & S.E.—Bleadon C. of E., '32.

17 N.W.—Banwell C.S., '32.

17 N.E. & 18 N.W.—Churchill S., '32., and Sidcot S., '35.

17 S.W. —Loxton and Christon C.SS., '32.

17 S.E. —Winscombe S., '31.

18 S.W.—Cheddar S., '31.

18 S.E. —Ubley C.S., '32.

19 N.W.—Bishop Sutton C.S., '31.

19 N.E.—Clutton C.S., '31.

19 S.W.—East Harptree C.S., '32.

19 S.E. —Farrington Gurney C. of E., '31.

20 N.W. & 21 S.W.—C. J. Goold, '35.

20 N.E.—Peasedown St. John C.S., and Camerton C. of E., '31.

20 S.W.—Paulton Wesleyan S., '31, and Welton C.S., '31.

20 S.E. —Radstock C.S., '33.

21 N.W.—Wellow C. of E., '31.

21 N.E.—Freshford C. of E., '32.

22 S.W., S.E. & 33 N.W.—B. Freeman and J. Archer, '33.

23 S.W., S.E., 33 N.E., 34 N.W., N.E., S.W., S.E., 35 N.W., N.E., S.W. & 46 N.E.—A. F. Harris, '36.

25 N.W.—Berrow S., '32.

25 N.E. & S.E.—Burnham-on-Sea C. of E., '34, and Brent Knoll S., '34.

26 N.W.—East Brent C. of E., '33, and Sidcot S., '35.

26 N.E. —Axbridge C. of E., '33.

26 S.E. —Wedmore Blackford C.S., '31.

27 N.W.—Cheddar C. of E., '32.

27 N.E. —Priddy C.S., '31.

LIST OF SURVEYORS OF FIELD SHEETS

27 S.W.—Draycott S., '31, and L. D. Stamp, '35.

28 N.W.—Chewton-Mendip C.S., '32.

28 N.E. & S.W.—T. G. Exford, '32.

28 S.E.—Binegar C. of E., '32.

29 N.W.—Chilcompton C. of E., '32.

29 N.E.—Kilmersdon S., '33.

29 S.W.—Stratton-on-the-Fosse C. of E., '32, and T. G. Exford, '33.

29 S.E.—Kilmersdon Coleford C. of E., '32.

30 N.W.—Hemington C.S., '33.

30 N.E., 31 N.W. & S.W.—Frome C. of E., '31.

30 S.W.—Dup. Frome C.S., '32.

35 S.E., 47 N.W., 48 S.E., 49 N.W., S.W., 57 S.E. & 67 N.W.—G. G. Cruickshank, '35.

36 S.W.—Watchet C. of E., '33, c. Department of Geography, King's College, '35.

36 S.E.—East Quantoxhead C.S., '32, c. Department of Geography, King's College, '35.

37 N.E. & S.E.—Stogursey C.S., '31.

37 S.E.—Dup. Stockland, Bristol S., '31.

38 N.W.—Otterhampton C.S , '31.

38 S.W.—Pawlett C.S., '31, and L. D. Stamp, '35.

38 S.E.—West Huntspill C.S., and Puriton C.S., '32.

39 N.W.—West Mark S., '31.

39 N.E.—Wedmore C.S., '33.

39 S.W.—Woolavington C.S., '34, f. L. W. C. Maidment, '35.

39 S.E. & 40 S.W.—Meare C.S., '31.

40 N.W.—Wedmore Bagley Close C. of E., '32, f. L. W. C Maidment, '34.

40 N.E.—Wookey C.S., '34.

40 S.W., S.E., 53 N.W., S.W., 54 S.E., 62 N.E., 63 N.W., N.E., S.W. & 73 N.W.—L. W. C. Maidment, '34.

41 N.W.—Wells Central S., '31, f. L. W. C. Maidment, '34.

41 N.E.—Crosscombe S., '31, f. L. W. C. Maidment, '34.

41 S.W.—North Wootton C.S., '32, f. L. W. C. Maidment, '34.

41 S.E. & 42 S.W.—Waterloo Road Boys' S., '31.

42 N.W.—Stoke St. Michael S., '32.

43 N.E.—Holy Trinity S., Frome, '31.

45 N.E. & S.E.—Exford C. of E., '32.

47 N.E.—Old Cleeve S., '31.

47 S.W.—Treborough S., '31, c. Department of Geography, King's College, '35.

48 N.W.—Williton C. of E., '32, c. Department of Geography, King's College, '35.

48 N.E.—West Quantoxhead C. of E., '31.

48 S.W.—Monksilver and Stogumber C. of E., '33, f. Department of Geography, King's College, '35.

49 N.E.—Cannington S., '34.

50 S.W.—Wembdon S., '32.

40 S.E.—Somerset Bridge S., '31.

51 N.W. & N.E.—Catcott C.S., '34, f. L. W. C. Maidment, '36.

51 S.W.—Westonzoyland S., '32, Dup. Sutton Mallet S., '32.

51 S.E.—Moorlinch C.S., '32.

52 N.W.—St. John's Boys S., '31, f. L. W. C. Maidment, '36.

52 N.E.—St. Benedict's Girls' S., '31.

52 S.W.—Walton C. of E., and Street C.S., '32.

52 S.E.—Street C.S., '33.

53 N.E.—Pilton C.S., '32.

54 N.W.—Evercreech C. of E., '32.

54 N.E.—Upton Noble S., '31, Dup. Batcombe C. of E., '32.

54 S.W. & 65 N.E.—Bruton C.S., '32.

56 N.E.—Hawkridge C. of E., '32.

57 S.W.—Dulverton C. of E., '34.

58 N.W.—Withiel Florey C.S., '31.

58 N.E.—Clatworthy S., '31.

58 S.E.—P. D. Evans, '31.

59 N.E.—Lydeard St. Lawrence C.S., '31.

59 S.E.—Lydeard St. Lawrence C.S., and Combe Florey C. of E., '31.

60 N.W.—West Bagborough C.S., '31.

60 N.E.—Enmore C. of E., and Broomfield S., '31.

60 S.W.—Bishops Lydeard S., '32.

61 N.W. & N.E.—North Petherton C.S., '33.

61 S.E.—North Newton C.S., and Lyng C.S., '31.

62 S.E.—High Ham, '31.

62 N.W.—Anon., '31.

63 S.E. & 74 N.W.—Westonzoyland S., Dup. Sutton Mallet S., f. L. W. C. Maidment, '36, Charlton Mackrell C. of E , '32.

64 N.W.—Baltonsborough C of E , '31, f L. W. C. Maidment, '34.

64 N.E. & 65 N.W.—Castle Cary Mixed S., '33.

64 S.W.—Anon., '31.

64 S.E.—Lovington S., '32.

65 S.W. & 75 N.W.—Rev. R. Moline, '32.

65 S.E.—Wincanton C. of E., '31.

66 S.W.—Wincanton C.S., '31.

67 N.E.—Dulverton C. of E., '31.

68 N.W.—C. Bower, '31.

69 N.W.—Goldsmiths College, '34.

69 N.E.—Milverton C.S., '31.

69 S.W., 71 S.W., 81 N.W., 82 S.W. & 89 N.E.—C. H. Puckett, '33.

69 S.E. & 70 S.W.—Oake C.S., '33.

70 N.E. & S.E.—Taunton Schools, '33.

70 S.W.—Bradford-on-Tome C.S., '32.

70 S.E.—Dup. Bishop's Hull Without C.S., '33.

71 N.W.—West Monkton C. of E., '32.

LIST OF SURVEYORS OF FIELD SHEETS

71 N.E. & S.E.—North Curry S., '32.

72 N.W.—Stoke St. Gregory C. of E., '33.

72 N.E. & S.E.—Huish Episcopi, Langport, and Drayton C.SS., '32.

72 S.W.—Curry Rivel S., '31.

73 N.E.—Somerton C. of E., and Somerton Monteclefe C. of E., '31.

73 S.E.—Ilchester S., '31.

74 N.E. & S.E.—Queen Camel Central S., '31.

74 N.E.—Dup. Sparkford S., '31.

74 S.E., 75 S.W. & 83 N.E.—A. Wyatt-Smith, '32.

75 N.E.—C. E. Brill and K. H. Brill, '31.

75 S.E. & 76 S.W.—Abbas and Templecombe C.S., '31.

75 S.E.—Dup. Horsington C. of E., '31.

77 N.E. & 78 N.W.—Stawley C.S., '31.

78 N.E.—D. R. Tancock, '31.

78 S.W.—Sampford Arundel C.S., '32.

78 S.E.—C. H. Haydon, '34.

79 N.W., N.E. & S.E.—Trull C. of E., '33.

79 S.E.—Dup. Pitminster Bladgon C.S., '33.

80 N.W.—West Hatch C. of E., '32, f. C. H. Puckett, '33.

80 S.W.—Staple Fitzpaine S., '31.

80 S.E.—Ashill C.S., '32.

81 S.W. & 88 N.W.—Whitelackington C.S., and Ilton C. of E., '33, f. C. H. Puckett, '33.

81 S.E.—South Petherton C.S., '32, f. C. H. Puckett, '34.

82 S.E.—Montacute C. of E., '32.

83 N.W.—Mudford C.S., '32.

83 N.E.—Marston Magna, '31, Dup. Coxton Denham, '31.

84 N.W.—Milborne Port C. of E., '31.

84 N.E. & 85 N.W.—Henstridge C. of E., '33.

84 S.W. & 92 S.E.—Milborne Port C.S., '32.

86 N.W., N.E., S.W. & S.E.—Churchstanton S., '33.

86 N.E.—Dup., Otterford C. of E., '31.

87 N.W.—Buckland St. Mary S., '31.

87 N.E.—Donyatt C.S., '32, f. C. H. Puckett, '34.

87 S.W.—Whitestaunton C. of E., '33, f. C. H. Puckett, '34.

87 S.E.—Combe St. Nicholas S., '31.

88 N.E.—Seavington C.S., '33, Dup. Loken C.S., '33.

88 S.E., 89 S.W., 92 N.E. & 93 N.W.—A. K. Mellanfield, '31.

89 N.W.—R. G. de H. Hoskyns, '34.

89 N.E.—Rev. G. A. Nicholson, '33.

89 S.W.—Crewkerne S., '31.

90 N.W.—Barwick C.S., '33.

90 S.W.—East Coker S., '33.

91 N.W. & S.W.—Chard C.S., '31.

91 S.E. & 95 N.E.—Tatworth S., '32.

92 N.W. & S.W.—Winsham C.S., '32, c. C. H. Puckett, '33.

The following sheets were surveyed by T. Stuart-Menteath in 1935-6: 10 S.W., 13 S.E., 21 S.E., 26 S.W., 27 S.E., 30 S.E., 33 S.W., S.E., 37 N.W., S.W., 38 N.E., 42 N.E., S.E., 43 N.W., S.W., S.E., 44 N.E., S.E., 45 N.W., S.W., 46 N.W., S.W., S.E., 47 S.W., S.E., 49 S.E., 50 N.W., N.E., 55 N.W., N.E., S.W., 56 N.W., S.E., 57 N.W., N.E., S.E., 58 S.W., 59 N.W., S.W., 60 S.E., 61 S.W., 62 S.W., 66 N.W., 67 S.W., S.E., 68 N.E., S.E., 70 N.W., 73 S.W., 74 S.W., 76 N.W., 79 S.W., 80 N.W., 81 N.E., 82 N.W., N.E., 83 S.W., 88 S.W., 89 S.E., 91 N.E., 93 N.E., 94 N.W.

The following sheets were completed by T. Stuart-Menteath in 1935-6: 3 S.W., 6 N.E., 11 S.W., 12 N.E., 13 N.W., N.E., 14 N.W., S.W., 17 N.E., 19 S.W., S.E., 21 N.E., 28 S.E., 29 N.W., 30 N.W., 33 N.W., 36 S.E., 38 S.W., 45 N.E., S.E., 48 S.W., 51 S.W., 52 S.W., 54 N.E., S.E., 58 S.E., 59 N.E., S.E., 61 N.W., N.E., S.W., 63 S.W., 64 S.W., S.E., 65 N.E., S.W., S.E., 68 N.W., 69 N.E., S.W., S.E., 71 S.W., 72 N.E., 73 N.E., 74 N.E., 78 N.W., 79 N.W., 83 N.W., 84 S.E., 88 N.E., 89 N.W., 90 N.W.

The following sheets were checked by T. Stuart-Menteath in 1935-6: 2 N.W., N.E., S.E., 4 S.E., 5 N.W., N.E., 6 S.W., 8 S.W., S.E., 10 N.W., N.E., 12 N.W., 14 S.W., 16 N.E., 18 N.E., 29 S.W., 30 N.E., 35 S.W., 37 S.W., 40 N.E., 48 S.E., 50 S.E., 51 N.W., 54 S.W., 56 N.E., S.E., 67 N.E., 70 N.E., 71 S.E., 72 N.W., 73 S.W., 78 S.E., 80 S.W., 86 N.W., N.E., 87 N.W., 87 S.E.

The following sheets were checked by L. D. Stamp in 1935: 6 S.E., 7 N.W., N.E., S.W., S.E., 13 N.E., 14 N.E., 17 N.W., S.W., S.E., 20 S.E., 27 N.E., S.W., 33 N.W., 37 N.E., 41 N.W., S.W., S.E., 42 N.W., S.W.

THE LAND OF BRITAIN

The Report of
The Land Utilisation Survey of Britain

EDITED BY
L. DUDLEY STAMP, B.A., D.Sc.

Part 91

CORNWALL

by

B. S. ROBERSON, B.Sc. (Econ.) (London)
Geography Master, The Grammar School, Tottenham

with an historical section by

L. DUDLEY STAMP, B.A., D.Sc.

and an appendix on Scilly by

MARYELLEN MORTIMER, B.Sc. (Econ.)

LONDON
PUBLISHED FOR THE SURVEY BY GEOGRAPHICAL PUBLICATIONS LTD
1941

NOTE

The publication of this Report has been made possible
by a grant from the Pilgrim Trust

The appropriate one-inch coloured map to accompany this Report is Sheet 146 (Land's End and Lizard, including the Isles of Scilly), price 4s. each (flat, unmounted) or 5s. (folded and mounted).

The remainder of the county has not been published on the One-inch scale but the manuscript maps have been reproduced on one-quarter the scale as coloured plates in this Report. Additional copies are available, price 9d. each. There are three plates involved : Sheet 127 (covering the extreme north of the county) ; Sheet 136–143 (covering the centre) and Sheet 137–144 (covering the east).

Maps and Report are obtainable from
THE LAND UTILISATION SURVEY OF BRITAIN

London School of Economics, Houghton Street, London, W.C.2
or c/o G. W. Bacon & Co., Ltd., Norwich Street, Fetter Lane, E.C.4

Part 91

CORNWALL

By

B. S. ROBERSON, B.Sc. (Econ.) (London)

Geography Master, The Grammar School, Tottenham

I. EDITORIAL INTRODUCTION

THE Survey of the County of Cornwall presented a combination of difficulties which rendered the work here as arduous, if not more arduous, as in any county in the whole kingdom. The distinction of the land categories is rendered difficult by the system of irregular long-ley so that it is sometimes almost impossible to distinguish between permanent and rotation grass ; as Mr. Roberson explains in this report, the " moorland edge " is a movable line which fluctuates with economic conditions and there is every gradation from land once improved to untouched moorland. Especially in the south the " pocket-handkerchief " fields often averaging only an acre or two in area are surrounded by high earth and stone banks surmounted by hedges and where this layout is found on level plateau surfaces the survey took five and six times as long to carry out as in more normal open country.

The county is a large one—roughly 300 quarter sheets of the six-inch maps—and in many parts is sparsely populated. The work began in May, 1931, when Mr. F. R. Pascoe, then Secretary for Education, promised the support of his Committee, and a complete set of field maps was ordered. Local volunteers came forward and undertook about a third of the county, but, despite the strenuous help and encouragement of Mr. Harold W. Pitt of the Training College, Truro (and by Mr. W. C. Primmer who succeeded him), the task proved too difficult in many cases and the work proceeded slowly despite some fine results from scattered areas. It became apparent that the survey could best be carried out by academically trained geographers, with field experience in other parts of the country. It has been stated on many occasions that the Land Utilisation Survey could never have been completed save for the untiring efforts of a band of volunteers, mostly graduates of the University of London who had passed through the Geography Department of King's College and the London School of Economics, and it was to them that the survey of Cornwall was eventually entrusted.

Following the early policy of publishing representative One-inch sheets from varied parts of the country, it was decided to complete and publish the large sheet 146 (Land's End and the Lizard, including the Scilly Isles). The Camborne area was surveyed by Dr. E. H. Davison of the Camborne School of Mines and certain areas had been covered by the schools. Led by Dr. Willatts, the remainder was surveyed and the whole checked in the summer of 1933 by R. F. C. Cropper, W. C. Donithorn, B.A., C. E. Fitchett, B.A., G. M. Hines, B.Sc., E. F. Mills, B.Sc., Miss W. A. Obendorf, B.A., C. H. Puckett, B.Sc., B. S. Roberson, B.Sc. (Econ.), and G. W.

Shaw, B.A. The Scilly Isles were covered by Messrs. Roberson and Shaw. The One-inch sheet was reduced in manuscript by C. J. C. Ewing, M.Sc., and published in 1935.

With the publication of this sheet, the work on the others was attacked again. In the heart of the county Miss Da Silva (also formerly of King's College) and Miss Cruickshank, who has helped in many counties, worked round Newquay and in August, 1935, most of the remaining sheets were undertaken by Messrs. H. F. Bew, B. S. Roberson, B. C. Heppel and Miss M. B. A. Young. In 1937 I completed the checking and revision.

On the Cornish half of the Sheet 144 (Plymouth) a large part was covered by Miss D. M. Parish, B.A., The Grammar School, Liskeard (formerly of King's College), whilst other parties from London, led by S. F. Wells, B.A. and J. May, B.A. (1936) and by J. Allchin (1937), covered most of the remainder. They were helped by Miss M. F. Hume of Saltash and other residents.

The northern prologation of the county, lying on Sheet 127, was surveyed by Mr. H. H. Griffin (Kilkhampton), Mr. G. S. Campbell (Launceston College) and the remainder by myself, the whole being checked and revised in 1938.

In the north of the County, lying on Sheets 136 and 137, great help was received from Mr. G. S. Campbell of Launceston College and a number of local schools helped. The remainder— the greater part—was surveyed in 1937 (completed 1938) by London parties, including Messrs. B. C. Heppel, B. W. Thompson, B. S. Roberson, D. A. Allen, J. Allchin, A. C. Black and H. F. Bew, and Miss D. M. Parish. I checked and completed some areas difficult of access in 1938.

It will be seen that, with the exception of the Land's End sheet (1933) the survey refers to the years 1937–1938. It will also be noticed that Mr. Roberson, who undertook this report, has been associated continuously with the field work since 1933 and with all parts of the county. Having combined a study of geography and economics in his University career at the London School of Economics he is particularly well qualified to examine the land utilisation from more than one angle and this he has done in the present Report. Mrs. Roberson is of an old Scillonian family and one long associated with the flower industry. Not only has she been able to introduce her husband to many phases of life in the county but has also contributed a valuable Appendix on the Scilly Isles.

Since I became a resident—at least part time—of the county some years ago, I have naturally been personally much interested in this Report which, incidentally, has been edited from the Survey's war-time headquarters in Cornwall.

The author has asked that his thanks should be recorded to the many farmers in all parts of the county who have so willingly given full details of their farms. He mentions particularly his gratitude to Messrs. Stephen Lewis and Lewis Hicks of St. Agnes, Scilly, from whom he has learnt much of flower farming in the past ten years and who have provided many helpful introductions on the mainland. Captain R. H. Hall of Hamatethy, St. Breward supplied much of the information about Bodmin Moor and throughout Mr. Alexander Gregg, County Agricultural Organiser, Mr. R. Abbiss, County Horticultural Officer and Mr. G. S. Campbell of Launceston College, rendered invaluable assistance. Our thanks are also due to the Meteorological Office for reviewing the section on climate and to the Ministry of Agriculture and Fisheries for the detailed statistics for 1936 used in the construction of the text figures. Fig. 23 was prepared, after extensive field studies, by Mr. G. M. Hines and Dr. E. C. Willatts in 1933.

L. D. S.

TABLE OF CONTENTS

II. AN OUTLINE OF THE GEOGRAPHICAL BACKGROUND

A. GEOLOGY AND RELIEF

THE greater part of the Cornish Peninsula is developed on Carboniferous and Devonian slates, shales, and grits, with intrusions of varying size of igneous rock. With the exception of the highlands which coincide with the outcrops of the granite masses, however, the solid geology is little reflected in the physiography of the county. There is little difference in either topography or soils between the various series of the old sediments, with the result that the landscape of Cornwall, apart from the granite masses, has a marked uniformity throughout. The most important element in the topography of the county is the succession of platforms, largely old marine denudation surfaces, now found at varying elevations above sea level and from the surface of which occasional higher hills rise as monadnocks. Among the more important plateau surfaces which thus result are those at 1,000, 750 and 430 feet above sea level. Much of West and West-Central Cornwall is rather lower, with a general level between 200 and 300 feet. The plateau surfaces reach the sea in magnificent cliffs for which Cornwall is famous and which are interrupted only at infrequent intervals by tracts of sand dunes. All these plateaus have deeply incised rivers and streams. There are thus no major alluvial lowlands, but many exposed areas (an important point in this maritime county) and many steep valley sides, features which are all reflected in the land use. " Generally, the physical characteristics of the area can be summed up in the statement that it is a region of deep narrow V-shaped valleys, alternating with flat-topped interfluves which rise in step-like formations to the east."[1]

It follows naturally from the shape of Cornwall that there is no great river system and no large rivers. The Tamar, flowing in its deeply incised valley, forms the eastern boundary of the County, and the steep, sunny, sheltered slopes of its west banks provide sites for the orchards of south-east Cornwall. Its longest tributary, flowing in a similar type of valley, is the Lynher. The Fowey and Camel rivers both rise in or near Bodmin Moor and flow southwards, the former, after an east to west course, making its way to the south coast, the latter turning north to reach the sea in the Padstow Estuary. The steep slopes of the valley sides of these rivers, particularly in the middle course of the Fowey, are clothed with the only considerable areas of woodland in the County, if one excludes recent planting. The valleys of the right bank tributaries of the Fowey, and those of similar streams draining to the coast south of Bodmin Moor, are also strikingly wooded.

So far as agriculture is concerned, a much more important part is played by the rias which cut into the coast, and bring maritime influences, already strong, farther inland. The Helford River, the Fal, and the lower Tamar, are the chief examples. The estuary on the north coast, at Padstow, is of comparable size, but being exposed to the north does not give rise to the special crops which are found neighbouring the southern ones.

The granite masses play the chief part in forming the higher relief features of the county. In the east, Bodmin Moor dominates the relief, and produces a considerable climatic effect, shown by the contrast between the bleaker areas of the northern slopes (the Davidstow–Otterham district) and in the milder lands to the south and east. Hensbarrow Down on the St. Austell

[1] Balchin, W. G. V., " The Erosion Surfaces of North Cornwall." *Geog. Jour.* July, 1937.

410

granite to the south-west (highest point 1,026 feet) is lower, smaller and more settled, and forms a smaller obstacle to communications. Pasture and even arable land has made a considerably greater penetration upon it than upon Bodmin. A minor relief feature of east Cornwall is the isolated mass of Kit Hill (1,091 feet), and in mid-Cornwall, St. Breock Down (700 feet), is developed on the Staddon Grit. Both of these show a high proportion of moorland. Also noteworthy is the northward extension of the high ground of the Bodmin mass to form Davidstow

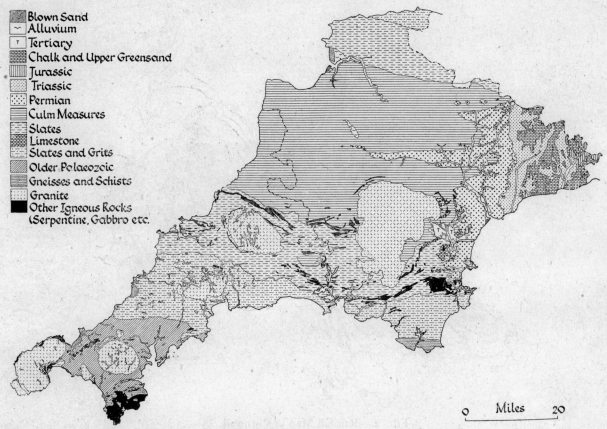

FIG. 1.—Geological Sketch Map of Devon and Cornwall.

Moor and the high area between Tintagel and Boscastle, which also rises to 1,000 feet, but which is characterised by an almost complete cover of permanent pasture and very little arable land.

The remaining granite masses form less conspicuous relief features. The mass south of Camborne-Redruth, with its highest point Carnmenellis (819 feet), and its detached portions at Carn Brea, Carn Math, and Tregonning Hill, can only be distinguished on the Land Utilisation Map by small patches of heathland or moorland. The St. Ives–Land's End granite mass is distinguished as a relief feature only to the north-west, where it rises sharply above the clearly marked platform, between 300 and 400 feet high, which runs from St. Ives to Land's End.

The area of pre-Cambrian rocks of the Lizard Peninsula forms a low plateau 300 feet high, not greatly dissimilar physically from the areas underlain by sedimentary rocks. The distinguishing feature is a large intrusion of serpentine which affords very little soil and so gives rise to the open dreary stretch of Goonhilly Downs. Scilly, a drowned granite mass, forms a unique region which will be considered separately.

No rocks of any importance younger than the Devonian and Carboniferous occur in Cornwall, with the exception of certain very recent deposits. These are areas of blown sand, practically negative from the point of view of agriculture ; the largest are at Hayle and Penhale, and smaller ones occur at Constantine and Rock. It follows from the rejuvenated river system that there

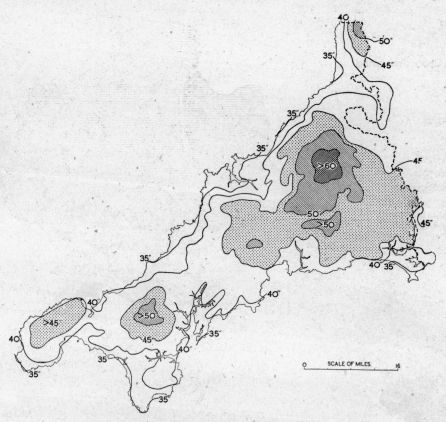

Fig. 2.—Rainfall Map of Cornwall.
Based on information supplied by the Air Ministry,
Meteorological Office, British Rainfall Organisation.

are no large areas of alluvium, though the small tracts near Gulval and the St. Erth beds of Pliocene age play an important part in the soils of the Penzance market-gardening region. Further, recent subsidence has converted old river valleys into marine inlets or rias.

B. CLIMATE

Cornwall is the most southerly county of Great Britain, and the most westerly of England, lying almost exactly between latitudes 50° and 51° North, and longitudes 4° and 6° West. It projects south-westwards into the large gulf of the Atlantic between southern Ireland and Brittany, and is thus the county of England most strongly subject to maritime influences.

Its shape increases the effect of its position. The greater part of its boundary is sea coast and the long inlets already mentioned increase the length of the coastline. Only on one side, for some forty miles, is Cornwall adjacent to a land mass; and it is so narrow that west of Bodmin no part is over ten miles from the sea. Well over half the county is less than five miles from the sea or a large estuary, and only about one eighth is over ten miles. The area which is farthest

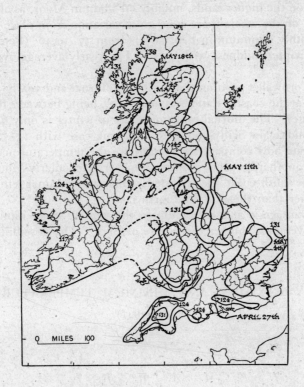

FIG. 3.—Average Floral Isophenes (35 years 1891–1925).

This map is based on that in the Phenological Report (1934) in the *Quarterly Journal of the Meteorological Society* (1935). It shows that along the sheltered south Cornish coast the average flowering date for 12 selected plants is before April 27th, compared with May 4th for London. In making the observations on which this map is based, twelve wild flowers common and widely distributed in Britain were chosen and volunteers all over the country have noted their earliest flowering dates over a period of 35 years.

from the sea includes, as it happens, about half of Bodmin Moor, which is also the most elevated portion of the county.

There are ample meteorological data to indicate the climate of Cornwall, and these are appended. With the one exception of Altarnun, however, the stations are on or near the coast, but with the peculiar shape of the county, differences inland cannot be more than a degree or so, except where temperatures are modified by height. Bodmin Moor is some four or five degrees cooler than the rest of Cornwall, both in summer and winter.

Temperatures

The maritime influence is shown in several ways; there is first the typically maritime phenomenon of " seasonal lag "—the coldest month is in every case February, and the warmest August. February is, on the average of 1906–35, colder than January, and August about half a degree warmer than July.

Over the whole of the county the average maximum temperatures for August on the coast are from 65° to 68°; on the higher lands, notably on Bodmin Moor, as already mentioned, they are slightly lower, but on the whole there is no great variation from place to place.

The average monthly minimum in February is from 37° to 40° (Penzance 41°), with Scilly showing the extreme winter mildness with 45·5°. The yearly average over the whole county is between 50° and 52°.

It follows from Cornwall's position that both the diurnal and yearly ranges are small. The average diurnal range at the coastal stations is about 10°, being between 10° and 12° in summer, and 8° and 10° in winter. The diurnal range of Scilly in winter is only 6°. The average yearly range is 17° to 18°, and again Scilly shows the extreme case with 15°.

The figures indicate how comparatively slight are the temperature conditions between one part of the county and another, but the south-west corner, particularly Mount's Bay, and, to a less extent, the whole of the south-coast, are favoured, winter and summer temperatures being on the average about 2° higher than those of the north coast.

This climatic advantage is at a maximum in the winter, when minimum temperatures at Penzance are on the average 4° higher than those of Bude. The possibility of frost is therefore much less.

MEAN MONTHLY MAXIMUM AND MINIMUM TEMPERATURES IN DEGREES

(Fahrenheit)

Station	Height above sea level		J.	F.	M.	A.	M.	J.	Jy.	A.	S.	O.	N.	D.	Year
Penzance	54	Max.	49·0	49·1	51·1	54·6	59·7	63·9	67·1	67·6	64·6	58·9	53·1	50·3	57·4
		Min.	41·4	41·1	41·5	43·9	48·7	52·6	56·0	56·4	54·1	49·7	44·7	42·7	47·7
Falmouth	167	Max.	47·7	47·8	49·7	53·3	58·7	63·1	66·5	66·7	63·3	57·7	51·9	48·9	56·3
		Min.	39·9	39·5	39·9	42·5	47·7	51·6	55·2	55·4	52·8	48·1	43·2	41·1	46·4
Fowey .	51	Max.	49·1	49·2	51·5	55·4	60·6	65·4	68·2	68·0	65·3	59·4	52·7	50·1	57·9
		Min.	39·3	38·6	39·2	41·6	46·9	50·9	54·8	54·5	51·7	47·4	41·4	40·0	45·5
Newquay	190	Max.	47·4	47·3	48·9	52·0	57·7	61·4	64·7	65·3	62·8	57·4	51·5	48·6	55·4
		Min.	39·6	38·8	39·4	42·3	47·1	51·2	55·1	55·5	52·8	48·1	42·9	40·8	46·1
Bude .	50	Max.	47·9	47·6	50·0	53·2	59·3	63·6	65·9	66·5	64·4	57·8	51·7	48·5	56·4
		Min.	38·3	37·2	38·4	41·9	46·1	50·8	54·4	54·9	51·6	46·7	41·4	38·7	45·0
Kew .	92	Max.	44·9	45·7	49·5	54·5	63·1	67·8	71·1	70·1	65·2	57·5	48·9	45·7	57·0
		Min.	36·0	35·6	36·7	39·8	46·4	51·1	54·9	54·3	49·9	44·5	38·7	37·2	43·8

MEAN MONTHLY TEMPERATURES (°F)[1]

Station	J.	F.	M.	A.	M.	J.	Jy.	A.	S.	O.	N.	D.	Year
Penzance . .	45·2	45·1	46·3	49·3	54·2	58·3	61·5	62·0	59·3	54·3	48·9	46·5	52·5
Falmouth . .	43·8	43·7	44·8	47·9	53·2	57·3	60·8	61·1	58·1	52·9	47·5	45·0	51·3
Fowey . . .	44·2	43·9	45·3	48·5	53·7	58·1	61·5	61·3	58·5	53·4	47·1	45·1	51·7
Newquay . .	43·5	43·1	44·1	47·1	52·4	56·3	59·9	60·4	57·8	52·7	47·2	44·7	50·7
Bude . . .	43·1	42·4	44·2	47·5	52·7	57·2	60·1	60·7	58·0	52·3	46·5	43·6	50·7
Kew . . .	40·5	40·7	43·1	47·1	54·7	59·5	63·0	62·2	57·7	57·0	43·8	41·5	50·4

Rainfall

The bulk of the county has about 40 inches of rain a year. Coastal positions are again favoured, most of the land within two or three miles of the coast having rather less. The granite uplands get appreciably more, the St. Ives–Land's End moors being noticeable in the west with over 40 inches, and Bodmin Moor in the east having over 60 inches. Scilly, low-lying and causing less uplift to rain-bearing winds, has only 32 inches.

The rainfall regime is also clearly maritime. Winter, of course, is the wettest period, and three-fifths of the rain falls in the period from October to March. The months of April, May and June are markedly drier, most places having 2 inches to 3 inches in these months; there is a steady rise to a December maximum, of 4 inches to 6 inches, with a secondary dry period in September (2½ inches—3 inches) and a secondary maximum in October.

RAINFALL (IN INCHES)[2]

Station	Height in feet	J.	F.	M.	A.	M.	J.	Jy.	A.	S.	O.	N.	D.	Total
Penzance .	55	3·8	3·3	3·2	2·4	2·2	2·2	2·7	3·2	2·9	4·7	4·6	5·7	41
Falmouth .	167	4·2	3·7	3·5	2·6	2·2	2·3	2·8	3·2	2·9	5·0	4·8	6·3	44
St. Austell .	300	4·3	3·8	3·4	2·8	2·4	2·6	3·3	3·6	3·2	5·3	4·9	6·1	46
Devonport .	20	3·3	2·9	2·9	2·3	2·1	2·2	2·7	3·0	2·5	4·0	3·7	5·0	37
Newquay .	190	3·0	2·6	2·4	2·0	1·6	2·0	2·3	2·6	2·7	4·0	3·6	4·3	33
Bude .	16	3·0	2·5	2·4	1·9	1·8	2·0	2·5	2·8	2·5	4·0	3·6	4·4	33
Callington .	450	4·1	3·5	3·3	2·6	2·5	2·5	3·4	3·7	3·0	4·8	4·6	5·7	44
Altarnun .	620	6·0	5·6	4·7	3·1	3·0	3·1	3·8	4·7	3·9	6·8	6·2	8·1	59
Kew . .	92	1·7	1·5	1·7	1·4	1·7	2·1	2·1	2·2	1·9	2·7	2·2	2·3	24

Sunshine

One would expect a maritime county to have less sunshine than other parts of England,

[1] From *Averages of Temperature*, M.O. 407 (Meteorological Office).
[2] 1881–1915, from the *Book of Normals*, M.O. 236 (Meteorological Office).

but Cornwall compares very favourably with them in this respect, having only slightly less sunshine than the correctly described sunny South Coast. In addition, the many sheltered hill-sides of the county give a favourable aspect, particularly in the case of the Tamar orchards. It has been seen from personal observations how cloud conditions often exist inland when the coast is clear, and the cloud-capped tors of Bodmin are a very common sight in summer, when other lands are in sunshine. On the other hand drifting sea mists round the coasts are common and cut down the sunshine average.

SUNSHINE. AVERAGE NUMBER OF HOURS PER DAY[1]

Station	J.	F.	M.	A.	M.	J.	Jy.	A.	S.	O.	N.	D.
Gulval	1·94	3·05	4·48	5·79	6·29	8·19	6·79	6·35	5·26	3·76	2·47	1·67
Newquay	1·91	2·88	4·45	5·96	6·63	7·42	6·65	6·16	5·14	3·68	2·50	1·67
Bude	1·92	2·88	4·45	5·90	6·38	7·54	6·33	5·81	5·00	3·53	2·47	1·76
Kew	1·41	2·16	3·49	4·87	6·40	6·76	6·25	5·91	4·88	3·10	1·77	1·21

Wind

Such mild conditions have their drawback. Its position, thrust out into the Atlantic, and its lack of sheltering highland, gives Cornwall the most exposed conditions in England. Shelter from the prevailing westerly winds becomes a factor of paramount importance ; the best lands are sheltered. Flower fields and farm buildings in all cases tuck themselves into folds in the ground as best they can, and houses are always solidly built. Shelter plantations, however, are rare, though there are a few even on Bodmin Moor. Their rarity may be due to the difficulty of getting trees firmly established ; strong winds appear to cause such loss of moisture through transpiration that trees planted in west Cornwall are often thought to have died of drought. The following figures, compared with those for Kew, speak for themselves :—

Station	Height above sea-level feet	Hours duration of wind						Highest hourly wind	Direction	Highest gust
		Over 39 m.p.h.	25–38 m.p.h.	13–24 m.p.h.	4–12 m.p.h.	0–3 m.p.h.	No Record			
Scilly	230	160	1,718	4,140	2,410	329	3	59	W. by S.	88
Lizard	315	210	1,424	3,693	2,729	687	17	62	S.W. by W.	90
Falmouth	256	203	1,259	3,154	3,164	934	46	60	S.W.	88
Kew	92	0	60	1,917	4,926	1,662	0	32	—	63

These figures are averages of the records of the last ten years ; in the case of the Lizard, of the last five years.

[1] From *Averages of Bright Sunshine for periods ending* 1935, M.O. 408 (Meteorological Office).

C. SOILS

No soil survey of Cornwall has yet been made, though soil conditions in the West of England are dealt with at Seale Hayne College, Newton Abbot. The following brief description is based on reports of field surveyors, verbal descriptions of farmers, and the writer's observations. There is actually remarkably little to add to the observations and descriptions of Borlase made nearly two centuries ago and quoted below. (p. 458.)

Cornwall was outside the area covered by the ice sheets of the Great Ice Age, so that the usual drift deposits of other parts of the country are absent.

Two broad classifications can be made. On the granite lands is a light black peaty loam, which when drained and cultivated gives quite good results. On the untilled areas of badly drained moorland, this becomes very acid, and in places on Bodmin is true peat moor, underlaid by sand ; six feet is an average depth, and peat cut from the surface is ready in a fortnight.[1]

The ancient shales and slates break down into a fairly fertile brown soil, usually a medium loam, with a few shaly stones, and sometimes a heavier clay. Towards Devon the soils are richer, redder, and heavier. Often these soils do not drain well, and many farmers speak of their tendency to get boggy and cut up in winter ; it is partly for this reason that cattle are brought in during the winter.

Cornwall has one natural disadvantage, and one great advantage, in this matter. The heavy rainfall causes constant leaching, and the effect of this is specially felt on the lighter soils. Most of the coastal sands and sand dunes, however, are rich in limestone shells, and the carting and spreading of this sand has long been important and the sand has for long ranked with seaweed as a fertiliser. It serves a double purpose by lightening heavy soils, and by supplying lime.

In a county where so much of the land is within easy reach of the coast, many farmers can fetch the sand supplies with their own haulage, which is thus the only cost.

[1] Malin, J. W., *The Bodmin Moors*. Methuen, 1936.

III. LAND UTILISATION IN CORNWALL

A. ARABLE LAND AND PERMANENT GRASS

IT must be emphasised that apart from the areas of moorland and sand dune, there are no marked differences in the types of land use from one part of the county to another. Over most of the area, heathland, wasteland, woodland and gardens take up a very small proportion of the land surface, and the chief aspect of land use is the relationship between arable and grassland. For this reason the two are dealt with together in this section. In the county as a whole, some 17

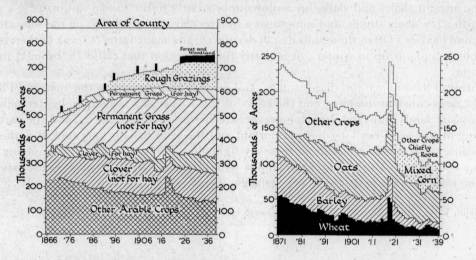

FIG. 4.—Graph showing changes in Land Use and Principal Crops in Cornwall, 1866–1938.

per cent., or 142,000 acres, is under crops, and 53 per cent., or 467,000 acres, under grass, including clover and sown grass. Of this last figure, 20 per cent. to 25 per cent. produces a hay crop, quite a usual practice being to seed a field to grass and to take a hay crop the first year. This may have caused a slight difference of practice among individual field surveyors, as this first year of grass could well be considered as arable. A better picture of Cornish agriculture is obtained, however, if the whole of the land actually under grass at any one time is regarded as grassland, though little is truly permanent. The proportion of ploughland to grass varies slightly in certain districts, as mentioned below, but these are local variations in what is fundamentally a single type of land use. (See Fig. 20 and the note on page 465.)

Individual farms over all Cornwall, except in the special areas such as Mount's Bay, have between 25 per cent. and 30 per cent. of their acreage under crops, and the remainder under long-ley or permanent grassland. This long-ley grassland, which may be under grass for from four to eight years, is typical of Cornwall as it is of many other counties on the west side of Great Britain. There are frequently present in farm leases clauses prohibiting the ploughing of certain fields.

There are, of course, grass lands which by reason of their position, on steep hill sides or river flood plains, are naturally permanent pasture in the more usual sense of the word. In Cornwall, however, the river meadow is rare, and the narrow floor of the deeply incised Cornish stream is often fit only for rough pasture. Much more common is the steep hillside which is too steep to plough and is thus under grass. Even then, a favourable southern slope may modify this rule, and good positions on a valley side will be under crops or fruit, for example, the orchards of the Tamar Valley. Because of the extensive plateau surfaces which can be ploughed and the limited areas which are truly permanent grass, the proportion of the county under crops is considerably higher than other Western counties.

In mapping the land utilisation certain difficulties arose. In Eastern England, rotation grass has of course been recorded by the field workers as arable, with the result that the published

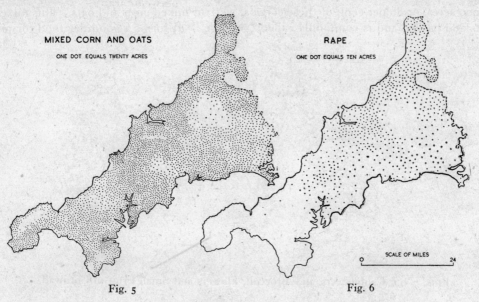

Fig. 5   Fig. 6

FIG. 5.—The Distribution of dredge or mixed corn (oats and barley) and oats.

FIG. 6.—The Distribution of Rape.

maps remain correct for long periods, except where fundamental changes have taken place in the farming practice, such as the war-time ploughing up. For the purpose of the Survey in Cornwall, long-ley grassland was recorded as grassland (M), and after four or five years, a field originally surveyed as arable (A) could quite correctly be recorded as M. As the first sheet of Cornwall (Sheet 146, Land's End) was published in 1933, there are changes between A and M in particular fields at the present time, but the important aspect, namely the proportion, remains constant. A reference to the pattern produced by the green and brown colouring of the published Land's End sheet shows this clearly. It is possible that this has caused some confusion among field workers, as the farmers of a district, when consulted, frequently regard a long-ley grass field as part of their arable land.

This proportion between A and M can be checked from the parish returns of the Ministry of Agriculture, from sample strips of the L.U.S. Map, and from sample farms, and a high degree of correlation obtained.

A very usual arrangement of the system is an eight-year rotation, giving four years of crops, and four years of grass, with certain other fields on the farm seldom being ploughed at all. Unless carefully grazed and tended, however, a field usually requires ripping at the end of four or five years, though circumstances may prevent the individual farmer from doing this, and fields may stay under grass for considerably longer periods. If a field is in good state, it is left alone ; it is the bad fields in many cases which are first ploughed. In districts such as North Cornwall, the Davidstow–Boscastle region, where the amount of arable land is markedly lower, this appears in the farming system as a longer ley of six or seven years, and also in a higher proportion of land, on each farm, which is never ploughed.

Arable Land and Crops

Of the 142,000 acres under crops in 1936, 103,000, or 72 per cent., were under cereals, and 82,000 acres, or 80 per cent. of these cereals, were of mixed corn and oats. This mixed corn is of oats and barley, and is commonly called " dredge." It forms a good dry food for pigs and

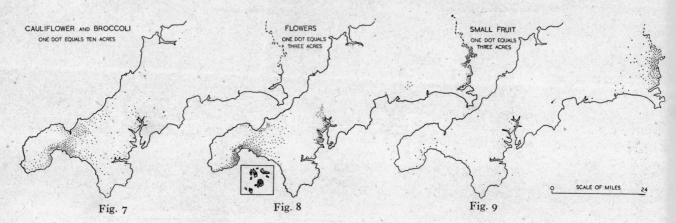

FIGS. 7–9.—Cauliflowers and Broccoli, Flowers and Small Fruit in Cornwall.

cattle and is a characteristic feature of the county. Out of a total acreage of 76,385 under " mixed corn " in England in 1938 no less than 40,936 acres were in Cornwall and 8,117 acres in neighbouring parts of Devon. Its popularity seems in the main to be the result of a local fashions and is of recent growth—especially during the Great War. It was first recorded separately in the Ministry's statistics for 1918. The mixture varies from $\frac{1}{4}$ barley–$\frac{3}{4}$ oats to $\frac{1}{2}$ barley–$\frac{1}{2}$ oats, the latter being more usual. It is claimed that there is less risk of crop failure, if the season does not suit one grain the other may flourish ; it usually gives a heavier yield than either oats or barley sown separately and 20 cwt. per acre is a fair average, with a heavy straw crop. As barley is more shallow-rooting than oats, two layers of the soil are tapped. The mixture is grown almost entirely for feeding to stock on the farm ; most farms have a small grinding machine and the resulting meal, with some cake added, is used for cattle, pigs, sheep and poultry. The acreage under dredge corn is roughly the same as that under oats. The large proportion of oats is to be expected, as the normal staple crop of a damp western and stock-rearing country. The distribution of mixed corn and oats (shown together on Fig. 5) is remarkably even over the whole area. With the exception of the moorlands, there is hardly any appreciable difference in the importance of its cultivation in various parts of the county ; there is a slight lessening of the amount of land under these crops to the north and west of the Carnmenellis region, and in the south-east of the county. The crop is frequently, especially in the west, cut just before it is fully ripe, and stacked without threshing, for winter feed. Wheat and barley occupy the other 20 per cent. of the land under cereals.

Apart from the special vegetable crops, the remainder of the arable land, the use of which is everywhere subordinated to the needs of stock, is under other fodder crops, particularly turnips, swedes and mangolds (11,000 acres) and rape (6,000 acres). In view of its usefulness as a sheep food, the latter crop (as shown in Fig. 6) is found mainly east of that line, noted below, which coincides with the change from pig-rearing to sheep-rearing.

The significance of Cornwall's mild climate is most clearly shown in the distribution of

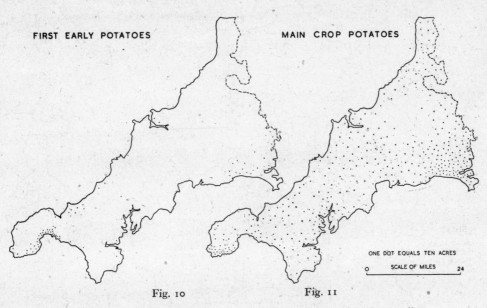

FIRST EARLY POTATOES   MAIN CROP POTATOES

ONE DOT EQUALS TEN ACRES

SCALE OF MILES

Fig. 10   Fig. 11

FIGS. 10–11.—First Earlies and Main Crop Potatoes in Cornwall.

fruit, flowers, and early vegetables. These crops overlap to a large extent, and occupy three clearly marked regions :—

    1. The Penzance–Mount's Bay area, with its extensions round the coast towards Land's End, and north-eastwards towards Hayle.

    2. The area on the west bank of the Fal.

    3. The area on the west bank of the lower Tamar.

The importance of the warmth near the sea is shown best in the case of flowers ; in Scilly, where the average February temperature is 45·5° F., only 1·4 ° warmer than Gulval, the flowers are ready about a fortnight before the same variety on the mainland. The better price obtained in the earlier period offsets the extra cost of carriage to Penzance. Scilly has some 500 acres under flowers (nearly all bulb flowers), the Mount's Bay area has 600, the Fal 250, and the Tamar 350 largely in the parishes of Calstock and St. Dominick. Shelter from the west and north-west— the direction of the dominant winds—is important, and is reflected in the grouping of the main-land flower regions on the west side of their adjacent body of water.

Although the actual area under flowers is small, they are an important cash crop. In Scilly

B

almost the sole aspect of farming is the production of flowers, but on the mainland, although there are farms almost entirely dependent on flowers for their main income, there are many who keep a small favourable piece under bulbs as an extra. The chief flowers are bulbs (daffodil and narcissus), but the increased production of anemones and violets in recent years is noteworthy.

There were 3,500 acres under cauliflower and broccoli in 1936, and 1,000 under first early

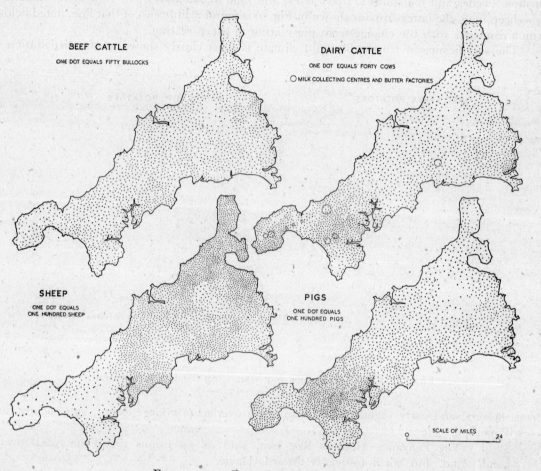

FIGS. 12–15.—Farm Animals in Cornwall.
The circles on Fig. 13, representing milk collecting centres, are proportional to the intake of milk.

potatoes. The whole of these come from the Mount's Bay region, where frequently both crops, which are complementary as regards marketing time, are obtained from the same field in one year. These crops are more fully dealt with in the regional section. Early potatoes should not be confused with main crop potatoes, which are widespread over Cornwall (see Figs. 10–11).

A somewhat similar distribution is seen in the case of small fruit (chiefly strawberries, but also raspberries, currants, and gooseberries). The two western regions produce, however, much less than the Tamar Valley, which, with its warm and sheltered inlets and hillsides, is by far the most important area.

Stock

There are some 240,000 cattle in Cornwall, of which nearly 100,000 are in milk or in calf, 270,000 sheep, and nearly 200,000 pigs. Cattle have steadily increased in importance in the last 70 years, there being only 130,000 in the county in 1871. Sheep have fallen in numbers as cattle have risen, from a maximum of 440,000 in 1875. Although there has always been a certain amount of pig rearing in Cornwall, pigs have attained their present importance only since 1918. The poultry industry is similarly of comparatively recent growth.

So far as stock is concerned, the county can be divided by a line running approximately from the Fal to St. Agnes Head. To the west of this line, are found chiefly Jersey and Guernsey cattle, which of course are almost entirely a milk-producing breed. To the east of the line are found mainly the useful dual-purpose South Devons, and also the hardier North Devons, which are primarily for beef. This line exists equally clearly in the case of pigs and poultry; there is a marked increase in their number to the west of it; the sheep, which are nearly all to the east of the line, are mainly South Devons, with some Devon Longwools.

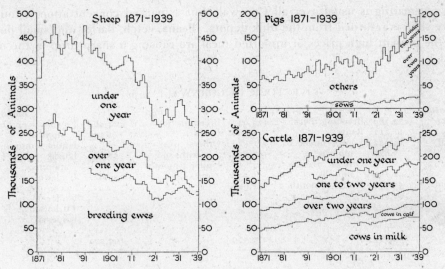

FIG. 16.—The Variation in Number of Animals in Cornwall—1871–1939.
On the Pig Graph for " years " read " months."

Dairy herds are found, of course, throughout the county, but there is a marked increase in the number of cattle in milk in the west; this coincides, as would be expected, with an increase in the number of pigs, and the importance of dairy production is shown most clearly by the map of milk collecting stations and butter factories (Fig. 13). It has been mentioned before that Cornish agriculture is a function of the mild climate, and the case of dairy cattle is no exception. The mildness of the climate, increasing towards the south-west, and, to a less extent, towards the whole of the south coast, causes a longer growing period of grass, and a shorter time when it is necessary to bring in stock for the winter. Examples of this can be seen in the various farm descriptions appended.

Although there is a slightly larger number of young cattle in the western area, coinciding with the larger number of cattle in milk, the distribution of bullocks over one year old is remarkably even. (See Fig. 12.) Nearly all farms carry some young stock, and much of the agriculture of the county is directed towards cattle fattening. In certain poorer areas, such as on

Bodmin and in the area to the north of it, all the young stock are sold as stores.   There are also rather fewer cattle for fattening in the west, the young stock being sold off for fattening in other parts.   In general, the smaller farms tend to go in for milk production, owing to the regular income this gives under the Milk Marketing Scheme.   The larger farms, and the old style farmers, prefer cattle raising for meat.   Another factor which allies the smaller holding, with its small area under crops, to milk production is the capital outlay involved in buying foodstuffs.

All over Cornwall there is a remarkable relationship between the numbers of cattle and the numbers of other animals.   In the west, the balance of the remaining stock are pigs, and in the east, sheep.   This division between west and east Cornwall is most striking in the case of sheep (Fig. 14) ;   there are very few indeed in the west.   Over Mid and South Cornwall they are important, while the most noticeable concentration is in Cornwall north of Bodmin Moor.   For example, the parish of Wendron, in the west, near Helston, has about 7,600 pigs, but only 160 sheep, while the parish of Davidstow, near Camelford, in the north, of comparable size, has 500 pigs and 5,000 sheep.   The western parish has 5,200 cattle, with nearly 3,000 in milk, while the northern one has only 1,800, with 600 in milk.

Some pig-rearing is usual over all Cornwall, but a marked concentration is found in the west, where skim is returned from the milk depots.   Beans, vetch, barley and small potatoes are also fed ;   the present high prices of imported meal are causing a sharp drop in the number of pigs reared.

LIVESTOCK IN CORNWALL 1936

Cattle		Sheep		Pigs		Poultry	
Cows in milk .	72,369	Breeding Ewes	123,947	Breeding Sows	24,464	Fowls over 6	
Cows in calf .	11,211	Rams . .	4,849	Boars . .	1,592	months .	736,308
Heifers in calf .	14,522	Lambs under 6		Others over 2		Under 6 months	877,452
Bulls . .	3,820	months .	118,598	months old .	58,094	Ducks over 6	
Others over 2		Others over 1		Under 2 months		months .	27,207
years old .	32,159	months .	5,537	old . .	109,922	Under 6 months	54,124
Between 1 and 2	53,974	Under 1 month	17,648			Geese over 6 .	6,020
Under 1 . .	47,799					Under 6	17,297
						Turkeys over 6	2,834
						Under 6 .	15,587
	235,881		270,579		194,072		1,736,829

The distribution of milk collecting centres shows the marked concentration on dairy production in Cornwall west of the Fal.   Nearly all milk sent to these depots is made into butter, though some is sent away for the liquid market.   The largest butter factory in the west is at Camborne, with an average daily intake of 7,500 gallons of milk, and a further supply from separating stations at Land's End and Helston, which have average daily intakes of 3,500 and 4,000 gallons respectively.   Two other butter factories, at Helston and Sancreed, have intakes of 6,000 gallons per day ;   the remainder are smaller, dealing with between 1,000 and 3,000 gallons.

The extra attention paid to dairying in south-east Cornwall is also shown by the collecting centre at Lostwithiel, which deals with nearly as much milk as Camborne, and the one at Saltash, which is rather smaller.   In the north, milk goes over the county boundary to a factory at Lifton, Devon.   Considerable amounts of milk from south-east Cornwall also go direct to Plymouth. Besides milk and butter, cream is produced and sold locally, particularly to summer visitors. Farms in summer often cut down their butter production, and send all their cream to the neighbouring seaside resort.

The following figures of gallons of milk marketed under the Milk Marketing Scheme in the year 1938–39, give some indication of the total output of dairy produce in Cornwall.

For liquid consumption, by wholesalers	6,778,000
For liquid consumption, by producer-retailers	2,924,000
For manufacture (largely butter) by wholesalers	13,695,000
Total	23,397,000

Most farms in Cornwall have a number of " barnyard " fowls, and their distribution is fairly even over the county. Certain areas, however, exist, where poultry keeping is thriving, and where egg and fowl production is of marked importance. The chief area is in the dairy-and-pig region of West Cornwall ; in regions 4 and 5, the extra numbers of fowls coincide exactly with that of pigs and dairy cattle. Another area where there is a concentration of poultry is the middle Tamar valley, between the south-east corner of Bodmin Moor and the river. This is partly in the Tamar Valley Fruit Region, but large numbers are also found in the adjoining parts of the Mid and East Cornwall Region. A minor area with extra numbers of fowls is behind the town of Bude.

B. HEATHLAND, MOORLAND, AND ROUGH PASTURE

There are some 112,000 acres in Cornwall which fall within this category, or 13 per cent. of the county. It occurs in clearly defined types.

The great bulk of it occurs in large continuous areas on the lands developed on granite, that is on Bodmin Moor, on Hensbarrow Downs, and on the St. Ives–Land's End moors. A smaller, separate area is found on Goonhilly Downs, on the serpentine rock of the Lizard peninsula. The St. Breock Downs between Newquay and Wadebridge are developed on sandstone. On Bodmin particularly, these moorlands provide considerable pasture for sheep, cattle, and ponies. Although underlain by granite, the Carnmenellis mass, and the southern half of the Land's End peninsula are not included in these large areas of heathland, both regions being largely under improved land. The remnant of the old moorland shows itself in a number of scattered patches. (See Wendron and St. Buryan, Fig. 17).

All these moorland areas have been nibbled away at the edges by the pasture areas of farms on the moorland fringe (but see below p. 441) ; the agricultural effect is also shown in the high numbers of sheep in the parishes surrounding Bodmin Moor. (See Fig. 14.) The disappearance of the Carnmenellis Moor is the most advanced stage of a process which can be seen in all these lands ; there are a few small farms in the very centre of Bodmin ; the Hensbarrow mass is clearly distinguishable, but has no continuous stretch of moor over two miles long, and inroads have been made on the southern side of the Land's End hump in the present generation.

In many areas poor drainage, especially on heavy soils derived from the shaley members of the Carboniferous Culm measures, is reflected in the extensive development of rushes in pasture fields. Such land grades insensibly into reedy " moors " and then into open cotton-grass (*Eriophorum*) moors. These cover wide areas in the north of the county and in adjoining parts of Devonshire.

In many cases, the sides of the young valleys are too steep for cultivation, and are not cleared of bracken or other rough vegetation. This is well seen on the sides of valleys draining to the north coast, e.g. behind Port Gaverne and Trebarwith Strand. This type of position is more usually occupied by woodland in the more sheltered south side of Cornwall.

Owing largely to the exposure to strong westerly winds comparatively little afforestation has

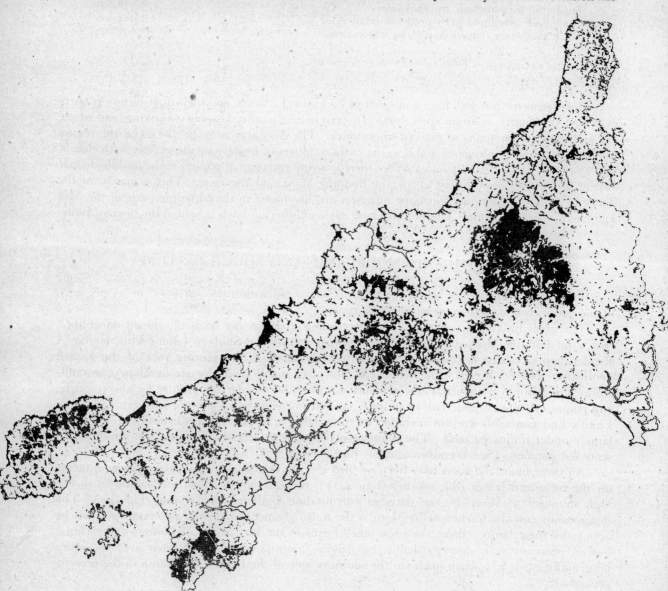

FIG. 17.—The Distribution of Moorland, Heathland and Rough Pasture in Cornwall.
Scale: 10 miles to one inch.

been attempted on the higher moorlands of Cornwall. One extensive area has been planted by the Forestry Commission on Wilsey Downs (Launceston–Camelford Road) and there are other areas on the slope of St. Breock Downs south of Wadebridge.

There is a narrow fringe of heathland, sometimes only a few yards wide, largely of heather, heath, gorse, *Senecio* and bracken, on the inaccessible portions of the cliffs round nearly all the coast of Cornwall. Where this cliff becomes steep, it is practically impossible to distinguish between heathland and true wasteland, with no agricultural value at all.

Rough marsh pasture occurs in many narrow valley lowlands, e.g. in the valley floors of the Camel, the Allen, and the Lynher, and where streams enter the estuaries there are very small areas of saltings, e.g. the estuary of the Lynher.

The areas of blown sand also form rough pasture, though this has often been improved for permanent pasture, e.g. at Hayle and Gwithian, and on Scilly the sandy regions are good bulb land. The sequence of vegetation developing on sand dunes is well seen in the extensive area at Perranporth. On the other hand many coastal areas with a light soil have been ruined by the activities of rabbits, which are also a serious menace in many inland areas.

C. FORESTS

There are no important forest lands in Cornwall. Some 29,000 acres of woodland exist, less than 3½ per cent. of the area of the county, and of this, only 14,000 acres are high forest. This area has remained remarkably constant in the past, as the following figures show :—

1871	. . . . . .	26,300 acres
1880	. . . . . .	29,500 acres
1891	. . . . . .	29,500 acres
1895	. . . . . .	30,400 acres
1913	. . . . . .	32,600 acres
1924	. . . . . .	27,985 acres

Most of this forest land is in Central Cornwall, and the wooded sides of the valleys of such rivers as the West Looe are mentioned elsewhere. The thin fringe of woodland on the east bank of the Fal is also noteworthy. There are few cases of considerable reclamation of moorland by planting, the square mile of this at Hallworthy (Wilsey Down, between Launceston and Camelford at 700 to 919 feet), being the largest. The Forestry Commission has 3,100 plantable acres, and of these 2,129 have been planted.

The comparatively small and constant area of woodland indicates that Cornwall is not one of the country's potentially important forest lands. The whole county is very exposed, and land which in other parts of Britain is suitable for planting, namely heathland and moorland, is in Cornwall even more exposed than the rest and the success of afforestation would probably depend on the gradual building up of shelter belts.

Details of woodland in Cornwall, as shown by the 1924 Census of Woodlands, published in 1928, are as follows :—

High Forest.
Conifers	3,081 acres
Hardwoods	5,022 acres
Mixed conifers and Hardwoods . .	5,100 acres
Coppice	6,183 acres
Coppice-with-standards . . .	1,930 acres
Scrub	2,580 acres
Felled or devastated	2,468 acres
Uneconomic (largely ornamental woodland)	1,621 acres
Total . . .	27,985 acres

To this should be added the recent plantings noted above.

D. GARDENS AND SETTLEMENT

The areas coloured purple on the Land Utilisation Maps are officially described as houses having gardens sufficiently large to be productive of fruit and vegetables. With the few small town centres (in red) the purple on the map thus reveals the distribution of settlement in Cornwall. Orchard land is purple-hatched, and is dealt with under the regional descriptions. The chief orchard areas adjoin the Tamar and the Fal. It is worthy of note, however, that Cornish farms usually have an apple orchard by the house, which is too small to be distinguished by separate shading on the reduced maps printed with this Report, or even on the One-inch map.

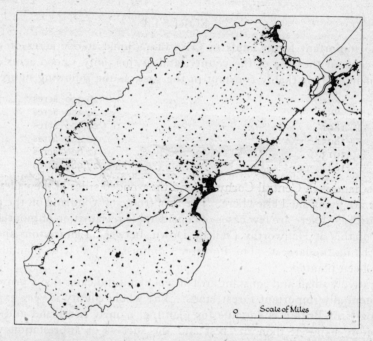

FIG. 18.—The Land's End Peninsula showing the main types of settlement in Cornwall. (a) dispersed farms ; (b) fishing villages and (c) towns with modern extensions (Penzance and St. Ives).

Types of settlement in Cornwall can be classified in three groups : towns, villages and isolated settlements. There are no large urban agglomerations in the county ; the only places remotely approaching industrial towns being the mining centres of Camborne and Redruth, and St. Austell. As the mining industry (except for the china clay associated with St. Austell) has long passed its maximum activity, the twin towns of Camborne and Redruth show little tendency to expand, and so are not typical of modern urban settlements. Linked with Camborne–Redruth, however, and also resulting from the former mining industry, is a considerable area of scattered settlements in the neighbourhood, extending north and east almost to Truro and recently expanding. The only other town areas of any size are Penzance, Falmouth, Newquay, Bodmin, Truro, Saltash, and Launceston. The first three have old harbour nuclei and modern expansions associated with their development as seaside resorts. Bodmin and Truro share the honours of county town ; the latter with its late nineteenth century cathedral growing at the expense of the former.

There is also a group of smaller towns, which act as local market centres, such as Helston, Wadebridge, Lostwithiel, Liskeard and Camelford, and fishing ports which are also pleasure resorts, such as Looe, Polperro, St. Ives, and Padstow. Bude in the north came into being in the early part of the last century at the seaward entrance to the now disused canal to Launceston : the sea-lock is still used but the later development is essential that of a seaside resort. True village settlements are few in Cornwall ; the most typical are fishing villages, closely packed around a small harbour, e.g. Mevagissey, Port Isaac, Mousehole, Boscastle and many others. In very many cases these are showing signs of expansion (indicated by purple colouring without the underlying symbol for a house) owing to the tourist industry of the present day. This is frequently a disturbing feature. There are many cases of land shown as " garden," which indicates the presence of holiday bungalows, a phenomenon more striking in other parts of England, but which has appeared in the last fifteen years with the development of motor traffic. The configuration of the Cornish coast in many cases hides these from the passing traveller,

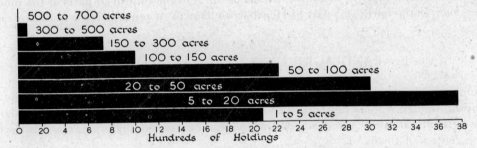

FIG. 19.—Size of Holdings in Cornwall.

but the Land Utilisation Survey reveals this growing coastal fringe notably near Looe, Porthleven, Gwithian, Polzeath, and many other places.

A detailed example of this phenomenon is found to the north of the Padstow Estuary, around the former villages of Polzeath, Trebetherick, Rock, and Stoptide. Rock and Polzeath were very small harbours, the others were mere hamlets. All are now rapidly expanding with " holiday houses," often built by speculative builders, without the slightest regard for either the scenic beauties they spoil or for the architectural atrocities they produce. Rock has now some attempt at planning ; the others, particularly Polzeath, straggle untidily along the cliffs. In some few cases the houses are built on moderately good farm land ; parts of Polzeath are on heathland or sand dunes, Trebetherick is on farmland or marshy pasture, Rock is on blown sand (though a much larger area of sand dune nearby, a golf course, is being avoided) and Stoptide is on farm or marsh land. The settlements are purely for summer residence, there being hardly any village nuclei. Rock, the oldest settlement, directly opposite Padstow, has a church and farm away from the new village, which straggles along the hillside between the public house and the older cottages. Trebetherick is simply a crossroad, with one general shop and a garage. Polzeath exemplifies this type of settlement best, as it has a good sandy and sheltered beach. It now consists of a collection of garages, tea rooms, a post office and general stores, a row of showy Edwardian terrace houses and numbers of modern bungalows. The terrace houses reflect changing tastes : they are now out of favour and frequently unoccupied. Singularly blessed by

Nature in the beauties of its coastal scenery, Cornwall too frequently exhibits man's depredations at their worst.

With a few exceptions, the rest of the settlement is either un-nucleated or hamletted, and occurs very evenly spread over the county. There are inevitably small clusters at cross-roads, and perhaps half-a-dozen houses round the parish church, but nothing approaching the agricultural village of south-east England. This is in part a reflection of the small size of holdings (Fig. 19), but it should be remembered in this connection that the Feudal System was never developed strongly in Cornwall, and that the county was enclosed much earlier than the rest of England. These scattered settlements consist usually of a farmhouse, a labourer's cottage, or at most three or four houses together. The distance of each settlement from the next keeps a remarkably constant one all over Cornwall, there being from eight to twelve in any one square mile. Most farms in Cornwall are worked entirely by one man and his family, and assuming on this basis that each of the eight or twelve settlements per square mile is a farmhouse, one gets an average of 50 to 80 acres per farm, which is, in point of fact, by far the commonest size of holding in the county. In a few special areas, such as the Mount's Bay region, the Tamar Valley region, and the Camborne–Redruth district, the number of settlements per square mile rises, and in the completely moorland regions, of course, it falls to nil. On the improved parts of the moorlands, however, such as the north east part of Hensbarrow Downs, it remains close to the average.

E. LAND AGRICULTURALLY UNPRODUCTIVE

Land agriculturally unproductive occupies an exceedingly small proportion on the surface of Cornwall, though it must be remembered that the bulk of the moorland and heathland is of very low agricultural value. Land entirely unproductive agriculturally can be classified as follows:

The centres of towns.

Mine workings (mainly disused) chiefly in the neighbourhood of Camborne and Redruth.

Quarries, of which the 400 year old slate quarries of Delabole are the outstanding examples.

China clay pits and waste dumps, accounting for by far the greater part of all the waste land, and found extensively all over Hensbarrow Downs where as much as 25 per cent. of some areas may be described as waste.

IV. THE LAND USE REGIONS OF CORNWALL

Introduction

Two criteria have been taken as a basis for the division of Cornwall into land use regions. The chief, of course, is the pattern shown on the Survey's maps. In the case of Cornwall this is an insufficient basis for the division of the county into regions since, using this criterion, it is only

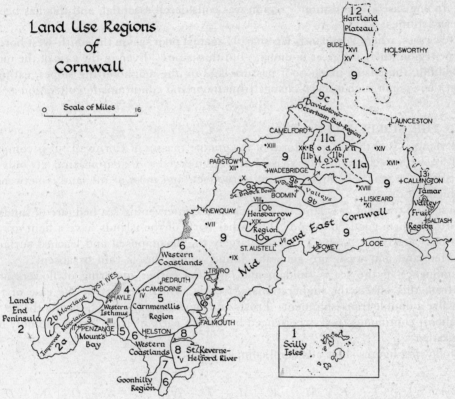

FIG. 20.—The Land Use Regions of Cornwall.
The dotted areas near the coast are extensive sand dunes.

possible to divide the county into two broad divisions, the moorlands and the tillable lands. In all cases but one, the moorlands coincide very closely with the granite bosses or the igneous complex of the Lizard, and the tillable lands with the sedimentary rocks. The tillable lands can however be sub-divided, and according to the type of farming and the attendant crops and animals. In support of this, summaries of many specimen farms are appended, and these afford details of the land use which cannot be shown on the general maps.

As Cornwall is fundamentally a county concerned with animals, types of farm and thus of land use must be considered with reference to the stock they carry, and in this connection must be stressed the line already mentioned which runs from the head of the Fal estuary to the north coast about St. Agnes, west of which one finds hardly any sheep, but a marked concentration of dairy cattle, pigs and poultry, and east of which there are few pigs but many sheep. This line is not indicated by the Survey's maps, since it marks no appreciable change in the land use pattern, though there are differences in landscape.

It marks nevertheless a very real change in the agricultural system.

There is a basic land-use pattern on the non-granite lands. It consists of a background of green, representing grassland, with small, evenly scattered patches of brown, representing land under crops, in a proportion of two or three to one. This is more fully dealt with elsewhere.

It must be emphasised that in most cases there is no hard and fast line to be drawn between the land use regions. With exceptions mentioned as they arise, one region shades gradually into the next. In one case a " transition " region was considered essential, and this has been named the Western Isthmus.

In a few cases, where good lands lap sharply against poor, as on the south-west border of the St. Keverne region, there is a clear boundary, but this is rare. Even in the case of the moorlands, such as Bodmin, there is so much poor pasture land on the neighbouring slopes, eating into its edges, that there is not such a sharp change from moorland conditions to cultivation as might be expected.

Region 1. THE SCILLY ISLES

Scilly shows a slightly different form of the granite masses of Cornwall. It is comparable in shape and size with the Carnmenellis mass, but is submerged so that approximately only 7 square miles are above the sea. The highest point is 160 feet, and most of the land is between 50 and 100 feet high.

Considerable tracts of coastland, and much of the intervening sea bed, are of sands, which, when improved, form good bulb land. The other parts of the islands have a light gravelly soil developed on " head " or " ram," which is largely the decomposed and leached surface of the granite. Moorland and waste are generally found where this is thin or absent.

The influence of the sea is fundamental, and the earlier maturing of flowers and crops resulting from this offsets the higher transport costs, which, except in the case of the main island, involve a double trans-shipment. Frosts and snow are very rare ; during the six or seven weeks of almost continuous frost experienced by Britain early in 1940, Scilly had only one week of such weather.

The following figures show a general comparison.

Station	J.	F	M.	A.	M.	J.	Jy.	A.	S.	O.	N.	D.	Year
St. Mary's, Scilly. Minimum ° F.	44·1	42·5	42·9	44·1	47·8	52·3	55·8	55·9	54·3	50·7	46·2	44·7	48·4
Gulval	40·4	39·3	39·6	42·4	46·5	51·4	55·5	54·8	52·3	47·7	43·0	40·5	46·1
St. Mary's Average ° F.	46·7	45·5	46·6	48·3	52·3	57·1	60·6	60·5	58·5	54·1	49·2	47·2	52·2
Gulval	44·9	44·1	45·5	48·4	52·7	58·8	61·6	61·0	58·4	53·2	47·9	45·0	51·7
St. Mary's Rainfall Inches	3·0	2·5	2·4	1·9	1·7	1·7	2·2	2·6	2·4	3·7	3·2	4·4	3·2
Penzance	3·8	3·3	3·2	2·4	2·2	2·2	2·7	3·2	2·9	4·7	4·6	5·7	4·1

The main climatic difficulty is wind ; trees are rare on the islands, save in very sheltered spots. Flower pieces for this reason are seldom larger than $\frac{1}{4}$ or $\frac{1}{2}$ an acre, and are bounded by temporary wooden fences, and shelter hedges of tamarisk, veronica and escalonia.

On the main island most of the land is cultivated, but on the others half or more of the land is open and mostly under heather. Nearly all the remainder is arable land, which is all for flowers, with the exception of an acre or so on each farm for potatoes, oats, and a grass field.

A typical farm is between 5 and 15 acres, run by one family and sometimes a labourer, with as much seasonal labour as can be obtained while the flowers are being picked and tied, during

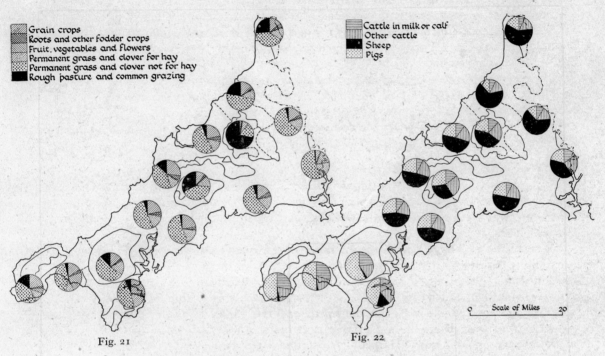

Grain crops
Roots and other fodder crops
Fruit, vegetables and flowers
Permanent grass and clover for hay
Permanent grass and clover not for hay
Rough pasture and common grazing

Cattle in milk or calf
Other cattle
Sheep
Pigs

Fig. 21   Fig. 22

FIG. 21.—The Utilisation of Land in each of the Regions of Cornwall.

FIG. 22.—The relative importance of Animals in each of the Regions of Cornwall.

The circles in these two figures represent sample parishes situated approximately in the positions covered by the circles.

January, February and March. All the land, with the exception mentioned, will be for bulbs. This provides the whole income ; a few dairy cows are also kept by most farmers for home-consumed milk and butter. War-time requirements now limit bulb-land to 75 per cent. of its former area, and as potatoes will not stand the cost of transport, incomes must fall, though lack of Channel Island competition may cause better prices.

One island, for example, has a surface area of 320 acres. Of this, 170 acres are heathland, 20 are permanent pasture, and 130 are under bulbs. There are nine farms on the island, which gives an average holding of about 14 acres. Seaweed is the chief manure, though some artificial is used ; and land will stay under bulbs for three or four years or longer before being rested by another crop. For further details of Scilly see Appendix II.

Region 2. THE LAND'S END PENINSULA

This can be divided into two parts :—

2a.   The Land's End Plateau or the Improved Moorland.
2b.   The Land's End–St. Ives Moorlands.

The Plateau or Improved Moorland

The whole of this region is underlaid by granite, and rises sharply from the sea in cliffs averaging 200 feet in height. The plateau lands are between 300 feet and 400 feet high, and the

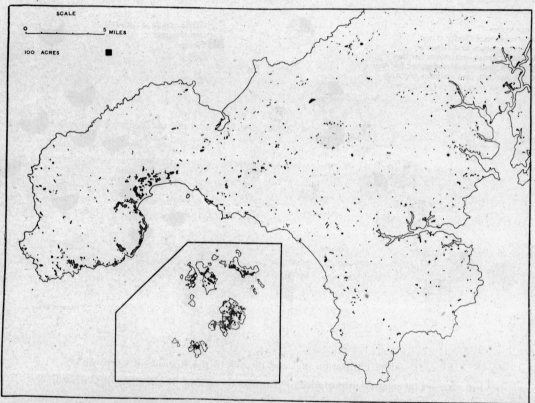

FIG. 23.—The Actual Area occupied by Bulb and Flower fields, 1933.

moorlands rise above them with a marked break of slope, particularly on the north side, to summit levels between 700 feet and 800 feet. The plateau is about four miles wide on the south, but north of St. Just, and from there to St. Ives, it narrows to a very clearly marked shelf averaging a mile in width, and in places less.

Rather more than half the land is under grass, and a little over a quarter is arable, growing oats, dredge corn, potatoes, and some broccoli. The remainder is moorland, occurring in scattered patches either where boulders at the surface make cultivation impossible or where soil is too thin. Field boundaries are of stone and earth and much of the area is characterised by the tiny size of the fields. Though cases can be found of new fields being taken into cultivation, the land being burnt over and later ploughed, the margin of cultivation, particularly on the north side, is clearly marked, and is usually found about 500 feet above sea level. The large number of geese, ducks, fowls, and even goats on the narrower northern section of the plateau (a reflection of the nearness of moorland) is worthy of note. The parish of St. Just has some 14,000 fowls, as compared with the 9,700 of Lanivet, a parish of equal size in Mid-Cornwall.

Fields of flowers and early potatoes are found in favoured spots as on the southern side of the moorland where the first rise above the plateau gives a warm southern slope.

The basis of the agriculture is the keeping of dairy cattle. They are predominantly of Channel Island breeds, with some admixture of Shorthorns and South Devons. The mild climate of the region makes possible the rearing of the more delicate breeds, as does, in general, that of the whole of Cornwall. The area is somewhat isolated, and agriculturally is in many ways a replica in miniature of the whole of west Cornwall.

Along the coast income is supplemented by summer fishing, some families making a regular summer migration to Scilly.

Specimen Farm I.

Typical of the region is the following farm, situated in the east of the parish of St. Just. The holding is of 50 acres, with over half the land under grass, and the rest under potatoes, dredge corn, and roots. At the northern edge of the farm, where formerly was moor, the owner has in the last eight years reclaimed two small patches of land, which are under bulbs, the sharp slope and south-east aspect compensating for the distance from the sea. There are about 30 cattle, with 18 to 20 cows in milk.

On the south coast itself, between Mousehole and Gwennap Head, a difference in agriculture is found. There are several sheltered inlets, e.g. at St. Levan and Lamorna, facing south-east, and here, and on steep east-facing cliffs, is a larger amount of flower and vegetable production.

The Moorland

The higher land, extending north-east from Land's End to St. Ives, is more exposed, and shows a fairly continuous stretch of moorland, although there are many " fingers " of cultivation extending into it from the south-east, up its south-easterly draining valleys. Over large areas the surface is strewn with granite boulder and cultivation is impossible. Numerous deserted mines indicate the former importance of tin and copper mining.

Region 3.   THE MOUNT'S BAY COASTAL REGION

This region in its typical development fringes the shores of Mount's Bay, from Mousehole to Perranuthnoe, and seldom extends for more than a mile inland. In this area, the most productive in Cornwall, the climatic advantages enjoyed by the county as a whole reach their maximum influence. Half the land surface is arable land, and a quarter produces early vegetables, fruit, and flowers. East of Gulval is a stretch of land about two miles long and half a mile wide, known as the Golden Mile, where the whole of the land is cropped continuously for vegetables, and where concentration on this type of farming reaches its highest point. East of Perranuthnoe, bulbs and the concentration of broccoli disappear, owing to the exposure on the western side of the Lizard Peninsula, and to the poorer soils.

Vegetable fields are seldom more than a mile from the coast, or on land over 250 feet high ; an exception is an extension of the region extending north-east towards St. Erth, across the neck of land between Mount's Bay and St. Ives Bay. Local farmers, whose holdings frequently include land in this region and land higher up, refer to " broccoli land " and " cow land," which reminds one that, although this is a highly specialised district, the basic Cornish type of agriculture is always near.

The flower crops are from bulbs, mainly narcissi, which come on the market from January to April, violets, from October to April, and in recent years, anemones, from September to April. In 1938 there were some two or three hundred acres of anemones in Cornwall. Within the region, most flowers are grown on the sheltered slopes between Newlyn and Mousehole.

The chief vegetable is broccoli, which is available from November to Mid-April, and early potatoes, which are ready by Mid-May or June. Frequently double cropping is found. Ground is often cleared of broccoli by January, a short rest given, and an early potato crop put in.

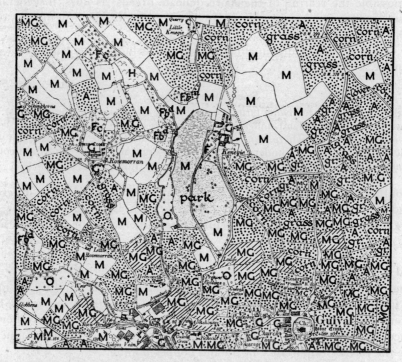

Based upon the Ordnance Survey Map with the sanction of the Controller of H.M. Stationery Office

Fig. 24.—The Land's End Peninsula.

This Map and Fig. 38 are reduced from the 6-inch field survey sheets and this illustrates the type of county found between the Land's End moorlands and Mount's Bay. The very tiny fields should be noted. Cultivated land stippled. M = pasture ; O = orchard ; MG = market garden (ruled for flowers) ; F = woodland. Scale 4 inches to one mile.

Immediately the potato crop is lifted, at the end of June, preparations are made for the planting out of the young broccoli, which are in by the end July. Fields at Gulval are said to have been cropped continuously for over a century. Certainly potatoes and broccoli have followed one another continuously for many years in the best fields.

Particularly good soil conditions favour this intensive cultivation. It is a light sandy loam, developed from Gulval to Ludgvan on alluvium. There are, however, difficulties. The high rainfall causes heavy leaching of soluble plant foods, and this must be replaced by manures. Nitrogen and potash are washed out, leaving a surplus of phosphate. The value of the land for market gardening also causes a shortage of stock in the immediate district, and consequent absence of farmyard manure. Penzance town refuse is used, being made into a compost and rotted down. Papers, of which this is partly composed, sometimes blow away, with the result that fields may look like a fair-ground after a holiday.

Manure from seaweed is sometimes available—heavy weather and spring tides favouring its accumulation on the shore—and, of course, supplies of sea-sand when required. There is however a constant competition to obtain manure to get the most out of this favoured patch of land.

As distance from Mount's Bay increases, the market gardening disappears, and the usual dairy-farming and stock rearing replaces it. Arable land in the region not under market gardening, produces oats or mixed corn. Hedges are of stone and earth, 6 feet or more high, and are frequently overgrown with bushes. Fields are small but bulb land is often subdivided even more, to obtain protection from wind, by temporary fences of wooden slats, until tamarisk hedges can grow up.

Specimen Farm II.

Locality. Behind Penzance ; 150 feet above sea level ; under 1 mile from sea ; south-east aspect.

Area and Crops. About 80 acres ; average value 50/- per acre. Half the land under crops ; 8 acres broccoli, 4 acres potatoes, 2 of flowers, remainder corn and fodder crops. 15 acres always cropped ; 50 acres broken every 5 years ; remainder once in 7 years.

Stock. 65 cattle ; 34 cross-bred Guernseys, and their young.

Notes. This is typical of farms of this area, as it includes land of varied quality. 20 acres of the best soil are on a clay subsoil, and are free of frosts in spring, 40 acres are on light black soils developed from granite, and the remainder poorer granite soils. The best land is heavily fertilised with 30 loads per acre of farmyard manure, and 15 cwt. of artificials containing potash and nitrogen. This is sufficient for the two crops per year which are often obtained. Income from early vegetables varies, but usually about one-third of the income is from these, and two-thirds from the dairy and sale of young stock.

The smaller holdings are from 10 to 40 acres, and rents of 60s. and 80s. are paid for these ; another farmer mentions 50 loads of mixed seaweed, sand, and farm-yard manure per acre, with 10 cwt. of artificial. Costs of production are high, with labour, manure, and carriage charges. Four men will be employed on 20 acres of vegetable land. Unless prices are good, there will be a loss on vegetable production, and the basic income of most farms is from their dairy.

Region 4. THE WESTERN ISTHMUS

This region is one of transition between the intensive market gardening of Mount's Bay and the general dairy-and-pig farming of the remainder of west Cornwall.

Some broccoli and early potatoes are grown throughout the region, but particularly in the west. Here, in the narrowest part of the neck of land between Mount's Bay and St. Ive's Bay, on the western shore of St. Ive's Bay, and about the Hayle estuary, climatic conditions are practically as good as on the south coast, although there is a northern aspect. Flowers, broccoli, and early potatoes are almost as important in this part as on Mount's Bay. The area is little more than an extension of the Mount's Bay coastal region, and the boundary is somewhat arbitrary. There are 70 acres of flowers and 400 of broccoli in the parish of Ludgvan, as compared with 30 of flowers and 140 of broccoli in the parish of St. Erth. The areas concerned are of comparable size, as the larger parish of Ludgvan extends on to poorer granite land. The sheltered north-east facing cliffs by St. Ive's afford good sites for flower patches, and much of the arable land about the main road from Hayle to Penzance is under potatoes and broccoli.

Over the whole region there is rather more arable land than usual, but the type of farm is mainly as in regions five and six, with the addition of early vegetable land.

Specimen Farm III.

Locality. Parish of St. Hilary ; buildings two miles from sea.

C

Area and Crops.   310 acres, but 70 roads and waste, leaving 240 tillable.   Rent £320 per annum. 40 acres broccoli, 10 acres spring cabbage, 10 acres potatoes (earlies and seconds), 70 mixed corn, all of which is for stock.

Rotation.   Early broccoli usually followed by corn, but sometimes by sugar beet, mangolds, or broccoli again ; next year is best for potatoes.   After another corn crop, land is sown to grass for four years, with a hay crop the first year.

Stock.   28 stores, and 30 fat cattle (Devons and Crossbred) ; 20 Guernsey heifers in calf, 13 cows, and 50 calves.   Some pigs.

Soil.   A medium loam, easily worked.   Much shelly sand used instead of lime, and cattle (which are

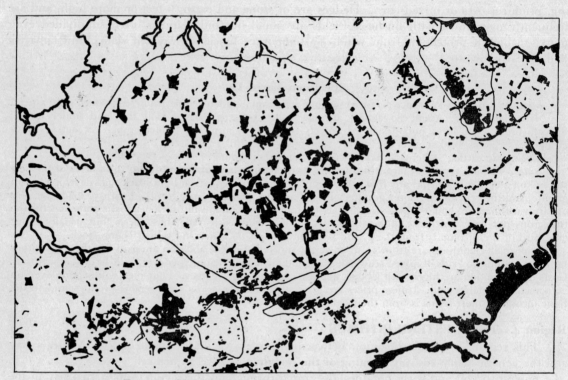

FIG. 25.—The Moorland of the Carnmenellis Granite Mass.

A good example of the successful conquest of the moorland areas of a granite mass.   Scale : 3 miles to one inch.   Granite outcrops enclosed by lines.

for this purpose housed all winter) and pigs provide farmyard manure.   When seeding to grass, 10 cwt. basic slag per acre.

Notes.   10 men, and sometimes more, permanently employed.   The land could produce two crops per year if required.   Though this farm is larger than usual, it is typical of the region, being near enough to Mount's Bay to get most of its income from early vegetables, but having a large part of its activities devoted to stock.

Region 5.   THE CARNMENELLIS REGION

This region has been named from Carnmenellis (819 feet), the highest point of the granite mass of Central West Cornwall.   It is bounded approximately by lines joining Helston–Camborne–Redruth–Truro.   It is unique, in that although a granite mass, it does not appear on the Survey's map as a solid area of moorland or heath.   The encroachment of farmland upon the moorland has reached here nearly full development ; heath or moorland remains only on high exposed hills, such as Carnmenellis, Carb Brea, Carn Marth, and Tregonning Hill, and on badly drained land. The general aspect is one of a bleak, treeless, and strongly undulating country, between 400 and 800 feet high, with many small holdings and isolated houses.

About 20 per cent. of the land is arable, a markedly lower percentage than is usual, 13 per cent. moorland, and the remainder grass, about a quarter of this grass producing a hay crop. This is the normal practice with grassland throughout the county. Of course in such an area as this, some of the grass is marginal, and is little better than rough grazing. Arable crops are dredge corn, oats, and roots, as usual. It is very striking that here staple grain crops disappear only on the completely moorland areas.

The normal rotation of the area, where heath is always near, is one of six years. Three consecutive years of arable (usually grain) are followed by three or four years grass. By the fourth year, unless carefully grazed, it relapses into heath or " croft " land ; this croft land is broken in again from time to time, and thus takes a part in the whole system.

Stock rearing (pigs and dairying) is the main aspect of the farming, though poultry-keeping is quite an important subsidiary. The diagram for Wendron (Fig. 21), shows this. There are larger numbers of cattle in milk as compared with the rest of Cornwall ; young stock are sold off and fattened more in Mid Cornwall. There is much pig-rearing, farmers using returned whey from the several butter factories of the district, besides grown fodder and bought meal.

The size of the fields in this poorer area is noticeably smaller than in mid and east Cornwall, and is related to the number of boulders. As the land was originally cleared, these were piled to make the walls. Fertility is also slightly increased by the prevention of downwash in the smaller enclosures. The soil is the light, black, peaty soil, frequently found on the granite lands.

In the north of this region a certain difference of land use is found, though not in the type of farming, through the presence of the tin-workings of the Camborne and Redruth area. Quite a considerable tract of houses with gardens appears, forming a built-up area five miles long. Parallel with this on the south side are tracts of waste land which total a thousand acres. Separate old tin workings, and quarries, account for another square mile altogether.

Specimen Farm IV.

Locality. Near Camborne. 250 feet. Northern aspect.

Area and Crops. 100 acres, nearly all in large grass fields. About 10 acres corn ; usually some oats and roots.

Stock. 28 Guernsey cows in milk, and 20–30 bullocks. 4–5 horses. 30 to 40 sheep. 2 or 3 litters of pigs.

Soil. Heavy marly soil, which easily gets wet and sticky.

Notes. Sheep tend to get foot-rot, and do not do really well. Main aspect of farm is dairying ; a milk station and butter factory is next door. Arable land is simply for a little fodder and bedding. There are large farm buildings, and cattle are brought in during the winter.

Region 6. THE WESTERN COASTLANDS

There is no appreciable difference between the land use pattern of this region, and that of Mid and East Cornwall, but the eastern boundary marks the change from the milk, pig and poultry production of west Cornwall to the cattle and sheep production of the east. This region, together with Regions 4 and 8, form in essence the non-granite lands of west Cornwall.

There is little moorland or woodland, and the proportion of arable to meadow land is as that of Mid Cornwall. Crops also are almost the same, with the exception that no rape is grown west of the Fal, and beans and vetch are grown together with oats as pig-food. A little market-gardening is found, there being some early potatoes and broccoli grown on the north coast as far as St. Agnes, and in the Helston district.

The farm type, however, is as that of the Carnmenellis region, and pig production was before 1940 usually the farmer's most paying line. Home grown fodder crops are of course supplemented by imported meal, and the difficulty of obtaining this is causing a drop in the number kept. Field boundaries and holdings are larger, and the country-side has not the bleaker aspect of the granite land.

The Fal Sub-Region

This small sub-division of the Western Coastlands consists of a narrow strip of land, usually less than half a mile wide, bordering the west bank of the Fal and its tributary creeks, Penryn Harbour, Mylor Creek, Restronguet Creek, and Truro River. Here is, climatically, a minor Mount's Bay. The presence of sea water keeps off winter frosts, and the south-west—north-east trend of the inlets, with their fairly steep banks, often wooded, gives a maximum protection from westerly winds. There are not the light soils of the Gulval-Ludgvan district, however, and sea-sand is not so readily available.

The region is distinguishable by its string of small flower patches along the shore-line, and a little small-fruit growing. Orchards (apple, pear and plum) are slightly more in evidence than in the rest of Cornwall, particularly in the peninsula formed by two creeks near Truro. There is, however, nothing comparable with the large areas of broccoli in the Mount's Bay region though farms in this district do grow small quantities.

Region 7. THE GOONHILLY REGION

This region consists of a clearly defined area of heathland or moorland (Predannack Downs, Goonhilly Downs, and Lizard Downs) which reaches almost to Lizard Point. It is one of the few moorland areas of Cornwall not on granite. The boundaries coincide closely with the area underlain by serpentine and associated igneous rocks, except where this extends to the coast east of the Lizard, in the parish of Grade Ruan, and where there is the usual type of land use of West Cornwall.

The surface is very level, and about 300 feet high. The highest point, on Goonhilly Downs, is 370 feet above sea level. There are no valleys nor surface streams, but several small pools, and the whole therefore tends to be marshy. There are some grass fields around the edge of the downs, but there is no encroachment upon the moor as there is in the case of the granite lands, and no moorland fringe, the land use changing quite abruptly along the northern and western edge of the serpentine.

The vegetation of the downland or " croft " is of coarse grass, heather, gorse, and black-berry, with many reeds in the damper parts. In the west, on Predannack Downs, much of the surface is covered with a dwarf gorse, 1 or 2 feet in height. The only animals found on the croft land, in places where the normal heathy vegetation obtains, are horses, and these are few. Cattle are pastured on the few bordering fields which have been reclaimed from heath.

Region 8. THE ST. KEVERNE–HELFORD RIVER REGION

This region, lying about the Helford River, chiefly to the south of it, comprises the parishes of St. Martin in Meneage, Manaccan, St. Anthony in Meneage, and St. Keverne. Local saying describes it as land within sight of St. Keverne Church, but this is not strictly true, as the southern half of St. Keverne parish is on the poorer land of the gabbro and serpentine of the Lizard.

Its boundaries are, for Cornwall, comparatively sharp. To the south and south-west it ends at the line mentioned above ; to the west it ends at wooded streams draining to the Helford River, and on the north-west it laps against the granite lands of the Carnmenellis region, where an immediate change in the size of fields and holdings is found.

The soil is a fairly heavy brown clay, developed on the Veryan and Gramscatho beds. Grain does well, and yields are better than elsewhere.

On the Land Utilisation Map (Sheet 146), 70 per cent. or 80 per cent. of the land is shown as arable. Percentages from the Ministry of Agriculture's returns show only 30 per cent., or about 50 per cent. if land producing a hay crop is included. It is probable that the field surveyors have here recorded long-ley grassland entirely as arable whereas the farmers in their returns record it as permanent pasture. There is, however, no doubt of the greater productivity of the region, which is reflected in the larger holdings, and larger, more prosperous, farm buildings.

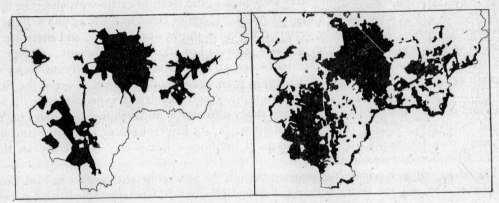

Ordnance Survey, First Edition 1813.   *Land Utilisation Survey* 1932.

FIGS. 26–27.—Changes in Land Use in the Lizard Peninsula.

The black areas are moorland. The Ordnance Survey One-inch maps (First Edition) 1813 show moorland clearly though probably did not record the smaller areas. On the thin acid ill-drained soils overlying the Serpentine and other igneous rocks there has clearly been an increase in the area of moor. Scale : 4 miles to one inch.

Certain individual cases offer some explanation. One farm, largely under grass, was run as a sheep farm but did not pay, and presumably will soon return to arable land ; another formerly good arable land, has more grass as the farmer relies more on visitors requiring land for camping and home dairy produce. In this connection it can be mentioned that throughout Cornwall are many farms where summer visitors are the most profitable of the farmer's activities. In so far as this is the province of the farmer's wife only, it tends to take labour away only from the dairy.

The basic type of farming is not greatly dissimilar from that of the rest of West Cornwall. The crops are as usual : oats, mixed corn, barley, roots and clover and grass. The amount of stock, cattle and pigs, is also as usual, but more attention is paid to cattle fattening than to dairy production, and the district has a local advantage in a higher proportion of home-grown feeding stuffs.

Specimen Farm V.

Locality. South of Helford River, 300 feet.

Area and Crops. 133 acres—45 under crops, producing wheat, barley, oats, and roots. Part of remainder is permanent grass.

Rotation. Four or five years ; less long-ley grass than usual.

Stock. 50 cattle ; three or four litters of pigs.

Soil. Marl, on clay subsoil.

Notes. Chief aspect of farming is production of fat cattle and pigs.

Region 9. MID and EAST CORNWALL

This land use region is by far the biggest, and includes practically the whole of the county east of a line running north-west from Truro to the coast, with the exception of two major moorland regions and the Hartland Plateau. It should again be emphasised that few land use boundary lines are hard and fast ones, and in this case in particular, the western limit does not coincide with any great change in land use. The basis of this western boundary is the marked change in the farming system from cattle-with-pigs in the west, to cattle-with-sheep in the east.

Over such a large area (Fal to Tamar 40 miles, St. Agnes Head to Bude 45 miles, Bude to the south coast 35 miles), there must be certain differences in physical features, and there are minor variations in land use, but the latter actually shows a remarkable homogeneity. Except in the north where Carboniferous Culm Measures are at the surface, the underlying rocks are of Devonian age, largely slates and shales, with at least one important series of grits, the Staddon Grits. The rocks as a whole are highly metamorphosed and hardened, especially near the granite masses and in the south, so that even where slaty cleavage is undeveloped the shales have been changed to silvery " killas." The soil in most parts is a brown light or medium loam, usually with many rock fragments, though in places it becomes a heavy clay—especially on the less altered Carboniferous rocks in the north.

The whole region is a dissected plateau, though the general height varies ; in Mid Cornwall it is between 200 and 300 feet ; between Tintagel Head and Davidstow much land is between 600 and 800 feet, and in places 1,000 feet ; most of North Cornwall is between 400 and 500 feet ; in South Cornwall the land is more cut up, but summit levels are between 500 and 600 feet. There is little level land, the different parts varying only in their degree of dissection. Mid Cornwall has a rolling topography, without such deeply incised valleys as the south ; the latter part, particularly between the Fowey and the Tamar, is cut by many deep south and south-east flowing streams, usually with closely wooded valley sides, and with short east and west tributaries, which make a regular pattern, and break up the whole district into one of steep slopes. As a result communication is difficult, but farm lanes can soon reach better roads which, clinging to the tops of the ridges, give access to the main roads and railway running east and west. East Cornwall, draining to the Tamar, is similarly strongly dissected, but north of Bodmin Moor is higher, flatter land, which is consequently more exposed to the strong west and south-westerly winds.

In general southern Cornwall presents a much softer aspect than the north. There is more woodland, fields are smaller, and the earth-and-stone walls have a greater amount of hedge on top. A comparison of the regular pattern on the Survey's map south-east of Lostwithiel and Liskeard, with the same essential pattern but with larger blocks of arable land, near Padstow, indicates this. The whole of the north-western side of this region—exposed to Atlantic gales— is noticeably treeless except where such a feature as the Allen Valley is well protected from dominant winds.

North of a line joining Camelford and Launceston, the Carboniferous Culm Measures— alternating sandstones and carbonaceous shales—are little altered and give rise to loams, often stoney, grading into heavy ill-drained clays on the shales. The country again becomes softer ;

the earth and stone walls are crowned with hedges, there are sunken lanes and nestling farmhouses of the type more often associated with Devonshire and patches of woodland in all sheltered spots.

In spite of local differences in topography, soil, and climate, the land use over all this region is fundamentally the same, though differences in farming practice from the point of view of stock will be indicated. A reference to the diagrams (Figs. 21–22) for the parishes of South Petherwin, Pelynt, Cuby, St. Allen, Mawgan in Pyder, and St. Kew, will show this. Twenty-five per cent, of the land, sometimes a little more, is under crops ; there is hardly any heathland (4 to 5 per cent.), and as little woodland. The remainder is under grass, of which a fifth produces a hay crop. This proportion of arable is the same as that for the whole county, as one would expect in this main region.

The objective of nearly all the farms is stock-rearing ; the numbers of cattle and sheep remain even over all the area. A typical large farm is 100 to 150 acres, though there are many small holdings, of 50 acres and less. One of the larger farms will have 40 or 50 acres under crops : 30 to 35 of these will be producing dredge or oats, the remainder potatoes, turnips, mangolds and rape. The typical rotation is one of eight years : three years corn, one of roots, then corn and grass together, and three years of grass. There is also on each farm some pasture which is seldom or never ploughed.

The number of cattle will be from 40 to 70, and in most districts these are for fattening and for dairy produce ; with these there will be from 2 to 6 litters of pigs. The number of sheep varies from farm to farm more, according to whether the farmer is a " sheep man " or not. Farms specialising in sheep will have flocks of 150 or 200. This is a composite picture ; the farm samples show the variations possible on this main theme.

To subdivide the region further on a basis of land use would only create artificial boundaries. Certain slight general changes, not indicable by a line on a map, are nevertheless present. In Mid Cornwall is mixed farming, with an increasing amount of cattle fattening as one goes north; towards the north also is an increase in the number of sheep ; in east and south Cornwall are big dairy herds, besides cattle for fattening, sheep and poultry.

Specimen Farm VI.

Locality. Outskirts of St. Austell, at 200 feet, one mile from sea.
Area and Crops. 95 acres—18 acres wheat, 20 oats, 3 roots, 15 hay, remainder grass.
Rotation. Three years in corn, and three years grass.
Stock. 18 cows and heifers in milk, 46 bullocks, 2 bulls (one Jersey for milkers and one Devon for beef cattle). 30 breeding ewes, with lambs. 2 sows and 20 feeding pigs. 4 horses, two for breeding, and pony.
Soil. Rich dark soil.
Notes. Cattle under one year old are housed for winter, remainder stay out. This farm is near a town, and thus has a ready market for produce.

Specimen Farm VII.

Locality. Mid Cornwall, north side. In parish of Newlyn East (near Newquay). Farm buildings in valley at 200 feet, opening north-west, farm land up to 300 feet. Sea 4 miles to north, and 5 miles to west.
Area and Crops. 160 acres, 50 acres ploughland.
Rotation. Wheat ; spring corn and roots ; mixed corn ; seed for hay ; three years grazing.
Stock. 70 head of cattle, chiefly Devon and Devon crosses. About 20 calves per year raised on their mothers and another 20 stores bought. All cattle fattened and sold for beef. Pure bred flock of South Devon sheep. About 200 run in summer months ; as many fat lambs sold as possible.
Soil. Mixed ; mainly a deep marl ; easy working and good cropping.
Notes. Most cattle are in yards or stall by December ; about one-third are in sheds in fields, and a few stay out all the winter.

Specimen Farm VIII.

Locality. Mid Cornwall ; north edge of Hensbarrow Region. Hilly land, from 200 to 400 feet. Sea ten miles to north, west, and south.

Area and Crops. 143 acres—32 acres mixed corn, 2 acres potatoes, 6 mangolds and turnips ; remainder grass.

Rotation. Two years corn, one year roots, one year corn ; seed for hay first year, and three years grazing.

Stock. 60 cattle, North Devons ; breeding and fattening ; 4 horses ; 100 South Devon sheep and lambs. 70 to 100 pigs, Large Whites.

Soil. A light loam in valleys, but black soil with stones on hilltops. This is typical of the moorland fringe. Soil does not allow cattle to run on it during winter, as the steep slopes cut up and spoil the pasture.

Notes. Main work of farm is cattle rearing, selling surplus milk, but best return has been from pigs, for which all meal is bought. Cattle have to be brought in from the end of October to the end of April. Much land is not tillable, and hardly good enough to call grazing, being on hills or on damp lowlands. Local pest is dock, which seems to be increasing generally. Smaller holdings in the neighbouring valleys grow a good deal of fruit (apples and plums).

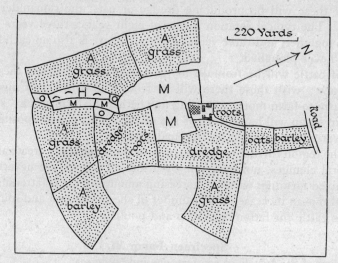

Fig. 28.—Specimen Farm XII.

Specimen Farm IX.

Locality. Mid Cornwall, south side, 250 to 300 feet. 5 miles to south-east is the sea, 6 miles to south-west is River Fal.

Area and Crops. 186 acres—8½ acres wheat ; 20 acres oats ; 26 acres dredge corn ; 2 acres potatoes ; 2 acres mangolds ; 4 acres swedes and kale. (This information was obtained since the war began, and shows one-third of the farm under crops, by order of the Ministry of Agriculture ; this is rather higher than the normal).

Rotation. Four years crops and five or six in grass, with first year for hay.

Stock. 60 cattle, mostly pedigree Guernseys, and extra stores bought for fattening. 125 cross-bred sheep and lambs.

Soil. Medium loam.

Notes. The farm is fairly sheltered with a southern aspect, and all cattle over one year remain out during the winter.

Specimen Farm X.

Locality. Mid Cornwall, north side. Farm building at 250 feet, with land rising to 550 feet on St. Breock Down. Sea 5 miles to west, and Padstow Estuary 3 miles to north.

Area and Crops, 564 acres, of which 264 are downland. 110 acres under wheat, barley, oats, dredge corn, mangolds, swedes, potatoes, and rape.

Rotation. Three years crops—wheat, roots, then barley or oats, then three years grass.

Stock. About 100 North Devon Cattle, some 70 bullocks, sold sometimes as stores and sometimes fat. About 80 South Devon breeding ewes, with lambs.

Soil. Clay soil, which can stand dry weather in summer ; near the downs black peaty soil.

Notes. Oats and barley do better than wheat. The farm has a northern aspect, and spring is late. This retards the new growth of grass. Cattle are in from mid-November to the end of April. Downland gives some summer pasture. This farm is much larger than usual in Cornwall.

Specimen Farm XI.

Locality. South-east Cornwall, near Liskeard. Farm buildings 350 feet, facing south. Sea 5 miles to south.

Area and Crops. 240 acres—12 wheat ; 20 dredge corn ; 40 oats ; 5 kale, remainder grass.

Rotation. Very little wheat grown ; usually four crops of oats, one of roots, then seed with oats for four or five years grass.

Stock. 50 cattle ; attested herd producing T.T. milk ; some young cattle fattened, but not of a good

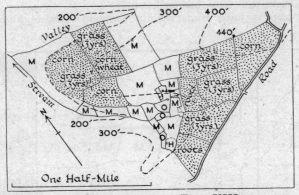

Fig. 29.—Specimen Farm XIII.

beef type. Large white pigs ; 12 to 15 sows, producing about 200 to 250 baconers yearly. 60 breeding ewes.

Soil. Light to medium loam.

Notes. This farm is much larger than usual ; there are a number in the district from 60 to 100 acres. This information obtained after the war began, and shows one-third of land under crops, rather more than usual. Good hay crops, with plenty of aftermath for silage. Access to sea-sand with high lime cement. Cattle can stay out all winter.

Specimen Farm XII.

Locality. Mid Cornwall, north side. Farm buildings 300 feeet, facing west.

Area and Crops. 62 acres. 21 acres under crops ; barley $6\frac{1}{2}$, oats 2, dredge 9, roots $3\frac{1}{2}$. Other arable fields give 22 acres of long-ley grass, and 10 acres are permanently meadow. A further 9 acres are of rough grazing, farm buildings, roads, etc.

Stock. 20–25 cows (Devons), of which 8 are in milk, and 13–15 young stock for fattening.

Notes. This is a typical small farm of Mid Cornwall, with income from dairy, and from home reared fat cattle. The farmhouse is larger than usual for a small farm, and there was a considerable extra income from summer catering. The equal area of cropped land and long-ley grass shows the eight year rotation exactly. The permanent pasture is richer, damper land, in a slight dip, where a spring begins.

Specimen Farm XIII.

Locality. Mid Cornwall, north side. Farm buildings 300 feet, facing north.

Area and Crops. 147 acres. 42 acres under crops ; dredge 25, wheat 6, roots (mainly turnips, rape and swedes) 11. 42 acres of tillable land under long-ley grass, of which 8 acres was giving a hay crop. 35 acres of permanent pasture, controlled by the lease, and 16 acres of rather poor hillside pasture with ferns. The farm buildings, yards, and orchards took up 4 acres, and the remaining 10 were rough woodland, roads, etc.

Stock. 10–12 cows in milk, with their young stock, and 20 stores for fattening. A flock of 60–100 sheep.

Notes. This farm uses a 6, or sometimes 7, year rotation ; 2 years of grain, 1 of roots, and 3 of grass. Sometimes there is an extra year of roots, or corn and grass sown together. In summer all the dairy produce was sold locally as cream.

Specimen Farm XIV.

Locality. Near Launceston, about 500 feet. Sea 13 miles to north-west.

Area and Crops. 102 acres—20 acres ploughland, corn and roots.

Rotation. From four to seven years.

Stock. 60 cattle ; 35 are pedigree Devons. Devon Longwool sheep ; 45 breeding ewes, 16 yearling ewes and 12–15 yearling rams for sale. 2 or 3 litters Large Black pigs. Indian Game and commercial poultry.

Soil. Rather light loam, with some heavier loam.

Notes. Most cattle taken in during winter months, owing to exposed position and heavy rainfall.

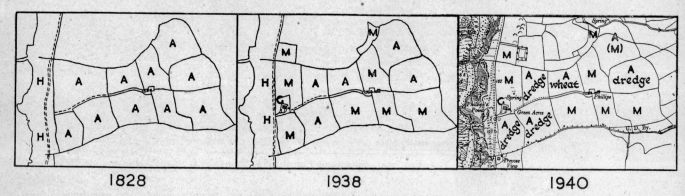

1828   1938   1940

Fig. 30.—Specimen Farm XVI

Specimen Farm XV.

Locality. North Cornwall, south-east of Bude. Sea three miles to west. Farm buildings 250 feet, fairly exposed.

Area and Crops. 187 acres—15 acres dredge corn, 23 acres oats, 5 acres wheat, 1 acre potatoes, 9 acres rape, mangolds, swedes, and cabbage. Remainder grass.

Rotation. Usual rotation is three cereal crops, one of roots and rape, then seeded to grass with a nurse crop of oats or dredge corn. Most of the fields will then stay in grass for a good many years (4 to 6) if carefully farmed. The difficulty is to prevent the first corn crop from lodging, and the best mixture is found in practice to be one of wheat, oats, barley and beans, sown together. With this system, manure is rarely used on the grass. White clover does best, and grows very readily. (It might be noted here that white clover is indigenous to Cornwall).

Stock. About 70 cattle, all pedigree North Devons, of a dual purpose type. Best bull calves are reared and sold for stock, the others are reared and fattened for sale at two years old, when they are about 10 to 11 cwt. The heifers are all kept for breeding ; after the first calf, the best are put into the herd of about 15 cows, the others fattened and sold. Surplus milk is sold to factory. Herd of pedigree Devon Longwooled sheep, producing a good carcase and a good fleece (12 to 18 lbs.). A few lambs sold fat, most of the ram lambs reared and sold for stock ; some have been sold for export to South Africa. Surplus ewes sold for breeding. Sheep do well on grass, and on folding on turnips and rape.

Soil. Fairly heavy, with clay subsoil ; tends to cut up in winter, and is better kept free of cattle. Basic slag is best fertiliser ; seldom need for nitrogen or potash.

Notes. This farm is typical of the larger ones of the district, and had a higher proportion of grass before the war.

Specimen Farm XVI[1]

Locality. Coast south of Bude, the single storied white washed stone farm house standing on an east west ridge at just under 200 feet, the land sloping away to north and south, 500 yards from coast road.

Area and Crops. 67 acres in 13 fields. When the survey was made in 1938, 4 of these fields were arable. In 1940 after the ploughing campaign of 1939-40 five fields were ploughed and under crops— four under dredge and one under wheat. The coastal location was evidenced by the dominance of *Festuca rubra* and *F. ovina* with some bent in the pasture—almost of downland type. The pastures were marred by thistles and reeds appeared in the damper parts.

Stock. 10 cows, Red Devons ; 50 sheep ; no pigs ; barndoor fowls.

Soil. Light brown clay-loam, passing to clay, with many angular surface stones—fragments of the Carboniferous shales and sandy shales of the subsoil.

Notes. In 1828 the whole farm (then of 10 fields one of which has since been divided) was recorded as arable, i.e. in rotation and the cliff top (then as now, of " furzey down," with fescue, thistles and gorse), was apparently used for sheep. It is not now attached to the farm. The crops illustrate the remarkable reliance placed in this part of the county on dredge corn, i.e. mixed oats and barley. The sale a few years ago of two acres and the building of a private hotel indicates the significance of " development values."

Specimen Farm XVII.

Locality. East Cornwall, near Callington, 450 feet.

Area and Crops. 330 acres, actually two farms run as one. Quarter of land under crops of wheat, oats, barley, potatoes and roots. No regular rotation followed: good pasture is left down for a considerable number of years, while poor pastures are broken up as necessary.

Stock. Pedigree herd of 80 Devon cattle, with 30 or 40 stores for fattening. 250 sheep, 80 to 100 pigs, and some poultry, all for local markets.

Soil. A light black loam on porous rock.

Notes. Farms in the district are from 150 to 250 acres, with numerous small holdings of 10 to 50 acres. On 200 acres a famer will employ 2 permanent labourers besides himself and family. Rents are from 26s. to 35s. per acre on the large farms, and 36s. to 40s. on the small holdings. As the district is near Plymouth, many farmers have found it more profitable to go in for milk production rather than cattle fattening, which occurs in more outlying parts.

Specimen Farm XVIII.

Locality. Southern fringe of Bodmin Moor. Farm buildings 400 feet, sea eight miles to south.

Area and Crops. 170 acres—45 acres of wheat, oats, barley, dredge corn, and a little cabbage.

Rotation. Four years crops, then long-ley grass.

Stock. 50 South Devon cattle; cows for milk, others fattened. 50 sheep, South Devon and Hampshire cross.

Soil. Black soil on granite.

Notes. Fairly sheltered; cows and calves in from end December to April ; others out.

9a. The St. Breock Down Sub-Region

This is a small but clearly marked sub-region of Mid Cornwall. A remnant of the 750-foot plateau, formed on the Staddon Grit, marked by an old shore-line on the north, and with a gentler southern slope, here forms an area of moorland or downland, mainly heather. Considerable inroads have been made on it, particularly on the south side, and in the central part the improved land from each side meets. Neighbouring farm holdings include some moorland which pastures sheep.

[1] By L. D. Stamp. Acknowledgments are gratefully made to Mr. J. C. Parkhouse, of Bude, for the loan of an MSS. Survey and maps of the Efford Manor (of which this farm is part), 1828.

9b. The Mid-Cornwall Wooded Valleys

This sub-region causes no more than a slight variation on the land use of Mid Cornwall. The farm land is under the usual crops of the main region, but there is an appreciable amount of dense woodland, of deciduous or mixed trees, with fairly heavy undergrowth. This woodland occurs on the steep sides of the valley of the Fowey, of its right bank tributaries, and of the Camel, in one case covering a continuous area of well over a square mile. In places this woodland has been cleared and not replanted, leaving rough heathland. Much of this is now Forestry Commission land.

9c. The Davidstow-Otterham Sub-Region

This sub-region can be distinguished by its greater height, more exposed position, and consequently lower amount of arable land. Less than 20 per cent. is under crops, and nearly

FIGS. 31–32.—The St. Breock Down Belt.

Moorland according to Greenwood's map (1826–27) (above)
and the Land Utilisation Survey (1932–38) (below).
As in most of the areas of sedimentary rocks there has been
a considerable diminution in moorland. St.E.—St. Eval ;
B—Bodmin.

Scale : 4 miles to one inch.

as much is heathland, mainly marshy pasture near the slow flowing streams draining east, or rough grazing on the sides of combes draining to the coast. The southern edge of this area, next to the moor, forms part of the moorland fringe referred to in the section on Bodmin Moor.

Region 10. THE HENSBARROW REGION

This region coincides approximately with the mass of granite of Central Cornwall, and can be divided into two parts.

10a.   The Southern Clay-working Sub-Region.   10b.   The Northern Improved Sub-Region.

The part of Hensbarrow Moor where the kaolinised granite is worked for clay is a clearly marked area, occupying some 15 square miles. Of this, nearly 4 square miles, or about a quarter, is waste land owing to clay workings. Part of this waste land is caused by the clay pits, from which the soft material is washed out, and part is occupied by the white quartz waste dumps which form such conspicuous features of the landscape.

Less than a quarter of the area is farmland, and is mainly in very small holdings under grass, which keep a few dairy cattle, sheep, and pigs. The rest of the region is open moor.

Houses for workers in the clay pits form quite a considerable amount of settlement in what would otherwise be a thinly populated region, though many workers travel out from the nearby town of St. Austell.

The Northern Sub-Region, so far as disappearance of heathland is concerned, is intermediate in state between the Bodwin and the Carnmenellis masses. Only $12\frac{1}{2}$ per cent. of the

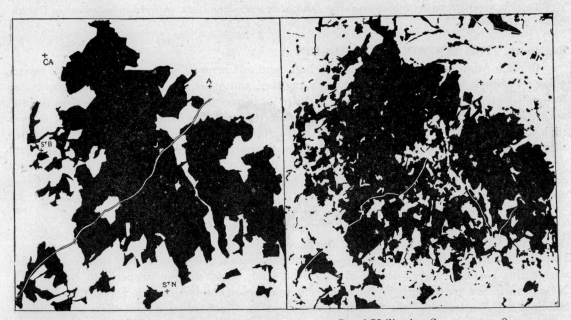

Greenwood's Map 1826–7.   Land Utilisation Survey 1932–8.

FIGS. 33–4.—The Changing Area of Bodmin Moor.

CA—Camelford ; St.B.—St. Breward ; A—Altarnun ; J—Jamaica Inn ;
C—Cheesewring ; St.N.—St. Neot.

Scale 4 miles to one inch.

Although the main bulk of the moorland remains the same, there has clearly been a general effort to wrest agricultural land from the fringing areas so that only the most stubborn and intractable areas remain. This is notably the case around and south of Jamaica Inn on the Launceston–Bodmin Road.

surface is under crops, and 30 per cent. is rough grazing. Nearly all this is marsh pasture, on the flat, ill-drained areas, of which Goss Moor is the biggest.

Farming is as usual in Mid Cornwall, with cattle breeding, and fattening, pigs, and sheep. The exposure of many farms, and frequent bad drainage, causes young stock to be brought in for a longer period than usual in winter.

It should be noted here that this region does not coincide exactly with the granite. The northern part is on soils developed on Devonian slates, but there are minor exposures of granite, and patches of alluvium, which give rise to heath or marsh pasture, and the same land use pattern is thus maintained.

Specimen Farm XIX.

Locality. In Hensbarrow Downs Region; nearly 500 feet up, with north aspect. Sea 7 miles to north-west and to south-east.

Area and Crops. Two holdings, one 100 acres, one 40 acres, worked together. 38 acres ploughed mainly oats and dredge, some turnips, mangolds and kale; 3 acres sugar beet.

Rotation. Varies between three and seven years, according to fields.

Stock. 15 cows, Devon and Guernsey cross; 30 stores, mostly Devons. 40 South Devon sheep. About 150 pigs before the war, now reduced to 50.

Soil. Light, black soil on granite.

Notes. Northern aspect is a disadvantage, and cows and young stock are in from beginning of December to mid-April.

Region 11. THE BODMIN MOOR REGION

Bodmin Moor forms the chief mass of high land in Cornwall, and occupies some 50 square miles. The highest point, Brown Willy, is 1,375 feet, and other tors, including the conspicuous Rough Tor, reach 1,200 feet. Practically all the moor is over 800 feet. It is developed on granite, with black, peaty, acid moorland soils, often waterlogged. The climate is wetter and severer than that of the rest of Cornwall, and there is much more cloud and sea mist, particularly when there is a west or south-west wind. Altarnun, though partly sheltered in a valley at 620 feet, with 59 inches of rain a year, may be compared with Bude, 15 miles to the north on the coast with only 33 inches. The streams are not deeply incised, and there are many badly drained areas, which are so marshy as to be practically waste, e.g., Crowdy Marsh and Stannon Marsh.

So far as land use is concerned, there are two sub-regions.

11a. The open moorland.

11b. The enclosed region and the moorland fringe.

Here a difficulty of demarcation occurs. What constitutes true moorland is clear enough, but within this area are many patches of improved land, which belong properly to Region 11b. Next to the moor, particularly on the north, e.g. in the parishes of Altarnun, Davidstow, Blisland, St. Breward, Warleggan, "the hermit parish," and St. Cleer, physical and climatic conditions are so similar that the type of farming is very like that of the moorland, though the region is not distinguishable from Region 8 (Mid Cornwall), on the Survey's maps. The River Camel on the west, and River Lynher on the east, indicate this boundary well enough.

There are two main groups of un-enclosed moorland, where the vegetation is of coarse grass, cotton grass, dwarf and ordinary furze (which has some nutritive value for stock) and heather. The latter two are burnt over from time to time to clear off the old plants. The larger portion lies to the north-west of the main road across the moor (Roughtor Downs, Garrow Downs. and Hawk's Tor Downs), and the smaller to the south-east (East Moor and Smallacombe Downs).

The open moorland is of some agricultural value, moorland rights to graze stock, and to cut turf and peat being incorporated in the title deeds of most farms adjoining the moor. Galloway and Highland cattle thrive best, with North Devons a bad third, these latter requiring more extra feed in winter. Cattle can live and breed on the moor all the year round, but benefit if changed to a different soil for a month or so each year. Scotch, Exmoor, and Devon Longwool sheep are usual. There are ponies in considerable numbers, but not so many as a few years ago.

The limit of cultivation has been reached; examples are fairly frequent of enclosed fields having gone out of cultivation, and the walls (of stone) have been allowed to fall in many places, so that they are stocked as open moorland. Sometimes these fields get taken back into cultivation by a new tenant.

The diagram for St. Breward, on Fig. 20, shows the use of the land in this region. Of the improved land, i.e. in Region 11b, 10 per cent. is arable, and the rest grass. Again we find about one-fifth of the grassland producing a hay crop. Oats and rape are the chief crops.

The usual size of the farms is from 30 to 100 acres, including a considerable portion of rough and often unploughable land which gives fair pasture ; in addition they nearly all carry moorland rights. The system on the tillable land is as that of the rest of Cornwall ; corn and rape is grown for three or four years, and then land is seeded to grass, which is left as long as the pasture is good. In this connection it should be mentioned that when moorland is being improved the farmer ploughs for oats, and follows this with grass. This accounts for the patches of arable land seen cutting into blocks of moorland.

A typical holding of 50 acres would carry 8 to 10 Devon cows and their young stock, and a

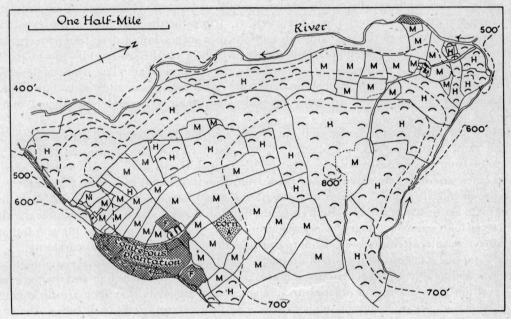

FIG. 35.—Specimen Farm XX (main farm).

flock of about 20 Longwool ewes and their lambs. Often Galloway or Scotch cattle may be kept in addition, also Scotch or Cheviot sheep, according to the amount of capital the farmer can put into them ; these latter are kept almost entirely on the moorl Almost always cattle are sold as stores, as yearlings or two-year-olds. Lambs are sold at lamb sales in July and August, and occasionally, but seldom, they are fattened on rape. Such farms do not provide a full living, and often the farmer goes to clay-pits or to other farms as a labourer.

Specimen Farm XX.

Locality. Western edge of the moor ; general level 700 feet, shelter plantation on both sides of building. This holding includes two other farms, one on the other side of the Camel, and the whole totals 411 acres of good arable and pasture, and about 2,000 acres of rough pasture and enclosed moorland.

Crops. On the main farm, no corn is grown usually. For sown grassland the best results have been obtained by the following mixture : 30 lbs. Rye Grass, 6 lbs. Timothy Grass, 4 lbs. Rough Stalk Meadow Grass, 1 lb. New Zealand Wild White Clover, per acre on the upturned sod, after considerable consolidation.

Stock. 200 breeding cows (Galloways) and their young, totalling 500 head. 100 Exmoor ewes and their lambs, also a few Longwool lambs bought in the autumn. About 40 sows, most of the progeny sold as sucking pigs, and about 100 per annum fattened out of doors for the good of the pastures. These are cut twice during the summer, for hay and for silage.

Notes. The main object of the farm is to produce high class beef cattle:; for this purpose the Galloway cattle are crossed with Hereford and Beef Shorthorn Bulls. Stock are sold at an annual sale in October. Surplus dairy produce goes to Lostwithiel, as liquid milk. The soil is a black light loam on granite and sand on the moor, and a brown loam away from it. This farm is not, of course, typical of the moorland farms ; it is exceptionally large and is farmed entirely for grass and silage for the stock (300 tons a year). It does indicate, however, what can be produced in a region which at first sight is of low agricultural value.

Region 12. THE HARTLAND PLATEAU[1]

The curious northern prolongation of Cornwall, north of Bude, belongs essentially to a larger region which embraces the north-western corner of Devon. It consists of an undulating plateau between 500 and 700 feet above sea level. A strip some three or four miles wide drains directly by small streams to the sea, and thus consists of a succession of deep, often steep-sided, " combes " with intervening sections of the plateau which reach the sea in cliffs 300 to 400 feet high. The inland section is drained by sluggish streams to the Tamar. The whole is developed on Culm measures, of which the sandstone beds give rather thin poor stony soils, but of which the dark shales or sandy shales afford heavy brownish soils, liable to become waterlogged on level or gently sloping areas.

Despite the small seaside resort of Bude, this is a curiously isolated and remote area. The single line railway to Bude was only opened in 1897 and even now the area round Hartland is a dozen miles from the nearest station. Most of the farmland can only be reached by narrow, tortuous lanes, and only one narrow main road, from Bideford to Bude, crosses the area.

In the inland, ill-drained section it is a region of small, semi-subsistence farms, some only from 20 to 40 acres, with farm houses, frequently built of " cob " and thatched, which are often only three or four-roomed cottages. Cream and butter are the surplus products for sale and only recently have serious attempts been made to improve means of collection and marketing.

The land use is mainly a function of drainage ; about a quarter of the surface is ploughland, a quarter is heathland, and the remainder is grass. In the gently undulating inland tract are large areas of cotton grass moor and old pastures so infested with reeds that they are little better, and are known locally as moors or moor fields. The farms have a few dairy cattle (Devons) ; where land is improved, this is done by ploughing, cropping, and re-seeding, so that the Land Utilisation Map shows large areas of yellow into which considerable tracts of brown form embayments. The better drained coastal tract has large arable fields on the plateaus, and little marshy land, but " down " and " furzey down " (terms which have been used for the past 200 years) on the steep slopes and seaward margins.

The prevailing, and frequently strong, westerly winds have driven a layer of blown sand over considerable areas, which has caused a marked amelioration of some heavy clay soils. In addition many of the more sheltered combes are pleasantly wooded and the common use of hedgerows on the top of the earth and stone walls make this a pleasant, intimate type of country, with a sprinkling of little stone or mud-and-daub (" cob ") farmhouses, and often old watermills on the streams. There are small weekly markets at Holsworthy and Kilkhampton.

Region 13. THE TAMAR VALLEY FRUIT REGION

This region occupies a clearly defined position on the west banks of the lower Tamar, and is a strip of land some ten miles long but seldom more than a mile wide. The central portion,

[1] By L. D. Stamp.

where there is a greater concentration of orchards, is only six or seven miles from north to south.

It comprises the eastern portions of the parishes of Stoke Climsland, Calstock, St. Dominick Pillaton, Landulph, Botus Fleming, and St. Stephens, all of which have the river or one of its inlets as their eastern boundary. Calstock and St. Dominick form the central part, and have a considerably larger output of fruit than the remainder.

The region is characterised by its large number of orchards ; out of a total area of about 13 square miles or 8,320 acres they occupy about 1,300 acres or between one-sixth and one-seventh of the land surface. As in the case of the other highly specialised regions of Cornwall, there is ample land surface for the usual type of farming to be carried on as well.

The topography is typical of south-east Cornwall ; the general level of the higher parts is between 400 and 500 feet, although near Calstock the land rises to 1,000 feet in the isolated Kit Hill, and in the southern half, towards Saltash, the general level is lower, with hilltops about 250 feet. From the waterparting between the Tamar and the Lynher are half-a-dozen small

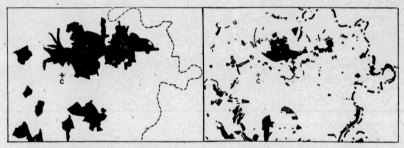

Greenwood's Map 1826–27.   Land Utilisation Survey 1932.

Figs. 36–37.—Changes in Land Use in eastern Cornwall.
The black areas are moorland.   C—Callington.
In this area of sedimentary rocks there has clearly been a great diminution
in the area of moorland, the main tract now remaining being Kit Hill.
Scale 4 miles to one inch.

streams draining south-east, and the lower slopes of their valleys provide the sites for the orchards, the northern sides, with southern aspects, being naturally preferred. Other orchards are found on the steep slopes immediately beside the Tamar, whilst outliers of the fruit industry are found in some of the small valleys draining to the Lynher, west of Callington.

The fundamental asset of the region is its mild protected site. The fruit-growing valleys face south-east, and the northward protection is increased by the ridge, nearly three miles long and 1,000 feet high, running from Kit Hill almost to the Tamar. Though orchards are found to the north of this, the greatest concentration on fruit is found immediately to the south-east of it. In the southern part, the lower lands in Botus Fleming and Landulph gain by their nearness to the large water-body of the estuary.

This situation is well-nigh ideal for fruit production ; hill slopes facing south, south-east or south-west, are abundant ; the south-west facing orchard has greater protection from possible north or east winds, while the south-easterly aspect gives the advantage of morning sun. Wind-protection is most important at blossom-time. In addition, the valley openings provide drainage for cold air currents, which can move easily down to the open Tamar and obviate the danger of

D

stagnant air and frost pockets.   The actual valley floors are marshy and owing to dampness and risk of frost fruit is not found.

The proximity of the body of sea-water gives a mild winter and spring, particularly to the farms adjoining the river, which are less affected by frost than those inland. The estuary also prolongs the late summer and autumn, when apples are still ripening.

The hillsides further provide good drainage, and the deep loamy soil retains moisture. In addition, at the foot of the slopes are damper sites for the small fruits, which require more moisture.

As a result of all these advantages, the Tamar fruit region gets its harvests between a week and a fortnight earlier than the other fruit districts of England.

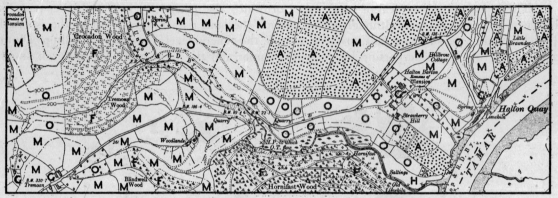

Reproduced from the Ordnance Survey Map by permission of the Controller of H.M. Stationery Office.

Fig. 38.—A Section of the Tamar Valley reduced from the six-inch Field Survey Map.
Scale 4 inches to the mile.

Notice the position of the orchards (which have strawberries, flowers or vegetables under the trees) on steep south or south-east facing slopes of tributary valleys having a good air drainage.   More level or exposed fields are largely arable and many north facing slopes are occupied by woodland.

The following figures in acres show the relative importance of the types of fruit.

Orchards   846
Orchards with small fruit between the trees   .   150
Small fruit   231

The varieties are :—

Apples	754	Strawberries	167
Pears	20	Raspberries	96
Cherries	97	Currants	55
Plums	89	Gooseberries	64

In addition there are 300 acres of flowers, chiefly in the parishes of Calstock and St. Dominick, while Calstock also produces some tomatoes.

The following table summarises the dates of production, and indicates the main markets.[1] The amounts refer to the production of the whole district about the Tamar ; it must be remembered in this connection that the Tamar is an artificial boundary, and fruit production is also important on the Devon side.

[1] Information and estimates of production supplied by Mr. H. Sherrell, Chairman of the Tamar Valley Fruit Growers' Association.

Fruit	Date of Harvest	Approximate Crop in tons	Market
Gooseberries . .	Marketed green from April onwards	40	Distant.
Strawberries . .	June, July	300–400	Distant.
Raspberries . .	July	80	Locally for dessert, but mainly to Bristol and Plymouth for jam.
Red and Black Currants	July	—	As raspberries, but smaller quantities.
Cherries . . .	July	—	Mainly local markets.
Plums . . .	Early varieties in July, finishing with Victorias in August ..	100	Mainly local markets.
Apples . . .	Early varieties in July for table, with later varieties for jam and cider until winter.	Over 500	Locally, mainly Plymouth

The bulk of the soft fruit is sent away to London, Midland, and Northern markets, but cherries, plums, and dessert apples are sold locally, chiefly in Plymouth.

Most of the fruit gardens have been reclaimed from woodland in the past 50 years; there are still quite large areas of woodland on the banks of the Tamar north of this region, and on the Devon side. The fruit farms are worked as small holdings, from 3 to 15 acres in extent. In these cases, fruit is, of course, the main source of income. There is no fixed rotation for fruit, but a common type of cropping on a small holding is 3 or 4 years strawberries, 1 year potatoes, and 3 years bulbs. Rents of these holdings are from £5 to £8 per acre. In the past 30 years, however, farmers have developed a profitable sideline by growing fruit and vegetables on suitable parts of their land. In this way there is a similarity again to the Mount's Bay area, both districts showing the specialised small holding side by side with the mixed farm with a few specialised fields. The small-holder frequently keeps a few pigs and poultry to supplement his income. The presence of increased numbers of fowls in this area has already been noted. The large farms are the usual mixed farms of east Cornwall; dairying plays an important part, with sheep largely to produce early fat lambs, and some fattening of store cattle.

V. LAND UTILISATION IN CORNWALL IN THE PAST

By

L. DUDLEY STAMP

CERTAIN distinctive features of farming and land use in Cornwall have their origin in the distant past, whereas others, even more important and characteristic at the present day, are of comparatively recent origin. The universal long-ley farming is very old ; the emphasis on dairying, flower and vegetable farming is modern.

There are several valuable accounts of Cornish agriculture between 1600 and 1820 but it is not always easy to reconcile some of the statements or fully to credit all the details given. Those accounts by native Cornishmen tend to exaggerate whilst those by visitors—" foreigners " from England—sometimes suggest hasty judgment or insufficient information. All agree, however, in emphasising the contrasts between agricultural practices in the south-western peninsula—broadly coincident with the old Kingdom of Dunmonium—and the rest of England. William Marshall distinguished this as his " South-western or Peninsular Department of England," and wrote in the Introduction to his *Review of the Reports to the Board of Agriculture* (London, 1817) : " Damnonian husbandry is as foreign to the practice of the kingdom at large, as the lands on which it has been nurtured are to those of its other departments."

Though the county has been well served by cartographers, the early maps available give little indication of land use. Thus the maps of Saxton (1576), Gascoyne (*c.* 1690), Overton (1712), Norden (1584–1728), Borlase (1758), Kitchin (1750) and Martyn (1748 and 1784), afford no evidence of the extent of the early " wastelands " or of cultivation. Indeed, the first accurate indication of the moorland areas then remaining is on the first edition of the one-inch maps of the Ordnance Survey (1813).

Richard Carew's Survey of Cornwall, 1602

This famous " Survey of Cornwall," the fruit of many years of labour, was first published in 1602, but the author, Richard Carew of Antoine, had previous supplied much of the information on Cornwall for Camden's Britannia. Carew long planned a second edition with corrections and additions, but it never appeared. More than a century later Thomas Tonkin of Pol Gorran prepared for press a re-issue with voluminous notes of his own but he died before its publication. Tonkin's preface is dated 1733, but it was not until 1811 that Francis Lord de Dunstanville republished Carew's Survey with Tonkin's Notes though the circumstances make this a valuable edition.[1] Carew shall be allowed to speak for himself.

" The Cornish soil, for the most part, is lifted up into many hills, some great, some little of quantity, some steep, some easy for ascent, and parted in sunder by short and narrow vallies. A shallow earth doth cover their outside, the substance of the rest consisteth ordinarily in rocks and shelf, which maketh them hard for manurance, and subject to a dry summer's parching.

[1] *Carew's Survey of Cornwall ; to which are added, notes illustrative of its history and antiquities by the late Thomas Tonkin, Esq., London ;* 1811. The quotations are from this edition.

456

The middle part of the shire (saving the inclosures about some few towns and villages) lieth waste and open, sheweth a blackish colour, beareth heath and spiry grass, and serveth in a manner only to summer cattle. That which bordereth upon either side of the sea, through the inhabitants' good husbandry, of inclosing, sanding and other dressing, carrieth a better hue, and more profitable quality. Meadow ground it affordeth little, pasture for cattle and sheep store enough, corn ground plenty." (pp. 16–17.)

" Touching the temperature of Cornwall, the air thereof is cleansed, as with bellows, by the billows, and flowing and ebbing of the sea, and therethrough becometh pure and subtle and, by consequence, healthful. . . ." (p. 12.)

" In times past, the Cornish people gave themselves principally (and in a manner wholly) to the seeking of tin, and neglected husbandry ; so as the neighbours of Devon and Somerset shires hired their pastures at a rent, and stored them with their own cattle. As for tillage, it came far short of feeding the inhabitants' mouths, who were likewise supplied weekly at their markets from those places, with many hundred quarters of corn and horse-loads of bread. But when the tin works began to fail, and the people to increase, this double necessity drove them to play the good husbands, and to provide corn of their own. Labour brought plenty, plenty cheapness, and cheapness sought a vent beyond the seas, some by procuring licence, and more by stealth, . . . so as, had not the embargo with Spain (whither most was transported) fore-closed this trade, Cornwall was likely in a few years to reap no little wealth by the same. And yet . . . the endeavour which the Cornish husbandman is driven to use about his tillage . . . the travail painful, the time tedious, and the expenses very chargeable. For first, about May, they cut up all the grass of that ground, which must be newly broken, into turfs, which they call beating. . . . After they have been thoroughly dried, the husbandman pileth them in little heaps and so burneth them to ashes. Then do they bring in sea sand . . . which by the plough's turning down, gives heat to the root of the corn. The tillable fields are in some places so hilly, that the oxen can hardly take sure footing ; in some so tough that the plough will scarcely cut them ; and in some so shelfy, that the corn hath much ado to fasten his root." Tonkin notes that this refers only to the " coarse, furzy and heathy grounds, which they beat up after this manner, and then call it breach."[1] (pp. 61–3.)

The common grains noted by Carew are two sorts of wheat, rye (" on worst grounds, which will bear no wheat ") and barley (increasing greatly in recent years, so that malt is made of barley instead of oats, as formerly).

" For fuel there groweth in all parts great store of furze. . . . The east quarters of the shire are not destitute of copsewoods . . . but in most of the west, either nature hath denied that commodity, or want of good husbandry lost it. Timber hath in Cornwall, as in other places, taken an universal downfall, which the inhabitants begin now, and shall hereafter rue more at leisure." (pp. 68–70.) In a footnote Tonkin notes how " large quantities have been cutting down ever since : neither is it indeed scarce possible to raise a new supply in the western parts, the shelter being destroyed, and these lying so much exposed to the raging west and north-west winds." (p. 70.)

" Of conies, there are here and there some few little warrens, scantily worth the remembering "—on which Tonkin comments " not so mean or contemptible, since we have many large ones, the rabbits very fat, and well tasted." (p. 75.)

" Beasts serving for meat only are pigs, goats, sheep, and Rother cattle. For meat, draught and ploughing, oxen : for carriage and riding, horses : for guard, attendance, and pleasure, dogs of sundry sorts."

[1] Compare brake and breck of Breckland.

" What time the shire, through want of good manurance, lay waste and open, the sheep had generally little bodies and coarse fleeces, but since the grounds began to receive enclosure, and dressing for tillage, . . . the sheep come but little behind the eastern flocks. . . . The Devon and Somersetshire graziers feed yearly great droves of cattle in the north quarter of Cornwall." (pp. 77–9.)

When Carew wrote there had evidently been a recent improvement in the standard of living of the husbandmen who " in times not past the remembrance of some yet living, rubbed forth their estate in the poorest plight ; their grounds lay all in common, or only divided by stitch-meal[1] ; little bread-corn ; their drink, water, or at best, but whey ; for the richest farmer in a parish brewed not above twice a year, and then, God wotte what liquor ; their meat, whitsul, as they call it, namely, milk, sour milk, cheese, curds, butter and such like as came from the cow and ewe, who were tied by the one leg at pasture."

" Suitable hereunto was their dwelling : walls of earth, low thatched roofs, few partitions, no planchings or glass windows, and scarcely any chimneys, other than a hole in the wall to let out the smoke." (p. 183.)

Borlase's The Natural History of Cornwall, 1758

Scarcely less famous than Carew's Survey is William Borlase's Natural History, published in 1758. He was a Fellow of the Royal Society and his observations have a scientific precision which renders them of great value. He gives, for example, some actual temperature observations, but specially valuable are his notes on soils. His description of Cornish soils was later para-phrased by Fraser (1794), whose account was utilised by Worgan (1808) who was in due course praised by Marshall (1817) for his valuable observations ! Borlase's account of soils is as follows :

" The vegetable Soils may be distinguished into three sorts, the black and gritty, the shelfy, slatty Soil, and the stiff reddish Soil, approaching more to the nature of Clay.

The highest grounds are covered with the black Soil, and on the tops and sides of hills, it is so lax and cold, and its salts so dispersed by the rain and snow,[2] that where it is dry at bottom it bears nothing but sour grass, moss, and heath, which is cut up in thin turfs for firing, or at best, short, dwarf, commonly called Cornish Furze; where the rains have not liberty to run off, bogs (though in Cornwall none dangerous or extensive) and marshes are formed ; here the Soil is less gravelly and deeper, but to be rang'd among the black Soils, and of little other use than that it yields a thick brick turf, full of the matted roots of sedge-grass, the *juncus*, and other marsh-plants, which, when thoroughly dryed, make a strong fuel. . . . In crofts, farther down from the hills, this black Soil serves as wintering for horned cattle, bears good potatoes, rye, and pillas, the *avena nuda* of Ray ; in fields, barley and oats, and serves as pasture for dairy and sheep, especially rearing young bullocks ; but seldom turns to any account when sown with wheat. It is more or less charged with gravel, and therefore called by the Cornish *grouan* (or gravelly), the earthy parts exceeding light, so that, in a dry summer, the sun quickly exhales its moisture ; and, in a wet summer or winter, the tilled grounds of this sort have much of the vegetable Soil washed away from the grain.

A great part of the Cornish soil, especially about the middle of the County, is of a shelfy, slatty earth. This is reckoned to bear better corn, especially wheat ; as also a stronger spine of grass than the black *grouan*. . . . The greatest enemy to this porous soil is drought ; for loose as it is, and perpetually dismissing part of its moisture through its shelfy foundation, it will yield the rest to the sun-beams above, after a long intermission of rain, by which means

---

[1] Stitch-meal : stitch = ridge between two furrows ; —meal, adverbial suffix (*cf*. piecemeal).
[2] This early reference to leaching and podsolisation should be noted.

both the grass and corn suffer ; but droughts of any continuance are so rare in Cornwall, that the husbandmen in those parts have seldom any reason to complain."

" The reddish, Loamy Soil is of closer texture, consequently retains the moisture of rain, the salts it receives from the higher grounds, the putrefied parts of plants and animals, and the bounty of manures, much longer than the Soils above-mentioned : it is not indeed so soon heated and animated (if I may so say) by the sun ; but as the spring and warm weather advance, it retains the influence of the day, notwithstanding the interposition of the night, in some degree, till the day comes on again, and ripens crops much sooner than the blacker and looser Soil. This soil is most common on level grounds and gentle declivities." (pp. 59–60.) Borlase notes that the three types of soil occur mixed and are often found on the same holding and that each requires different treatment and manuring.

Borlase has little to add to Carew's account of husbandry which he quotes, but deals in some detail with manuring. He notes the use of lime made of coarse marble in the east, but regrets a lack of appreciation of "marle" largely through the wide use of sea-sand and oreweed (" Fucus, Conferva "). Animal manure is used " in this county as elsewhere," but " near fishing towns, the husbandman in Cornwall has the advantage of purchasing, for a small matter, bruised, decayed pilchards, not fit for market, and also cast salt, that is, bay-salt which has been used already for salting pilchards . . . these off-casts of the pilchard cellars consisting entirely of salt, oil, and putrefied fish, and easily carried, because little of it suffices, may therefore be reckoned the cheapest as well as the richest manure anywhere to be procured. It will warm the coldest land . . . demonstrates it's lasting enlivening virtue even some years after it has been laid on." (pp. 86–87.)

Borlase records also wheat, barley, oats, and rye, besides avena nuda, called in Cornwall pilez (in the poorest land), as the seeds sown. Contrary to Camden and Carew's estimates of 150 years earlier, he says Cornwall can just be self-supporting in corn by balancing good years with bad and allowing the richer areas to supply the mining districts.

Borlase has his own explanation of the relative treelessness of western Cornwall, "not owing to any incapacity of soil, or sourness of climate, but to this ; that husbandry and planting, which separates counties into fields and inclosures, came late into use here in Cornwall, and have not yet prevailed upon the planter, at least in the westernmost parts, to surround his meadows with poplar, willow or alder, or edge his hills with elm, oak, and beech. . . . All the Duke of Cornwall's ancient parks in which there was a great number of forest-trees, and much copse, being disparked by Henry VIII upon a supposition that the ground would turn to better account in tillage, the wood was destroyed ; but, by some mismanagements, the royal intent was never answered." (p. 217.)

" Fruit trees have been at least as much cultivated of late years in Cornwall, as those of the forest. There is no gentleman now without his peaches and nectarines, as good as any." (p. 219.)

Borlase repeats Carew's information regarding sheep but notes the improvement of breeding in the east where the people (from the scarcity of tin) devote themselves to tillage and pasture. This may be the origin of the curious distribution of sheep noted above by Mr. Roberson (p.423).

"In coarse grounds the black-cattle are small, and live mostly (especially in the summer months) upon the heath and furze ; but in large tenements where the soil is improved, and the owner chuses to breed them, the Cornish have as large cattle as elsewhere, and with these the markets are well supplied, particularly in the larger towns." (pp. 286–7.) This statement remained true in 1939 ! Clotted cream was as characteristic of Devon and Cornwall then as now, " the cream is not skimmed off raw, as it naturally rises to the surface of the milk ; but after it has rested in the vessel about twelve hours, the milk is scalded in an earthen pan, over a slow, gentle fire, till it is as hot as a person can well bear his finger in, by which means the cream, settling into a wrinkled furrowed pellicle about a line thick, grows hard and *clouted*. This method of managing the milk is peculiar to Cornwall, and some parts of Devonshire." (p. 287.)

At the present day a distinction is drawn between Devon clotted cream and Cornish scalded cream ; the above is described as a method of making butter.

Borlase does not distinguish between the varied regions of Cornwall. Norden's descriptions[1] of the different hundreds are concerned mainly with other matters, but on p. 83 he gives the following details of the Stratton Hundred—the northern extension of the county. " It is the leaste hundred in *Cornwall*, but as frutefull as anie, both of Corne, Cattell, fish and other victualls; and the inhabitantes to be comended for planting orchardes, which yieldeth greate store of Apples, Peares, and such like frute, wherof they make *Syder* and *Perye*, healthsome and profitable drincke. There is also great aboundance of *Garlick*, the use wherof the Countrye-man holdeth salutarie, wherof they also make a comodious vente into manie other Shyres."

This picturesque account is a fanciful variation of Carew's and probably quite unreliable.[2] Tonkin stigmatises Norden's maps as inaccurate, Borlase records Stratton as one of the least productive hundreds, there are no fishing harbours and few streams which could have yielded river fish. If orchards and cider-making did then exist, they have since disappeared.

Robert Fraser's General Vew of the County of Cornwall, 1794

This is one of the early reports prepared for the newly constituted Board of Agriculture. It is brief and shows signs of hasty preparation and many statements suggest that the author had but a slight acquaintance with the county. His accounts of soils, manuring, deforestation, crops and animals are clearly derived from Borlase or Carew, where he writes from his own knowledge or observation, he becomes very unreliable. He claims that both Devon and Cornwall are too remote to have shared in " those new improvements in the rural arts, which have of late years excited so much zeal and enterprise in the more internal parts of the Kingdom," and states that " the internal parts of the county have remained hitherto uncultivated wastes and undivided commons, entirely in a state of nature, and, excepting the mining districts, almost without inhabitants. The admiration (*sic*) of a stranger is naturally excited by observing, in a country so anciently settled, that cultivation has proceeded so short a space from the coasts." This suggests that Fraser's view was coloured by travelling over the main road across Dartmoor and Bodmin moor since the one-inch maps of the Ordnance Survey (First edition, 1813) actually show the moorlands of smaller extent in certain cases than at the present day.

Fraser appreciates the main features of the climate and mentions the recommended trial of Guinea grass, adding a sentence which is prophetic of the modern flower and vegetable industry—"others may be found of great importance, which will not bear the winter cold, and sudden changes of temperature in other counties."

" The management of the land is uniform : here and there an exception will be found. The whole is convertible sometimes into arable, and sometimes pasture. Arable is sown with wheat, barley, or oats, as long as it will bear any ; and then grass for eight or ten years, until the land is recovered and capable again of bearing corn. There are many instances of what is called furze crofts, where they are so run out by this management that they do not recover themselves more than once in a generation." He condemns the whole system of management and estimates one-third of the county to consist of these furze crofts, " only broke up once in twenty-

---

[1] Norden, J. *Speculi Britanniæ Pars. A Topographicall and Historical Description of Cornwall*, 1728.
[2] Carew's description reads : " His circuit is slender, but his fruitfulness great, and the inhabitants' industry commendable, who reap a large benefit from their orchards and gardens, but especially from their garlick (the country-man's triacle) " (p. 278).

CORNWALL 461

five or thirty years," one-third under a regular course of husbandry and one-third wholly un-inclosed consisting of marshy grounds, rocks, mountains and waste—of which he believed 100,000 acres at least could be improved. At the present day more than two-thirds of the county are regularly farmed, but the system of outfields or brecks has largely disappeared, though examples can still be found and the land is still called croft land. Rough grazing recorded in agricultural returns is now less than 15 per cent of the county.

"Horses and oxen are generally both used for the plough. The country is very hilly, not admitting the use of carts, the horses are wanted for some carriage or another, and are almost always under the pack-saddle. The plough-team is sometimes four oxen, and sometimes only two, with always one or two horses as leaders before the oxen, with a man or boy to drive them. . . . Everything is carried on the pack-saddle." The veracity of these statements is doubtful.

Fraser repeats Borlase's information about forests and deforestation, tracing coppicing to the demand of tin smelters for charcoal; his information on manuring is also from Borlase. Cornish farms are described as small but a special word of praise is accorded to the many public-spirited gentry and land-owners.

Worgan's Report, 1811, Marshall's Review, 1817 and the Ordnance Survey Maps, 1813

The Board of Agriculture entrusted the preparation of the revised Report on the county to G. B. Worgan, of whose qualifications little is known. Although he does not once mention Fraser's report, he has clearly drawn largely on it and earlier writings, whilst his own observations were made in the course of a winter tour on foot. Evidently the Board found his MSS. (of which the preface is dated November 30, 1808) unsatisfactory and it was entrusted to three Cornishmen to revise. Their note is dated 1810 and the first edition of the Report was issued in 1811.[1] The pompous William Marshall, in his Review[2] of all the Reports, relates these circumstances with gusto, but in the few words of his own composition, displays a lamentable ignorance of the county when he says, " Cornwall comprizes a greater proportion of *inarable lands*, than any other English county." This was *after* the publication of the Ordnance Survey one-inch maps which show clearly the true extent of the moorlands.

Worgan's Report, as revised by Robert Walker, Jeremiah Trist and C. V. Penrose, presents a picture of Cornwall which differs in very many ways from that of Fraser prepared only 15 years before. Although great progress is reported as the result of the establishment of the Cornwall Society for the Encouragement of Agriculture and Industry in 1793, it is hard to believe that all those changes had taken place since Fraser wrote. Thus Worgan devotes a chapter to Implements (with many illustrations) and says, "no county affords a greater variety of wheel and other carriages than Cornwall. In most parts of the county may be met with the waggon, the wain, one and two-horse carts, the ox-butt, gurry-butt, slide and sledge." The inevitable conclusion is that Fraser's hasty report, quoted above, is quite unreliable.

Worgan repeats Borlase's notes on soils; he has some comments of his own on climate : " A kind of languid spring prevails through the winter, which brings forth early buds and blossoms, raising the farmer's and gardener's expectations, to be too often disappointed by blighting north-east winds, in March, April, and even sometimes so late as May."

On the estimate of Mr. Wallis, Secretary to the Cornwall Agricultural Society, unenclosed waste lands affording scanty year-round pasturage for "a miserable breed of sheep and goats"

[1] *General View of the Agriculture of the County of Cornwall*, London, 1811.
[2] *A Review (and Complete Abstract) of The Reports to the Board of Agriculture from the Southern and Peninsular Departments of England*. London, 1817.

are computed at 150,000 to 200,000 acres plus 10,000 acres of summer pasture for cattle and sheep. The goats are described as climbing and browsing the rocky summits, wild conies as feeding and burrowing among the sandy hillocks. Reference is made to sheep left on the moors becoming "moor-sick." "Though there be no case, till very lately, of enclosure by Act of Parliament . . . there are numerous instances of parcels of land being taken up from the waste and enclosed with temporary dead fences, for the purpose of securing two or three crops of corn : after which the land is consigned to waste again."

The moorlands are clearly shown on the 1813 one-inch maps of the Ordnance Survey and their area can be exactly calculated. In some areas they are of less extent than at the present day but it would seem that only the entirely unenclosed moors were shown and that the temporary enclosures are included as farm land. Greenwood's one-inch map of 1827, said to be based on a new survey of 1826–27, also shows moorland but the outlines of the moors are almost exactly those of the Ordnance Survey, with certain omissions (probably accidental).

In view of the present reputation of Cornwall Worgan's section on the "objects of husbandry" is peculiarly interesting. "Cornwall not being a dairy county, and the generality of the farmers having an idea, that there is nothing like corn in sacks, for making money, they are very fond of the plough, and consequently the tillage for white crops is large ; perhaps it may be hazarded, that full one-third of the cultivated lands are under the plough" (p. 53). Again, on p. 140 "The dairy does not constitute a very important department in the husbandry of Cornwall," the concentration as far as cattle are concerned being upon store cattle for sale to Somersetshire graziers (p. 138).

"The general course of the crops, in the county of Cornwall, is extremely reprehensible ; there is no circumstance evinces the truth of this assertion more, than the wretched, exhausted, foul appearance of the grounds, laid down with grass-seeds ; nor can it be otherwise, after having been cropped with corn, as long as they will bear any."

Apart from the temporary enclosures[1] on the moorland fringe, the general land-use pattern must have been very similar in 1808 and 1938. Meadows (of permanent grass) were restricted to slopes, valleys, level and moist land on the banks of rivers or near villages, and the selected "home meadows" of the farmsteads ; the rest of the farm land was cropped for two or three years with corn, with the last crop of which grass-seeds (red clover, trefoil and rye-grass, with or without white clover) were sown and the resulting pasture was left from 2 to 5 years before being again broken up for corn.

The Nineteenth Century

A comparison of Worgan's descriptions with the present day conditions makes clear that the chief changes have been :—

(1) The substitution of dairy produce for corn crops and store cattle as the chief commodity for sale off the farm. This change could not have come about except for the improvement of communications between Cornwall and the rest of England, especially the construction of the main line in the 'sixties. The change-over was assisted, as elsewhere in Britain, by the repeal of the Corn Laws and the flooding of the English markets with cheap foreign corn.

(2) The maintenance of the system of 2–3 years ploughing and 2–5 years grass, but the substitution of feeding crops for white corn crops and a consequent improvement of rotation.

(3) The introduction of specialist agriculture—flowers from the Scillies and south-west ; later

[1] It seems that in Cornwall the term "croft" should be restricted to these though sometimes apparently applied to unenclosed moor.

early vegetables from the south-west. Hops, grown in Roseland in Worgan's time, have gone but orchards have increased in those fertile sheltered tracts.

(4) Although there is no longer the system of cultivating temporary " breaks " in the moorland fringe, there is no doubt that the moorland edge fluctuates with economic conditions. Thus there is the apparent paradox that the area of cultivated land in the county (78 per cent) is greater than a century ago, but the area of true unenclosed moorland (13 per cent) is almost as large as it was then.

An illuminating picture of conditions in the middle of the nineteenth century is afforded by W. F. Karkeek's Prize Essay " On the Farming of Cornwall," published in the *Journal of the Royal Agricultural Society* (Vol. VI, 1846). Reviewing the changes since Worgan's Report, he notes the increase of turnip culture since 1815 and the gradual abandonment of the iniquitous practice of growing a succession of white crops till the ground was exhausted. Even so two white crops in succession (wheat followed by barley or oats) were still usual and then three years grass. The chief crops in 1846 were wheat, barley, oats, hay, turnips, potatoes and vetches with a recent introduction of rape, cabbage, mangolds and carrots. Amongst animals the west had, as now, few sheep but many pigs ; long-woolled sheep had almost completely replaced the short-woolled, Devon cattle, the old Cornish black cattle, horses (the breeding of which was much neglected) had driven oxen off the roads but had only begun to displace them as plough-animals. There was breeding and rearing of cattle and a trade in hides, but there is no mention of a dairy industry. The flower industry was not yet born, but already 12,000 to 15,000 bushels of early kidney potatoes were being sent to the London markets from the sheltered lands of Penzance (where best soils rented at £10 per acre), Lizard, Looe and Tamar-side.

Influenced by De la Beche's geological work, Karkeek distinguishes the soils of (a) the granites—grovan ; (b) the serpentine of the Lizard ; (c) the schists, clayslates or grauwackes and (d) the carbonaceous deposits of the north—affording stiff yellow clays over three-quarters of their outcrop. Waste land, much held in common, and regarded as improvable, was estimated to cover 200,000 acres. In a county so long associated with mining and fishing, farmers in 1841 still numbered only 7,668 (out of a total of 25,799 engaged in agriculture or 7–9 per cent of the population).

APPENDIX I
STATISTICAL SUMMARY
The Land Utilisation of Cornwall according to the Official Statistics of the Ministry of Agriculture and Fisheries
All areas in acres

Year	Total Area	Crops and Grass	Arable Land	Permanent Grass For Hay	Permanent Grass Not for Hay	Rough Grazing
1866		436,071	340,581		95,490	
1867		471,289	349,069		122,220	
1868		481,169	371,269		119,900	
1869	873,600	490,640	346,805		143,835	
1870		492,361	368,587		123,774	
1871		507,336	375,311		132,025	
1872		512,669	377,391		135,278	
1873		515,999	366,214		149,785	
1874		518,254	361,947		156,307	
1875		525,017	362,144	18,453	144,420	
1876		527,470	362,192	16,909	148,369	
1877		529,022	361,898		167,124	
1878		538,635	368,289		170,346	
1879		546,862	367,772		179,090	
1880		551,224	368,691		182,633	
1881		558,757	363,553		195,204	
1882	869,878[1]	564,459	364,865		199,594	
1883		575,624	359,883		215,741	
1884		579,610	359,903		219,707	
1885		583,421	357,364	23,905	202,152	
1886		585,965	365,409	33,776	186,780	
1887		589,649	366,135	35,764	187,750	
1888		594,802	375,394	36,841	182,467	
1889		598,557	379,217	39,118	180,222	
1890		599,901	382,530	37,903	179,468	
1891		601,918	374,634	37,785	189,499	
1892		601,667	363,754	39,486	198,427	
1893		602,479	359,059	34,713	208,707	
1894		603,121	361,509	40,341	201,271	
1895	868,208[2]	603,948	356,870	41,161	205,917	
1896		604,784	357,115	38,822	208,847	
1897		604,751	366,178	32,817	205,756	
1898		605,025	366,979	32,807	205,239	
1899	866,239[3]	605,741	365,151	32,381	208,209	53,679
1900		606,139	367,333	32,069	206,737	54,117
1901		606,524	361,434	32,637	212,453	55,519
1902		606,464	363,002	32,844	210,618	56,715
1903		606,919	360,089	33,969	212,861	58,451
1904	866,250[3]	606,548	353,115	36,362	217,071	64,755
1905		607,304	352,578	34,548	220,178	66,038
1906		607,246	355,311	36,231	215,704	67,577
1907		607,648	355,400	38,040	214,208	69,835
1908		608,691	356,497	38,695	213,499	71,438
1909		608,625	359,403	39,198	210,024	73,250
1910		609,610	365,783	38,927	204,900	72,102
1911		611,116	361,234	41,203	208,679	71,387
1912		611,111	351,197	40,033	219,881	73,920
1913		611,930	318,088	45,478	248,364	71,175
1914		611,695	311,772	44,475	255,448	71,251
1915		611,893	314,332	43,555	254,006	67,894
1916		613,687	317,370	43,131	253,186	75,387
1917		616,800	334,698	40,544	241,558	77,477
1918		617,327	369,721	32,825	214,781	78,900
1919		611,237	369,791	34,022	207,424	79,697
1920		610,888	359,899	35,180	215,809	81,145
1921		606,066	346,670	33,966	225,430	100,693
1922		607,683	342,703	40,666	224,314	104,705
1923	866,320	607,945	341,080	38,193	228,672	106,939
1924		609,511	334,112	42,157	233,242	107,852
1925		609,190	334,553	39,735	234,902	109,877
1926		610,027	343,404	40,578	226,045	110,315
1927		609,513	342,894	41,495	225,142	111,068
1928		609,446	337,476	43,439	228,531	111,464
1929		609,989	337,219	44,483	228,287	111,322
1930		610,145	337,595	47,269	225,281	111,231
1931		609,945	333,993	44,444	231,508	111,687
1932		609,646	334,544	46,410	228,692	111,565
1933		609,328	324,233	51,037	234,058	111,979
1934		609,399	330,459	49,116	229,824	112,029
1935		609,114	331,167	43,777	234,170	112,702
1936		609,515	325,424	43,971	240,120	112,324
1937		608,255	326,976	45,146	236,133	112,855
1938		609,197	319,819	42,310	247,068	114,296

[1] Land and water.   [2] Not including tidal water.   [3] Exclusive of water ; includes Scilly Isles (3,980 acres).

SUMMARY OF FINDINGS OF THE LAND UTILISATION SURVEY
CORNWALL

Acreages calculated approximately from the 1-inch maps.

	Ministry of Agriculture 1933–1938 *Average*		Land Utilisation Survey 1933–1938	
	Acres	*% of County*	*Acres*	*% of County*
Forest and Woodland[1]	27,985	3·2	30,200	3·5
Arable (including orchards) ..	326,346	37·7	187,980[3]	21·7
Permanent Grass[2]	282,789	32·6	483,510	55·8
Rough Grazing	112,696	13·0	112,250	13·0
Houses with Gardens	—	—	21,880	2·5
Land Agriculturally Unproductive	—	—	27,000	3·1
Orchards	3,500	0·4	3,500	0·4
Unaccounted for	116,504	13·5	—	—

[1] 1924 Census of Woodland.   [2] Including long-ley rotation.   [3] Excluding orchards.

The above figures should be compared also with those given on page 418. It is clear that the Land Utilisation surveyors have included as arable only land under crops or newly laid down to grass ; all other grassland has been recorded as permanent grass (including long-ley) whilst some neglected grass returned by farmers as " rough grazing " has also been included as grassland. The Survey's total of rough grazing is nearly all true unenclosed moor, some of which escapes the agricultural returns.

APPENDIX II

NOTES ON SCILLY AND THE FACTORS INFLUENCING LAND USE ON THE ISLANDS

By MARYELLEN MORTIMER, B.Sc. (Econ.) (Mrs. Roberson)

ANCIENT.

Two main factors and several lesser ones seem to have affected Land Use on Scilly.

a. Population.

   i St. Martins. Second largest and now a highly cultivated Island, was uninhabited till the time of Charles II.

   ii Sampson, also Pentile, was finally de-populated in 1875. (See Walter Besant's story "Armorel of Lyonesse.")

   iii Annet (now a famous bird sanctuary), Tean and St. Helens, were at one time used for grazing and have remains of habitation, and a hermitage.

   iv The Gugh—untouched through history except as a kings' burial ground, was leased by Mr. Cooper, an Irish engineer after 1918. He cleared land and experimented with stock and crops. When he died in 1931, he left a good workable farm, which is still running.

   v When the Dorrien Smiths took over Governorship in 1834, they insisted that only one son of a family should stay at home. This helped to ease poverty, and altered the course of land use and size of holdings, which are all held on yearly tenancy to the Crown. One cannot buy land.

b. Religion.

The sacredness of the soil and its extensive use as burial ground in Celtic times limited the use of soil to some extent. (Scilly is reckoned to contain more ancient remains than the whole of Cornwall, and Cornwall is rich in them). The tradition carried on, for the only Roman altar in Britain was found on Scilly, and in the early days of Christianity the Abbey of St. Nicholas (on Tresco), See of Exeter, was founded, and is recorded to have made the conversion of Olaf Trygvasson of Norse Saga fame.

This factor is non-existent now.

c. General.

   i *Tin.* There are remains of ancient workings on Tresco, and while tradition suggested Phoenician trade, they were more likely worked when the Romans held the Islands as a convict camp.

   ii *Stock.* Strabo, the Roman historian, speaks of Scilly and mentions Scillonians as being very civilised and clad in garments made from wool of their own sheep. Sheep rearing seems to have been general up to recent times. As in Cornwall the rise of flowers has been co-incident with a decline in sheep. (My cousin, who kept the last sheep on St. Agnes till 1926, gave as reasons : (a) the wild land, Wingletang, was not sufficient grazing. (b) Pasture was wanted for flowers and cattle. (c) Sheep which broke into the precious flower patches did more damage than their own value).

   iii *Fishing.*

This occupation is mentioned throughout history and appears to have supported large numbers of people— on a low standard. St. Agnes is quoted as having 3-4 hundred people, mostly fishers, in the 18th century. There are now 60 people on it. Fishing is rapidly dying as a main occupation, though it remains as a sport, and a potential supply. As late as the last war, the men of the Islands would go out in the autumn to Powl and other known grounds, and the women set aside a week for salting for the winter. That is non-existent to-day. The fleet from Sennen that came each year has practically disappeared, and also the French men from Camaret and other parts of Brittany.

For various reasons, life on Scilly deteriorated greatly between ancient and comparatively recent times. For instance, in the time of Richard II the Islands were described as being worth a few puffins in peace time and nothing in war. They were greatly reduced by Barbary pirate raids, and suffered considerably from being the last Royalist out-post in the Civil War. Charles and Cromwell have both left grim relics of occupation. The Dutch captured them in the 17th century, and they suffered the general 18th century decay of Cornwall.

For books on these later years there are :—

Borlase, W., *Islands of Scilly.* Oxford 1756.

Heath, R., *Account of the Islands of Scilly.* London 1750.

Troutbeck J., *A Survey of the Ancient and Present State of the Scilly Islands.* Sherborne, 1780-96.

Woodley, G., *A View of the Present State of the Scilly Isles.* Truro 1822.

North, W., *A Week in the Isles of Scilly.* Penzance, 1850.

Whitfield, H. J., *Scilly and its Legends.* Penzance 1852.

Uren, J. G., *Scilly and the Scillonians.* Plymouth 1907.

MODERN.

Because Scilly is isolated, one can study in unusual completeness the rise and utter disappearance of certain occupations during the last two centuries. No one for instance to-day would know anything about the old straw hat making.

Kelp.

Kelp making was a considerable occupation in the 18th and early 19th centuries, and there are vivid descriptions in some of the old books. That had completely vanished towards the end of the 19th century.

466

Smuggling.

This was such a major occupation that, on its severe suppression in 1828, a serious famine overtook Scilly, and charities had to rush to aid.   Needless to say, it is not entirely gone now, and rum running to and from Brittany remained till the 20th century.   The customs books on St. Mary's, which are largely unknown, make valuable reading on trade and wrecks.

Potatoes.

This industry was started after the famine, to help Scillonians to some means of livelihood.   It remained profitable until the rise of flowers, and foreign imports defeated it.   Since the Spanish war, and now of course in this war, more potatoes have been grown again.

Ship-building.

Although there is no trace of it to-day, except that skilled carpenters and boat builders can be found there, Scilly had a flourishing and famous ship-building industry in the 19th century.   It was ousted eventually by the coming of iron and steam.

Flowers.

This most profitable 20th century industry was begun in a humble way by a St. Mary's farmer who sent a few Scilly Whites across to a mainland market in a hat box.   There are many legends about its beginnings. Its rise in tonnage and profit has been phenomenal since the last war, and since the acquistion of the S.S. Scillonian, and the Research Station which has been working for 15 years under Mr. Gibson.   The air service makes no appreciable difference, except for those who try direct retail trade.   New types of flowers are tried out each year and the season is gradually extending.   Instead of Jan.–April (Scilly Whites, Soleils d'Ors, Iris—down to King Alfreds and Arums at Easter) the season begins in November for real earlies, lasting down to May, and going straight on to potatoes·

Tourists.

This industry has risen since 1918, and had reached a peak just before this war.   Every Island now runs some kind of boarding house, and the population of St. Mary's (1,200) doubles in the season, not to mention day visitors, which can be as many as 400 a trip.

Future.

It has been suggested by more than one observer that it is time for the flower industry to give way in its turn to something new, and enterprising farmers are already on the look out.   Some are developing bulb culture.   The Governor has encouraged crab and certain fish breeding.   But the war has suspended foreign and glasshouse competition, and it is not possible to say what may develop.

THE LAND OF BRITAIN

The Report of
The Land Utilisation Survey of Britain

EDITED BY
L. DUDLEY STAMP, B.A., D.Sc.

THE CHANNEL ISLANDS

by

G. DURY, M.A. (London)

LONDON
PUBLISHED FOR THE SURVEY BY GEOGRAPHICAL PUBLICATIONS LTD

1950

CONTENTS

LIST OF ILLUSTRATIONS

THE CHANNEL ISLANDS

by

G. DURY

EDITORIAL INTRODUCTION

It was not part of the original plan of the Land Utilisation Survey of Britain to include the Channel Islands. Consequently this Report is additional to Parts 1 to 92 of *The Land of Britain* as planned and published in nine volumes.

The survey of the islands and the preparation of this Report are due entirely to the interest and enthusiasm of Mr. Dury. Mr. Dury's interest in the work, in fact, antedates the establishment of the Land Utilisation Survey of Britain in 1930 for he had a part in the pioneer Survey of Northamptonshire published in 1928. He volunteered, about 1939, to survey the islands himself and had carried out some of the work when the German occupation of the islands forcibly interrupted it. This has had one most interesting result : the field survey is unique in that it was carried out photographically from the air and the whole of the islands " mapped " within the space of two hours ! The photographs have been interpreted stereoscopically—work in which Mr. Dury, who held the rank of Flight-Lieutenant in the R.A.F., is an expert—with the help of adequate ground controls. For his studies on the geography of Guernsey, Mr. Dury received the degree of M.A. of the University of London in 1944.

L.D.S.

I. INTRODUCTION

THE Channel Islands lie in the St. Malo bight, remnants of an earlier and more extensive Armorica. They range in size from Jersey, about 45 square miles, and Guernsey, about 25, down to numerous tiny islets and points of rock. All those of any size at all are inhabited, and it is with these that this Report will be concerned; namely Jersey, Guernsey, Alderney, Sark, Herm and Jethou, in all a total of some 75 square miles of land area.

This is about half the size of Rutland, but carries a population as great as that of the County Borough of Northampton, i.e., in round figures 93,000 (in 1931); put in another way, the average density of settlement is in the neighbourhood of 1,200 per square mile, which is particularly remarkable in view of the small development of nucleated settlement and of industry.

The map and diagram (Fig. 1) show the relative sizes and the positions of the islands named.

An introduction to the study of the Channel Islands would be incomplete without some mention of their political status. They have retained in addition to their several patois, which are still spoken along with English, a considerable degree of independence, and exercise much legislative power. They have their own governing bodies, responsible not to Parliament but to the King in Council, and impose their own taxes, customs and excise duties, all of which are notably lighter than the corresponding dues in England.

For governmental purposes the islands are divided into two groups: Jersey stands alone, while the Bailiwick of Guernsey includes, besides Guernsey itself, Alderney and Sark, which have their own governments subordinate to that of the main island, and Herm and Jethou, which are considered part of Guernsey.

In this Report, the treatment accorded each island is not exactly similar, so that mere repetitive description of conditions observed in more than one case may be avoided.

I should like to thank all those whose help I have enjoyed in preparing this Survey, especially the authorities of the islands and the librarians who have made available so much material.

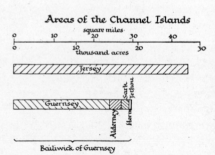

FIG. 1.—The Channel Islands—
Position and Relative Areas.

II. THE PHYSICAL BACKGROUND

THE islands are blocks of ancient rock which for the most part descend steeply to the sea in cliffs. They are notably flat-topped, and have evidently at some stage been subjected to a prolonged period of erosion.   The plateau surfaces are, however, not necessarily level ; in fact, it is only in Sark that horizontality obtains, for in Guernsey, Herm and Alderney there is a general slope to the north or north-west, while the plateau of Jersey inclines to the south.

Exposures of sedimentary rocks are less extensive than those of igneous ; the latter are mainly deep-seated, and probably represent two or more series of differentiations from magmas which, though all of great age, intruded at widely separated times. The more ancient of the groups of rock exhibit marked metamorphism.   Nearly all the formations are highly resistant to weathering and erosion, but the length of time throughout which these factors have been in play has permitted them to affect some of the rocks, especially the schistose types, to a considerable degree, and reduce their upper surfaces to residual sands and boulders.

Marine erosion also has wrought great changes in the shapes of the island blocks.   It is probable that the general outline is due to faulting, but the resultant horsts have been fretted and bitten into by the sea.   The northern lowland of Guernsey, the corresponding portion of Herm, and the various enclaves or niches of low ground let into the plateaux of the former and of Jersey and Alderney, are due to marine attack.   The assault has not always been carried on at the same level, for the floors of the niches are now above the sea and they appear as bays of low, flat land terminating to landward in cliffs which remain steep.

Raised beaches are known at various heights ; their deposits are not extensive, except in the niches, and recent rocks are otherwise composed chiefly of residual materials, some blown sand, and *limon*. The last of these occurs widely on the plateau top of each island.

A. JERSEY—RELIEF, GEOLOGY AND SOILS

Jersey seems to have been sculptured from a roughly rectangular block about ten miles by six. The highest land occurs in the north, close to the coast, and the highest point of all, some 460 feet O.D., is but a few hundred yards distant—in the horizontal sense—from the shore (Fig. 2).   From the most elevated area the land slopes away gently to the south, and still more gently to the south-east and west, and it is not until the general surface passes below 225 or 200 feet that the well-defined ancient cliffs begin their sharp fall to 50 feet O.D. or below.   The " general surface " signifies the heights of the flat interfluves, for the plateau is being dissected by a number of streams flowing in incised valleys.   The present cycle of erosion is in a very early stage, as the narrowness and steep sides of the valleys demonstrate, but it has already been subjected to interruptions, and the thalweg curves each exhibit a number of knick-points. This would naturally be expected in view of the several raised beaches known.

Drainage is principally southwards into St. Aubin's Bay, which receives the three largest of the Jersey streams.   These have incised their valleys back nearly to the 300 feet level, and St. Peter's Valley, the westernmost, marks off from the centre and east a portion of the plateau which curves round from Grosnez Point in the north-west to Corbière and Noirmont Points on either side of St. Brelade's Bay in the south-west. This area, which is the whole of the parishes of St. Ouen and St. Brelade, and nearly all of St. Peter's, differs somewhat from the rest of the high ground ; it is less dissected and also more nearly horizontal. Since there are also features of utilisation peculiar to it, it will be called in this Report the " western plateau," to distinguish it from the main plateau.

The low land is also naturally divided into two parts. The St. Ouen's Flatland is that area between St. Ouen's Bay and the western plateau ; the Southern Lowland is taken to include the niches which scallop the plateau edge all the way from St. Aubin to Gorey.

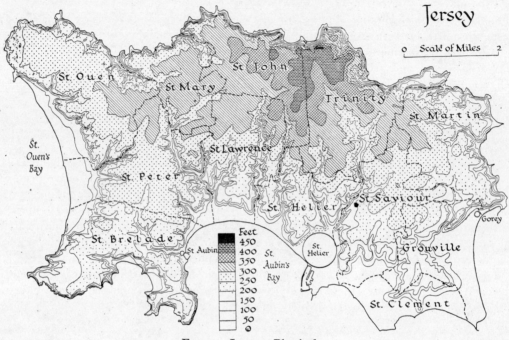

FIG. 2.—Jersey—Physical.

Geological features are here dealt with separately from those of relief because the configuration of the surface is little dependent on the subjacent structure, except in details of recent erosion and in the cases of the two large bays cut into the schists.

These pre-Cambrian schists are the oldest rocks of Jersey. Their main outcrop is between St. Ouen's and St. Aubin's Bays, extending northwards into the plateau (Fig. 3). They are highly metamorphosed ; in general they are more easily eroded than most of the later rocks, and from place to place are deeply weathered, although their resistance varies laterally.

The Plutonic Group next in succession is a series of resistant igneous rocks which traverse the schists. They have undergone regional metamorphism, and now exist as an epidiorite, occurring in small patches ; an amphibolitic granite widespread in the north-west, also found in the south-west and represented by a syenitic type immediately east of St. Helier ; and granulite invading the granite.

Most of the eastern half of the plateau consists of rocks of the Hypabyssal–Eruptive Group, which again are resistant rocks, including a varied assemblage of microsyenites, microdiorites, tuffs, breccias and nodular rhyolites. The last of these is the youngest of the Group, and outcrops the most widely ; to the north-east it bounds on the Rozel Conglomerate, which represents the sedimentary stage following close on the eruptive and includes materials torn from the rocks previously enumerated. The manner should be noted in which the surface passes from rhyolite to conglomerate with no break of slope ; similarly with the junction of members of the Plutonic Group with the softer schists, particularly in the western plateau.

Orogenic movements which took place long after the formation of the conglomerate brought about some metamorphism and opened the way for a number of minor acid intrusions, which however are of small extent and need not be examined here. They are not distinguished on the geological map.

In all the islands the existing state of the soils is in part due to the application, over centuries, of vraic, sea-sand and animal manure. Supply of dung is decreasing, while the demand for

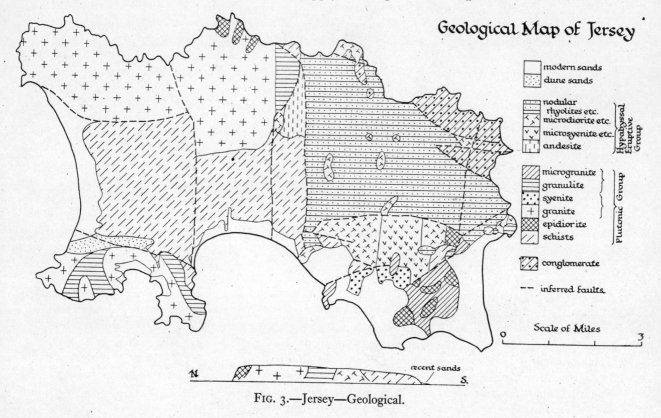

FIG. 3.—Jersey—Geological.

fertiliser is rising. The following discussion will, therefore, take account particularly of the measures adopted to maintain the land in good heart.

The recent deposits shown on Fig. 3 are largely littoral sands, beaches formed when the old cliffs of the plateau edge were cut. There is comparatively so little low land that the deposits of the plateau top are more important agriculturally, but the light sands must be noted, if only because of their natural earliness for the market-gardener. Their possibilities vary with the state of drainage, for where the run-off is good they tend to be dry, while where the water-table lies close to the surface they support only marsh vegetation or damp Heath. The pond in the centre of St. Ouen's Bay flatland is typical of an enclave, and other examples may be seen to exhibit various stages in the degeneration of lagoons, for instance behind Vazon Bay in Guernsey and Longy Bay in Alderney.

The sands of Jersey tend to be alkaline ; they respond well to treatment with potash, which needs to be applied with some care on the heavier soils because it lengthens the growing period. The largest areas of naturally sweet soils are found in parts of St. Saviour and St. Clement, and in the south-west near the Quennevais.

The geological map and relief maps of Jersey, being compared, show that sands blown inland from the southern shore of St. Ouen's Bay have heaped themselves up against the plateau edge and invaded the high ground. In the windward part of the dune area relief is broken and drainage seasonal. The south-east of the island also suffers a little from blowing sand, but since it is well sheltered from the prevailing winds the effects here are not serious.

On land between 200 and 400 feet O.D., that is over most of the plateau surface, limon is widespread, overlying in parts the sandy residual material of weathered " solid " rocks, and agricultural land ranges up to medium heavy clays. Despite the application of vraic, most farm soils tend to be sour, although of recent years there has been an improvement in this respect and the effects of long periods of continuous cropping are being counteracted by more adequate fertilisation. Nowadays rank sourness is rarely encountered except in new pieces being broken from old grass or from unworked land.

The question of fertilisation is a complex one. The annual loss of basics affecting balance may be considered equal to 8½ cwt. of carbonate of lime per acre, and therefore a corrective is necessary after a few seasons. On the other hand, soil conditions are constantly varying, and it is highly desirable to adopt a mixture specially prescribed for a particular piece of land, which many cultivators now do. Even then it is practically impossible to allow for the weather, which in a very dry season can make the dressing much less effective. Again, on the late soils which form the bulk of Jersey potato land, potash as stated will set back the date of ripening if used too liberally ; and to increase yield nitrogen is recommended with phosphate to encourage early ripening. On the heavier soils where tomatoes are grown, often as a first crop, manures must be low in nitrogen.

Liming as such is now more frequent than formerly, when the black sand " vase " from several bays was spread on the land. This material contains bases equivalent to 10–75 per cent. carbonate of lime ; it was applied together with vraic, which gave that moisture and humus not present in artificials and which are particularly beneficial in a dry year. Nevertheless modern methods have proved themselves by restoring to profitable yields some areas which had been planted with potatoes for 50, and even 80, consecutive years.

Sweetening mixtures are usually skimmed in the autumn, applied after ploughing or incorporated in a special dressing with the normal fertiliser.

A special case of deficiency is to be noted in fruit and flower gardens, which may become alkaline by excessive dressing with ashes from burnt garden refuse, lime, chalk, soot or slag.

The soils of the Channel Islands generally, like those of Brittany, are so deficient in lime and phosphorus that the local cattle are all on the small side, but they possess an advantage, small though it may be, in the heavy deposit of salt by rain which reduces the need for salt licks. It has been calculated that the average quantity of salt thus received each year is about 270 lb. per acre in Jersey, and may be twice as much in parts near exposed coasts.

B. GUERNSEY—RELIEF, GEOLOGY AND SOILS

The irregular outline of Guernsey has a rough resemblance to an isosceles right-angled triangle, whose hypotenuse, the north-west coast, would be over nine miles long. A glance at the relief map shows that physically the island falls naturally into two parts, the southern plateau and the northern lowland or shelf.

The shelf, which comprises about two-fifths of the whole island (Fig. 4), lies mostly below 50 feet, although there is more variety of relief than this fact alone would suggest. The Clos du Valle, the area north of the neck of land between Grand Havre and St. Sampson, is much broken up by small hillocks of igneous rocks, called hougues, and also includes the undulating land of L'Ancresse Common and some small low-lying patches, poorly drained. The Braye du Valle, a former tidal channel, now provides flat low-lying land, which passes southward into land of

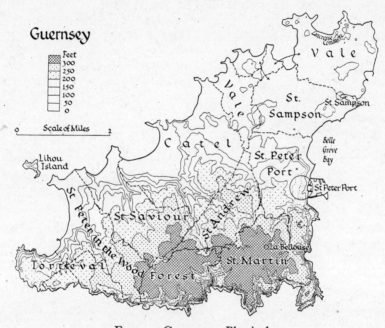

FIG. 4.—Guernsey—Physical.

slight but noticeable relief where small streams flow in little dips. On the west, hougues and flat sandy patches vary the coastal strip, while on the east is a low, flat, circular patch, cut off from the sea by a shingle bar and broken by two knolls, on one of which stands the ruined Château des Marais.

Many of the hougues have been reduced or levelled by the extraction of stone, and a relief feature of great importance, although man-made, is the number of abandoned quarries of varying size which pit the surface of the shelf in the rocky parts.

The niches of lowland in the west need little description since this type of feature has already been dealt with in the case of Jersey. The southern plateau which is the second major relief region of Guernsey is divided from the lowland by a steep edge, whence it rises gently southward from 200 feet to 345 feet at its highest point near the south coast. The general downward slope to the north gives this part of the island, which up till the latter end of the last century was the main cultivated region, a less favourable aspect for primeurs than Jersey's. Drainage is to the north and north-westward, with the typical incised streams whose valleys open out at the head into broad and scarcely noticeable folds in the ground.

The same independence of structure and surface occurs in Guernsey as in Jersey, although at first sight there may appear to be a general correspondence between the northern shelf and the Differentiation Suite and between the pleateau and the southern gneisses (Fig. 5). However, rock of the younger age is to be found incorporated in the plateau, while it is certain that the low-lying outcrops in the north are for the most part more resistant than the rocks forming the high ground.

The small exposure of Jerbourg Schists is the oldest of all Guernsey's rocks. They are thought to represent the sedimentary cover of pre-Cambrian to the Metamorphic series of gneisses. These are somewhat difficult to separate and classify, as boundaries are in places hidden and in others indefinite, and the rocks themselves highly metamorphosed. They are granite and diorite-gneisses, in the main resistant although having been long-weathered, and it is only in small exposures that decomposition is marked.

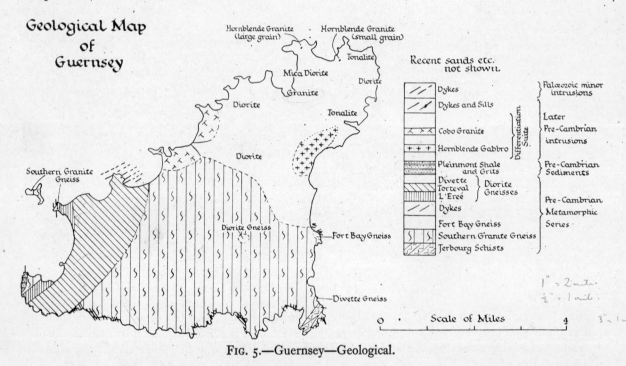

FIG. 5.—Guernsey—Geological.

The next succeeding deposits, the Pleinmont Shale and Grit, occupy a limited area in the south-west; they probably post-date the main pre-Cambrian earth-movements.

The later pre-Cambrian was marked by the intrusion into the southern rocks of dykes and sills related to the diorites of the north. These, with the probable inclusion of the Cobo and L'Ancresse granite, constitute the Differentiation Suite, a plutonic series thought to represent a number of separations from a single invading magma. They are all very little metamorphosed, and most resistant, especially the blue diorite which has been particularly in demand for export.

The members of the Suite vary in acidity from granite through mica-diorite and tonalite to hornblende-gabbro, which outcrops on the shore of Belle Greve Bay and has been correlated with the Lizard gabbro.

Again, in Guernsey there is a contrast between the limon of the plateau and low-lying sands. Here, however, clay is also found on some of the lower ground. The niches behind

Vazon and Perelle Bays are sandy and flat ; drainage is mostly sufficient, with the aid of tidal sluices, and these areas tend to be dry and support mostly thin crops of grass. North of the town the part near the Château des Marais is damp and remains Meadow ; on the opposite side of the island, also on the shelf, dry sandy patches occur inland from the bays, and are not yet all brought in, although they are being invaded by houses and cultivation. In the north of the island the sands of L'Ancresse Common, still a little liable to blow in the west, occur up to and above 50 feet O.D., heaped round the hougues which protrude from the underlying masses of igneous rock, and although a very little enclosure has taken place they remain largely an area of dry Heath.

South of the Common, the soils are on the light side, increasing in heaviness as one approaches the plateau edge and passing into clays, with a few patches of raised beach materials in places. The light soils well repay fertilisation, are easy to work and easy to irrigate, and their texture has made cultivation a simple matter, whether by the spade or by larger implements drawn by a man. The reclaimed Braye du Valle and the immediately surrounding part is a notable fertile area.

The clays extend up to the highest land on the plateau. They have been described as " a fine ochreous clay, ranging in colour from a dark or light yellow to red-brown . . . not a sedentary deposit, but to be compared with the French limon ; in places the thickness is as much as 50 feet." Rafts of true loess have been exposed in brickfield workings, and also concretions which would appear to be loesspüppchen.

Below the limon residual materials have been identified, and these outcrop on the surface where it is closely approached by the solid rock.

One may note in addition to the rocks described that small deposits of peat are known at two horizons near the coast ; they also occur on Jersey, and on both islands have been used in addition to vraic. There is also some marshiness to be seen in tiny patches just above some of the knick-points in the incised valleys, and this was an obstacle to improvement for a long period.

C. CLIMATE AND WATER SUPPLY

The islands are all subjected to strong oceanic influences ; the prevailing winds are westerly, rainfall is well distributed throughout the year, and diurnal and annual temperature ranges are both small. In order to avoid repetition, and to permit the study of climate to be pursued in some detail, it may be permissible to deal almost exclusively with a single island—Guernsey, whose climate is slightly more equable than Jersey's, and where meteorological effects produced over the French mainland have slightly less effect.

Forty-seven per cent. of the winds of Guernsey blow from a westerly quarter ; south-easterlies are the least frequent. It is necessary to note the great force of the winds experienced here. For instance, in 1938, when wind-strength was less than average, the total run recorded for the year was 87,930 miles ; that is to say, the mean speed throughout that year was in the neighbourhood of 10 m.p.h. In such conditions tree-growth in exposed localities is faced with the gravest difficulties ; sand from beaches on the windward side is blown inland (more so in Jersey, where raised beach material is widely exposed) ; the less sturdy types of outdoor plant are protected by the earth banks, or the less common stone walls, which divide the fields one from another.

Mean annual temperature range is 17° F. (Fig. 6) ; the occurrence of maximum in August and minimum in February emphasises the maritime character. Mean daily range is only 9·1° F. ;

mean minimum is correspondingly high, ranging from 57·5° in July and August to 40·3° in February. The mean underground temperature falls no lower than the February figures of 42·2° at 6 inches, and 45·7° at 4 feet ; snow is uncommon and frosts are rare, occurring on an average 27 times a year. The growing season is long, and a number of wild plants are scarcely affected by the winter.

It is highly significant that the mean minimum temperature is only about 1·3° F. above the mean dew point ;[1] there is little difference in this respect between months. The high

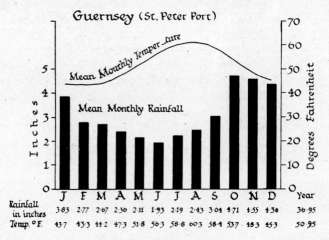

FIG. 6.—Guernsey—Mean Monthly Temperature and Rainfall.

relative humidity thus indicated averages 85 per cent., a figure which accounts for the very heavy dews experienced. Mean cloudiness is 5·6 (tenths). There are few days without sun, even in December, which is the cloudiest month but which records a mean of 47·8 hours sunshine, with sun on 20 days. The annual duration averages 1,721 hours, which is equivalent to a daily period of 5·2 hours. This is a notable stimulant to plant life, and is relevant not only to agriculture generally on all the islands, but to one aspect of it on Guernsey in particular, as will appear. Moreover, exposure to the ocean, and high humidity, both tend to increase atmospheric clarity, so that insolation is especially powerful. The black-bulb temperature is therefore high, averaging 97·5° F. throughout the year and 119·6° F. in July.

The similarity between the climates of Guernsey and Jersey is shown in the accompanying table. Jersey is a little more sunny, a little more liable to frost, and somewhat drier. The similarity of means does not preclude considerable differences between the respective records for a single year.

Guernsey growers, with so much land under glass, have achieved a measure of independence of temperature conditions. In Jersey, however, glasshouses are rare, and the important potato crop may suffer severe damage from cold waves spreading from the mainland. Thus, in mid-March of 1932, frosts affected the earliest potatoes, and there was further damage in that same year on the night of May 7. There was bad frost damage in some areas on April 13, 1936, following snow on the 12th, and in 1938 the crop was frozen in many parts of the island on May 9 and 10. Little can be done to combat frost. On the other hand some action is possible to counteract certain of the effects of unreliable rainfall. Drought, when it occurs, is a grave

[1] Grass temperature is about 4° lower than the dewpoint.

problem, and reduces yield (for example in 1938) without so much affecting the quality ; but excessive rainfall, in spring and early summer, fosters the spread of blight, and is the chief danger. In this case spraying is a sound defence (p. 22). Wet and cold springs do not themselves reduce the potato crop ; in 1935 these conditions persisted into May, and the crops were very heavy. Tomatoes, by contrast, were handicapped in that year, and also in the year following, when a dull, wet summer, with low soil temperatures, caused the first crop in particular to be poor. Summer fogs would have the same effect.

The following table, for the year 1923, illustrates the remarkable contrasts between Guernsey and Jersey in rainfall and temperature from month to month, which sometimes occur though not apparent in average figures.

	Jan.	Feb.	Mar.	Apr.	May	June	July	Aug.	Sept.	Oct.	Nov.	Dec.	Year
RAINFALL—inches : Guernsey, St. Peter Port	1·00	5·44	1·60	3·37	1·80	3·58	0·87	1·41	3·21	4·76	8·10	7·50	42·64
Jersey, States Farm, Trinity	7·00	3·32	3·30	2·03	0·95	3·16	5·03	1·20	3·02	1·86	5·16	1·98	38·01
TEMPERATURE of Guernsey	46·1	42·6	47·1	46·3	52·2	57·0	59·2	60·8	60·0	53·0	48·1	46·0	51·5
TEMPERATURE of Jersey	44·4	41·0	46·6	46·9	54·0	58·5	60·0	61·3	60·9	52·3	46·2	44·3	51·4

The consideration of rainfall has been deferred to this point so that it may be taken together with water-supply. In Guernsey, St. Peter Port recorded a mean of 36·95 inches over a ninety-five-year period. There is no doubt, however, that some parts of the island receive less, and that the fall at sea to the north is considerably smaller. The island appears to act as an obstacle to the steady flow of air, and its smallness seems to be offset by the sharp rise from the sea and by the high degree of humidity. The heaviest rainfall occurs on the eastern rather than on the western side, a fact which may be due to the deflection of the falling rain down-wind, and to the propagation in the same direction of the turbulences set up. Indeed, on some days small clouds may be observed to the leeward of the islands, while the sky above them is clear ; and the disturbances which occasion the clouds are experienced by aircraft. However, a comparison of the rainfall maps for Guernsey and Jersey (Figs. 7 and 8) indicates that such effects are not alone involved. These maps have been constructed by the usual method of extrapolation for short series referred to a control station. Although their accuracy is influenced by the degree of reliability of observers and by the lengths of the various series, it is thought that they do represent an approximation to true conditions. In Guernsey the mean annual total increases eastwards, and also towards the highest part of the plateau, and there is a difference of more than 5 inches between driest and wettest parts. In Jersey more than 40 inches per annum is received on the highest ground, and less than 30 inches in the extreme south-east.

In Fig. 6, October is seen to be the wettest month; pressure is then low, and autumn cyclones pass freely from the sea to the continental land-mass. Conversely, the small amount received in spring, when pressure is also low, shows the combined effects of a cool ocean to the west and

higher pressure over the continent to the east. Rain-days are least frequent in June, which
has 11 (in Guernsey), and most frequent in December and January, with 20 each, but in these
last two months the ocean is already cooling and the continental high is building up. It is in
January, too, that absolute humidity reaches its lowest point.

Guernsey may serve as a type area for the study of water-supply as it has served for climate.
Its problems are more pressing than those of Jersey, since it has so many glasshouses, while the
larger island is more dependent on natural rainfall.

The limon and residual arenaceous materials which together constitute such a large proportion
of the surface deposits of the southern plateau are able to retain water to some extent owing to
their insolubility, their lack of jointing and stratification, and their fineness. At the same time their

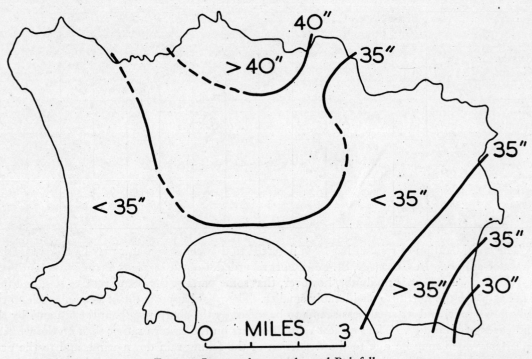

FIG. 7.—Jersey—Average Annual Rainfall.

very porosity makes for a rapid soaking-in of rainfall, which diminishes evaporation, while the
small natural slope of the subjacent surface gives little assistance to run-off. Consequently, the
water table on the plateau is able to remain high in spite of the incised valleys, supplying many
shallow wells.

If the rainfall were reliable the problem in farming areas would not be grave, but there are
irregularities due to cyclic and also to probably non-periodic variations, so that the amount
received from year to year shows great differences. In a 104-year series, one year recorded over
56 inches and another under 20 inches (Guernsey) ; the standard deviation was 5·94 inches.

In such a small island with no resource other than its own fall, the effects of drought can be
serious. The large population makes great demands on the supply, and glasshouses always need
more water for irrigation than a corresponding area in the open. It was the incidence of a group
of dry years that led to the setting up of a public undertaking, with pumping stations at points

in the lower parts of the incised valleys or on the plateau top where deep wells tap fissures in the gneiss and draw on a supply less dependent on climatic fluctuations than the sub-surface table.

Extension of the mains northward was proceeding up to 1940, to include those parts where the drift is thin, low-lying, and underlain by impervious igneous masses. At the same time a dam was under construction in St. Saviour, to bar a valley and have a capacity of 250 million gallons.

It is precisely in the north, where the natural supply is most precarious, and where the demands of growers with land under glass are heaviest, that an important source of supply is found in abandoned quarries, which, cut deeply into impervious rock and often shaded by overhanging trees, provide large storage tanks for rain-water. In many of them a small stationary engine works a pump which supplies water to nearby land and glasshouses for irrigation and heating.

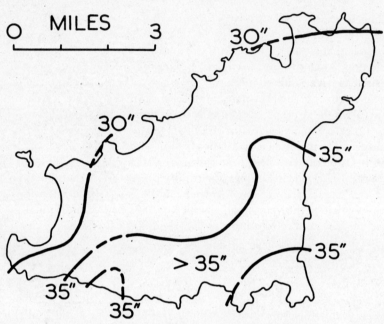

FIG. 8.—Guernsey—Average Annual Rainfall.

A fitting footnote to this section is supplied by the table set out below, which was published in Guernsey about 1900 :

EFFECT OF EVAPORATION IN GUERNSEY

Mean annual rainfall   =   36·52″   =125·44 million gallons
Evaporation allowance   =   29·72″
Surface drainage   =   3·63″

EFFECTIVE FALLS (INCHES)

Jan.	Feb.	Mar.	Apr.	May	June	July	Aug.	Sept.	Oct.	Nov.	Dec.	Year
3·02	2·14	1·16	0·17	—	—	—	—	1·01	3·51	3·46	3·59	18·06

B

The apparent discrepancy in the totals is due to the power of evaporation given for the summer months being more than sufficient to absorb the rainfall received. While the table of effective falls may be accepted with reserve, and some allowance should certainly be made for dews, the figures do emphasise the need to assure a supply of water during the growing season.

III. LAND UTILISATION

BEFORE proceeding to examine the land use of individual islands, it will be well to note certain characteristics that are common.

The first of these is that arable cultivation is the dominant interest ; Arable (with rotation grass) is more extensive than Meadow, and furthermore employs more labour per unit area than grass-land, especially since cultivation is so intensive. Secondly, there is to note the distinction between farming proper and growing (market-gardening). Within the arable much more land is given to growers' than to farmers' crops, although it is naturally not possible to distinguish rigidly between the two types. Finally, growing is principally directed to production for the English market, which absorbs the major share of the crops raised.

It must not be thought that the pastoral side of farming is negligible ; it still retains a considerable importance. Dairying enjoys a naturally protected market for milk, and there is also breeding for export. Stock farming on the other hand attracts little attention.

A noteworthy feature is the very small size of holdings and of individual fields, which is the result of the inheritance system referred to elsewhere, combined with heavy pressure of an increasing population and the fixity of the sea boundaries.

A. JERSEY—CULTIVATED LAND

Statistics are available for crop returns of both arable and grassland, but there are no details of the remaining Land Utilisation Survey categories except some gardens. The cultivated area will, therefore, be dealt with first.

Sixty-seven per cent. of the total area of the island is under crops or grass (1939); out of a total of 28,665 acres,[1] 19,375 are worked, 6,000 being put to grass and the remainder ploughed or dug. About half of the grassland is Meadow, and half rotation grass, which gives totals of 16,011 acres for Arable and 3,364 for Meadow. These figures do not however present a true picture since some 8,500 acres are cropped twice in a year, and it will be necessary to distinguish the actual area of land put to a particular use each year from the returned figures. The latter will be referred to throughout as *crop acres*. It is shown in the statistics that crop acres in 1939 amount to nearly 28,000, giving an effective productive area little smaller than that of the island itself.

Fig. 9 is based on the actual areas cultivated, and represents in a diagrammatic fashion the varying distribution of Arable, Meadow and other land. Worked land is clearly relatively least extensive in the parish of St. Helier, where the bay of lowland so well defined on the relief map

[1] Approximate.

is occupied by built-up Waste and Gardens, and in the three westernmost parishes, which include the western plateau and the St. Ouen's flatland. Their non-cultivated total is made up chiefly of the sands of the flatland, except in the centre, the plateau edge, some high Heath in the north-west, and in the south the airport and the drifting sands. It is on the plateau that cultivation is most widely developed, reaching 85 per cent. of the area of St. Lawrence and St. Martin and 82 per cent. of St. Mary, which include but a small proportion of cliff or valley side. The north-eastern tip of Jersey is especially noteworthy for the manner in which cultivation is pushed to the edge of the cliffs, and again in the south-east it extends over the low land to the very shore, except for a small sandy crescent along Grouville Bay.

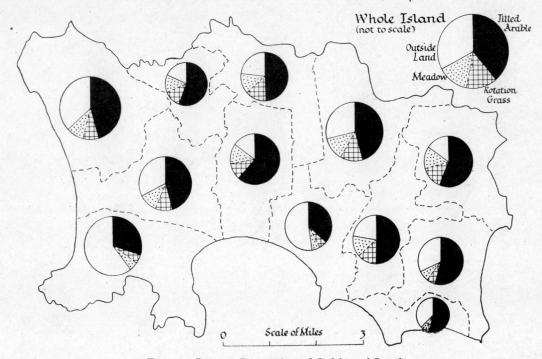

FIG. 9.—Jersey—Proportion of Cultivated Land.

There is considerable variety in the distribution of grassland, which is more important on the main plateau than elsewhere. In the south-eastern lowland, with its light soils, early and rapid growth favours primeurs rather than grazing, while the very flat western plateau is little dissected and offers few of the valley sides which are usually made over to Meadow.

The returns of crop acreages, illustrated in Fig. 10, show the dominance of Arable, which accounts for nearly nine-tenths of the whole. Potatoes alone occupy 10,614 of the 27,901 total crop acres, that is 38 per cent., and this supreme position demands first consideration for them.

In Fig. 14 no allowance has been made for double-cropping, but the distribution shown is very close to that of the actual land area devoted to potatoes, as the early crop amounts to 97 per cent. of the entire returns and there is little difference between parishes; the high northern parishes of St. John and Trinity, and St. Ouen in the north-west, have a slightly greater proportion of earlies, while St. Helier and St. Saviour have least, a fact probably to be explained by the proximity of the town to the latter areas and the consequent fractionally less dependence on the export market.   In 1939 the returns were as follows :

Earlies	.	.	.	10,260 acres
Late 1st crop	.	.		112 ,,
Late 2nd crop	.	.		242 ,,
Total potatoes	.	.		10,614 acres

In every parish but St. Clement the potato is the most widespread crop ; there it is over-shadowed by the tomato. Although the two are in competition elsewhere in the east and also in the south-west, potatoes nowhere account for less than 33 per cent. of the crop acreage and rise to 45 per cent. in Grouville, where tomatoes are also popular.

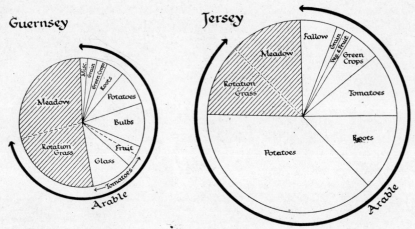

FIG. 10.—Guernsey and Jersey—Proportions of Crop Acreages.

Potato growing is primarily concerned with the export trade. In the five years 1934–8 the export of early potatoes averaged some 65,000 tons and a value of £780,000 annually, and this crop occupies the same leading position in produce export as it does in the use of land. Exports are destined for the English market ; the imports, small by comparison, are mainly for consumption and not for seed, which comes chiefly from locally grown tubers to the extent of 2,000 tons a year. Imported seed is liable to degenerate after a very few years, and most growers rely on the Jersey Royal (International Kidney).

Planting is in progress in mid-February, banking takes place in late May, and most lifting has in an average season been completed in the second or third week in June and the produce exported ; the earliest potatoes go out in the first week in June. The need for haste to catch the market and to prevent deterioration from blight calls for more labour than the local population can supply, and French, English and Irish workers are brought in for the lifting season. Although the crops carried are heavy, numbering about 27,000 plants per acre, and the price realised is great, the return varies from year to year ; in 1938 potatoes from the States Experimental Farm brought £17 per ton, in a year when crops were small, whereas in 1936 the price had been £11 17s. 6d. A crop of 10–16 tons per acre would, therefore, in any case bring in a considerable amount, but against the gross return must be offset the cost of labour and of fertilisers and sprays, which are an expensive item, but essential to combat blight.

The potato blight has been referred to previously in connection with climate. It is due to the fungus, *Phytophthera infestans*, and would probably ravage the whole of the island's crop in all but the driest years were it not for spraying. The disease is particularly serious in relation to the export market and in 1935, when it was both severe and widespread, prices fell rapidly

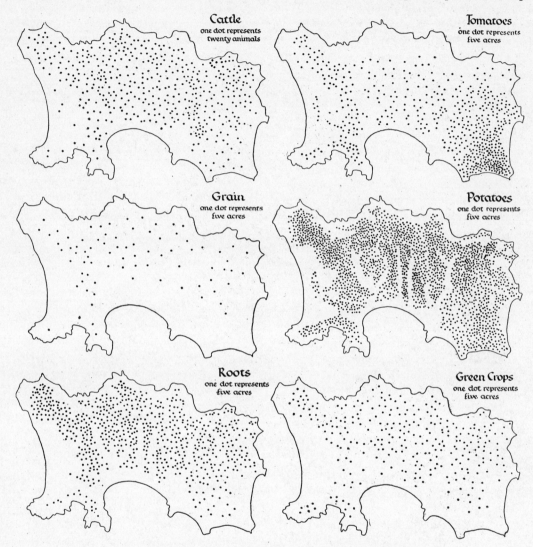

FIGS. 11–16.—Jersey—Distribution of Cattle and Crops.

while the bulk of the produce was being exported ; it is not surprising that agricultural inspectors have power to stop digging in affected fields. The spores of the fungus are usually transmitted to the tubers from diseased haulms, and may cause a loss of up to 90 per cent. of apparently healthy potatoes in 6 days. That is to say, the disease may develop in transit, and although certain packing methods render it less likely to do so, the remedy does not lie here, but in keeping the haulms as healthy as possible. This is a major undertaking, for the leaf area of a full-grown crop is 5½ times the area of the land in which the crop is planted, and to be effective spraying should commence before banking—that is to say, from mid-April onwards—and be repeated every two weeks thenceforward, or more often in wet or foggy weather. The value of spraying has been well shown in some seasons by the better yields obtained in the south-eastern parishes of Grouville and St. Clement than elsewhere on Jersey, for it is precisely the south-east which is most liable to blight and where in consequence growers are more conscious of the need to employ a safe-guard regularly. When the spray, a mixture of copper sulphate wash and caustic soda, is used thoroughly and often enough, it stops the attacks. When on the other hand blight has set in early and has killed the haulms while leaving the tubers intact, the procedure best adopted is to scorch the haulms with sulphuric acid to destroy the fungus and protect the crop during lifting. Disease may be warded off from potatoes intended for seed by immersing them in formaldehyde (1 per cent. solution).

Two other dangers threatening potato growing remain to be noted. Legislation was intro-duced in 1935 designed to prevent the import of potatoes infested with eelworm, for this pest would necessitate, as a counter-measure, the adoption of a five-year or longer interval between successive crops on the same land. It is ironical that the onset of eelworm would ruin the crop without involving the prohibition of exports, whereas the arrival[1] and spread of the Colorado beetle would mean the collapse of the trade with England and yet in the view of Jersey experts permit yield to remain reasonable. It is not surprising that stocks of anti-Colorado beetle spray (arsenate of lead and carbon disulphide) have been held ready.

The prospects of potato growing have also been affected by certain economic and industrial developments. In the early 1930's a canning factory was established on the island, after a series of tests which proved that the time elapsing between lifting and canning must be kept down to a minimum. This is not a sign that early ripening is no longer the advantage it was, but rather a movement in the direction of price stabilisation, and should be taken in conjunction with the minimum price-fixing scheme which came into operation in 1938. The fact that this was a year in which yield was low but produce sound, and the intervention of war which soon followed the introduction of the scheme, must prohibit any comment on the success or otherwise.

Tomatoes come second to potatoes in the list of grower's crops, with 3,008 crop acres in 1939, about twice the 1930 area. They are not equally popular in all parts of the island, being most thickly distributed in the south-east, especially in Grouville and St. Clement parishes (Fig. 12), and thinnest on the north and centre of the plateau. Out of the 42 acres of glasshouses in Jersey, tomatoes occupy 40, but this form of cultivation is of little importance. The 1939 figures were :

```
            Tomatoes under glass :
                1st crop      .      .        36 acres
                2nd crop      .      .         4  ,,
            Tomatoes (outdoor) :
                1st crop      .      .     1,303 acres
                2nd crop      .      ..    1,665  ,,
                                          ─────────
                Total      .      3,008 acres
                                      Total :  1st crop  .  1,339
                                            ,,   2nd crop  .  1,669
```

This is also principally a crop for export, and Jersey now takes a large share in the Channel Islands tomato trade. By 1937–8, £450,000 was being realised annually from about 28,000 tons exported.

[1] The Colorado beetle was in fact discovered in Jersey before the outbreak of war.

The same fungus which causes blight on potatoes attacks the tomato, and can be transferred from the one plant to the other. Spraying is again the remedy. Steam sterilisation was introduced for glasshouses as late as 1932, and has been tried on outdoor soils, but is thought to be less preferable than the use of a fungicide.

Growers' crops other than the two above are of little note, although the interest taken in vegetables is increasing and growers' interests are well served in this as in other connections by the States Advisory Service. Cabbage crops, i.e. brussels sprouts, cabbages, cauliflower and broccoli, are the principal items.

The extent of farming proper may be judged from the combined acreages of roots, grain, and grassland. In St. John and Trinity, that is on the highest land, on the north of the main plateau, farming attains its greatest relative importance, returning just over half the crop acreages; elsewhere it accounts for upwards of a third, except the south-eastern tip of Jersey, where it is much reduced by the great deal of land under both tomatoes and potatoes. In general, the grassland-tillage ratio within the farmed parts is around 5 : 4, but as some half of the grassland is of the rotation variety, arable working predominates here also. For the whole island in 1939, farmland was divided as follows :

Grain crops . .	404	acres
Roots . . .	3,573	,,
Green crops . . .	1,446	,,
Grass : rotation . .	3,364	,,
permanent .	3,364	,,
Total .	12,151	(crop acres)
of which .	8,787	arable

Grain is now one of the minor crops of Jersey, even when all varieties are taken together. The area it occupies is shrinking each year, not solely because of a fall in the numbers of cattle, but because green crops and imported feed—which is as cheap as locally grown grains—are supplanting it in farming practice.

The breakdown of the grain figures for 1939 gives :

Oats . . .	329	acres
Wheat . . .	60	,,
Barley and tremain .	9·5	,,
Rye . . .	5·5	,,
Total grain .	404	acres

Oats are thicker in the west, and wheat in the east.

Like grain crops, roots are concentrated chiefly in the north, but they are much more extensive, with acreage of 3,573 made up in this manner :

Turnips . . .	1,870	acres
Mangolds . . .	1,306	,,
Swedes . . .	397	,,
Total . .	3,573	acres

It is interesting to observe the contrast between the maps of root and tomato distribution, which are very dissimilar, and show how farming has been driven back to the higher land.

Green crops are increasing greatly each year : they occupied 1,446 acres in 1939 but **are** naturally found in the farming districts, being thickest in the north and showing a slight concentration in the north-east.

The total area of grassland, 6,728 crop acres and about 6,000 acres of actual land, is divided, as already stated, almost equally into rotation and permanent grass. The last year for which separate figures are available, 1930, recorded this use of grass crops :

Clover, sainfoin and temporary grass : mown . 5,264 acres ⎫
                                         grazed . 3,702 ,, ⎬ Total rotation 9,024
                                         lucerne . 58 ,, ⎭

Permanent grass : mown . 2,463 acres ⎫ Total meadow 9,646
                       grazed . 7,183 ,, ⎭

That is, about two-thirds of the grassland was for grazing purposes, the same proportion as for 1939, and the remaining third for hay.

The general distribution of grass has been referred to previously. It is most extensive on the main plateau, away from the lighter soils. Four types of grassland may be distinguished : the Meadow of the incised valleys, whose sides are in spaces too steep for tillage, and well shaded by terrain and trees ; Meadow occurring at the edge of cultivation where the land is not yet fully under control, with which may be classed patches of permanent pasture interspersed with the Arable : Meadow of parts of the sandy lowlands, and rotation grass, which may be found anywhere. It will be seen that Meadow tends strongly to be restricted to the less desirable lands. Nevertheless, grass farming, and more particularly temporary grassland, has received much attention because of the value of the island breed of cattle. The usual period of ley is three years for hay and clover mixtures, of which the following is an example which gives good results on good soils :

Lb. per acre :

Perennial ryegrass . . 9
Italian . . . $4\frac{1}{2}$
Red clover . . . 5
Red clover late flowering . 5
Alsike clover . . . $2\frac{1}{4}$
White Dutch . . . $2\frac{1}{4}$
Provence lucerne . . $2\frac{1}{4}$

Total . $30\frac{1}{4}$ lb.

Cattle

The distribution of cattle is given in the statistics and Fig. 11. They are found everywhere on the plateau and in the valleys, but are less numerous on the niches of lowland. The table shows that steers are not kept ; the whole emphasis is on dairying and on breeding for export. Legislation has provided against contamination of the herd either by cross-breeding or the introduction of bovine tuberculosis, which has been eradicated by stringent measures in all the islands. The high quality of the animals as milkers, which accounts for the esteem in which they are held, is well shown in the record of one of the herd at the Experimental Farm :

1935 : cow born in 1927, days in last lactation 361 : 10,992 lb. milk of 6·04 per cent. fat content (about 1,063 gallons).
1935 : 782·34 lb. butter from the same animal.

The cows are grazed in the open the whole year round, except on a few inclement days, and moved (being tethered) and milked three times daily. For winter feed, turnips are used until

January, followed by mangolds from January onwards. Imported feeds play an increasingly important part in the dairy farmer's economy, which is progressively less linked to the home production of grain.

A note is in place here on the origin of the Channel Islands breeds of cattle. Although at the present day there are differences between them, mainly of size and colouring, they are held to have had a common ancestry, possibly in a cross between the Breton "Froment du Leon" and the Norman brindle, in the eleventh century. The divergences between the Guernsey and Jersey types are due to selective breeding and restricted interchange.

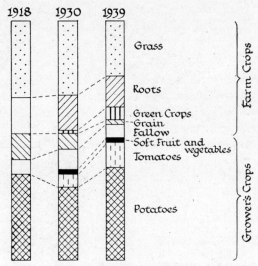

FIG. 17.—Jersey—Cropping Trends, 1918-39.

RECENT TRENDS IN THE USE OF CULTIVATED LAND—JERSEY

The published statistics relating to the years 1930-9 inclusive[1] should be accepted with caution, as it is known that in 1930-3 and again in 1935 they are to some extent incomplete, especially regarding second crops. However, where a certain crop shows a decline over the period, this trend can be accepted with confidence. The crop returns should be read in conjunction with the trade figures[1] which, besides showing movements in the export market, also indicate changes in deficiencies of various agricultural items.

Crop acreages of potatoes and potato export figures, even allowing for the inaccurate early returns, are not too closely related because of the varying fortune of the crop year by year, but in general it may be said that the island's chief crop has more than maintained its position. There has at the same time been a rapid increase in tomato land and trade, both of which have almost doubled over the ten years, and tomato exports are now nearly half those of potatoes by weight, and more than half by value. Jersey therefore has two principal cash crops, which practically exclude all others from the export market. Both are growers' produce, and it is not remarkable that while cultivated land and arable alike were about as extensive in 1939 as in 1930, farmland proper should have lost ground, falling by 2,000 acres, or 14 per cent. of its 1930 total. Grassland was the chief type to be reduced, losing some 1,500 acres. This corresponds to a diminution in the

[1] See statistical tables in the Appendix.

numbers of cattle, which fell by 2,333, but even so imports of feed, hay and straw rose, a movement due to improved methods of management as well as to the inability of the land to supply all the maintenance needed. Within the tillage farming area, roots have changed little, but grain has continued to decline as it has been doing for a long time. Green crops have greatly increased, and it is only for this reason that the farmed tillage has not declined more severely.

A diagrammatic summary of the relative extent of various crops at the beginning and end of the period here discussed is made in Fig. 17.

Changing methods in cultivation generally are also well brought out in the figures for agricultural machinery, transport, workers, and import of sprays and fertilisers.[1] Mechanisation has reduced the need for workers, down by about one-third since 1930, and for horses ; transport figures need no comment in view of the destination of so much produce for export ; while artificial fertilizers are now in about twice the 1930 demand.

B. JERSEY—OTHER LAND

The categories of Heath, Forest, Inland Water, Waste and Gardens remain to be considered. Between them they amount to 9,290 acres, nearly a quarter of the island and an area nine-tenths that of the chief crop.

The published figures relate only to holdings of more than one vergee (four-ninths acre), and therefore although they show 116 acres of kitchen garden and 490 of orchard, they are not of great assistance in discovering the true extent of the Garden area, but they do show how each of these sub-categories is being restricted in size from year to year. In rural areas, kitchen gardens, like the population, are widely dispersed, mainly alongside the roads, while the town of St. Helier is ringed by a belt of Garden continued along the coast in both directions, especially eastwards, where it swings round La Roque and stretches half-way up the shore of Grouville Bay.

Forest is represented only by bands of trees which partially clothe the sides of incised valleys, more thickly in the west of the island than in the east ; Saint Peter's and Millbrook valleys are the most notable in this respect. The sum area of these narrow and winding strips of woodland is small, and they are almost a negligible feature of land use. Inland Water is still less significant, being hardly perceptible apart from some tiny dams.

Waste[2] is of three types : built-up areas, bare rock, and roads. This last form is not inconsiderable, for roads are numerous in all parts. St. Helier provides the chief concentration of fully built-over and other urban Waste land, an estimated 325 acres, but there are very many small uncultivated enclosures scattered throughout the island. The airport, possibly 125 acres, may be considered a special type. As the cliff coasts are very steep the long stretches of naked rock there do not reach far inland ; quarries, mostly in the north, account for a small area.

It is Heath that constitutes most of the outside land, and that shows up blank on the western side of the island in the dot maps. Here, where it is most extensive, three main forms may be observed next to one another. The loose sands of the dunes district shown on the geological map are given over to golf links and a race-course where they extend over high ground, and grade into sand hills to the westward. The St. Ouen's flatland is watered in the centre by a small stream from the plateau, and a cultivated patch over a mile long, which appears on the distribution maps, lies between the foot of the slope and St. Ouen's pond. Between it and

---

[1] See statistical table in Appendix.   [2] Land agriculturally unproductive.

the sea runs sandy Heath, widening out on the north and south to stretch the whole way across the floor of the niche. A small development of the same type of low, dry sandy Heath is to be noted in the golf links at Grouville Bay. It abuts on the high Heath of the exposed plateau edge, a type which resembles in every respect the Heath of the south-west and the entire north coast. For the most part, this coastal Heath is confined to the degraded slope which lies between the edge of the plateau above and the sheer cliffs below ; only in the extreme north-west of the island has cultivation failed to conquer the flat land, where the uncultivated land, Les Landes, is used as a rifle range.

A Summary of findings is included in the tables of statistics.

C. SIZE OF HOLDINGS : LABOUR

A study of these two topics will serve two purposes ; it will emphasise the intensive nature of cultivation in general, and at the same time throw into relief certain contrasts between conditions in Jersey and Guernsey respectively.

In 1939, there were in Jersey 1,829 holdings of an average size of 10½ acres. Comparatively few were above 25 acres ; those below 5 acres[1] and between 10 and 20 acres were more numerous than the other groups, which would appear to indicate a division between property holders with small estates and those with medium-large areas (i.e. " small " and " large " as understood in the Channel Islands). This may correspond to the distinction between farming and growing, although it is probable that it has also something to do with the amount of land which one man can work. There were 1,839 regular workers, that is about one per holding (in addition to the large force of owner-occupiers, who hold the majority of lands), or about one man for ten acres. When the variation of labour needed per unit area according to the crop is taken into account, and also the smaller size of growers' than farmers' holdings, it will be realised that a holding of between five and ten acres would probably not in general be large enough fully to employ one man more than the smaller type.

The number of holdings is increasing ; the figure given above may be compared with the 1930 total of 1,808 ; it is exactly in the under-five acre size and the ten to twenty-five that the increase has taken place, while the intermediate and larger types have lost ground. The conclusion drawn is merely tentative, for the loss of workers contingent on mechanisation must be considered.

Guernsey had about 400 farmers in 1939, whose farms ran on the average to some 14 acres. There is a very sharp contrast with the average size holding for all worked land, which was 3½ acres, and the division between farming and market-gardening is clear-cut. Growing under glass is responsible (see below) ; here cultivation is at its most intensive and every individual plant is given attention. Cash returns per unit area are high. It is not surprising to find that the number of regular workers in Guernsey was double the Jersey figure. In 1939 there were over 4,000 compulsorily insured employees (i.e. those earning less than £3 a week) in market-gardens, in addition to some 2,000 growers. Farm land called only for 730 employed workers.

Attention must be drawn to the fact that the comparision just made takes no account of seasonal labour ; it is nevertheless a sound indication of the more definite demarcation of the growing from the farming area in Guernsey.

[1] The sizes dealt with are approximate. Official statistics record areas in vergees and summarise holdings of 1–10, 10–25, 25–50 and over 50 vergees. About 2¼ Jersey and 2½ Guernsey vergees are equal to one English acre.

D. GUERNSEY—CULTIVATED LAND

Turning now to consider the distribution of Arable, Grass and outside land in Guernsey, one sees that 56 per cent. of the area of the island is under crops or grass (Fig. 10). The map with wheel diagrams (Fig. 18) demonstrates the much greater proportion of cultivated land in Catel, St. Saviour, St. Andrew and St. Peter in the Wood than in the other parishes, where considerable areas are in Heath (along the south coast), built over (in St. Peter Port, and to a lesser degree in St. Sampson), or in Heath or rocky Waste (in St. Sampson and Vale).

The two northernmost parishes display the smallest ratio of grassland to Arable, and this fact corresponds to another feature of land-use distribution which should be borne in mind throughout the examination of the cultivated area which follows ; that is to say the percentage of cultivated land occupied by farms is everywhere above 60 on the plateau, while on the shelf it never rises above 40. The plateau is in fact the retreat of farming proper, which just as in Jersey has been pushed on to the higher land ; here the marked division of high land from low and the manner in which the growing industry has developed have led to a separation of the growing from the farming districts far more marked than anything in the larger island, just as there is a distinct difference in the size of holdings for the two purposes.

Arable

On the plateau, Arable occurs widely except in the valleys ; in the north it is broken into by blocks of Meadow where the drainage is unsatisfactory, reaching its greatest relative extent in the old Braye du Valle. Arable with rotation grass accounts for nearly three-quarters of the worked area, and 4,000 acres are actually tilled or dug.

The chief crop raised is the tomato. Since separate statistics are not available for types of fruit grown in the open, the total tomato acreage has been taken as equivalent to that of the crops grown under glass plus two-thirds that of outdoor fruit, giving a total of 1,225 acres; the distribution (Fig. 26) is far thicker on the shelf than on the high land.

Cultivation of the tomato began in Guernsey towards the end of the last century, when there was already much land under glass for grapes. It rapidly became the chief crop, but the early methods of cultivation were crude and by 1900 much of the soil was sick. Sterilisation by heat was commenced in 1904 ; a steam steriliser was patented, and although the idea was taken up slowly at first, the practice eventually became well established. Improvements in packing and grading in the first decade of the present century were followed by the introduction of better methods of despatch in 1915, when the Royal Court was provoked by wartime difficultes to pass Ordinances in this connection. The official control of exports has incidentally since 1934 been extended to all items of growers' produce, which are now liable to inspection.

Tomato planting takes place under glass, in both hot- and cold-houses, from late February to the end of March. The plants are kept under glass until the beginning of May, for a light frost will destroy them. Hardening is effected by slackening the fires and increased ventilation, and the plants are set out to yield mostly in mid-May to early June. All the three methods are common of ripening in the open, in hot- and cold-houses.

Each plant is usually kept to one leader, supported by a bamboo outdoors or by string or wire under cover. Outdoor tomatoes are generally a main crop, although on rare occasions they figure as a catch crop after potatoes on early slopes.

It is interesting to compare the tomato exports of Guernsey with those of Jersey (see statistics) ; the higher yield under glass is self-evident.

Tomatoes grow best on a light, well-drained loam. Systems of soil management vary ; in low-lying regions with a high water table controlled by tidal sluices watering is rare; but in other areas it is very necessary ; there is no formula, though it may be said that plants in pots should in most cases be watered daily and those in trenches three times a week.

The soil sickness referred to above may be due to more than one tomato disease, most of which are due to parasitic fungi ; for instance, the *Verticillium albo-atrum*, transmitted by thrips,

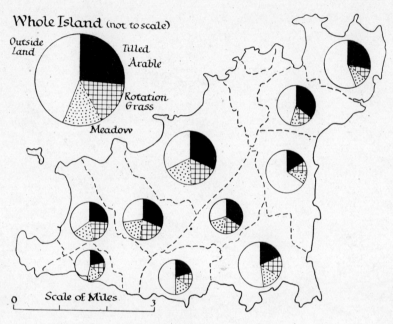

FIG. 18.—Guernsey—Proportion of Cultivated Land.

causes the sleepy or wilt disease, which flourishes in hot-houses ; stem canker is caused by *Didymella lycopersici*, while club root is spread by the cellworm. Depletion of chemical properties must also be reckoned with, and the vraic with which the soil was at first dressed was unable to remedy the deficiencies brought about by years of continuous cropping. Nowadays proprietary fertilisers are common, and steam sterilisation popular. It is effective, although rather expensive, for when the whole floor of a house is steamed, it should remain pest-free for two seasons if the practice is to be economical. Unfortunately, re-contamination after one season is most frequent. When trenches only are steamed, the treatment must be repeated annually, some two months before planting. Other methods of sterilisation include the use of fungicides, mostly formaldehyde. A form of rotation is also known, consisting of the bodily interchange of soil under glass with an equal amount of soil from grassland ; this means that the grower must own or rent grassland close to his glass, and he is therefore involved in the management of stock. This method is not considered likely to have a lasting effect.

Glasshouses

Glasshouses are separately indicated on the three-inch Ordnance Survey map of Guernsey, which should be studied. The amount of land under glass on Guernsey, nearly $1\frac{1}{2}$ square miles, is the most distinctive feature of land use in the island. Its distribution is summarised in Fig. 24, where it is seen that the plateau has far less per acre than the shelf; in the north over a third of the cropped land is under glass.

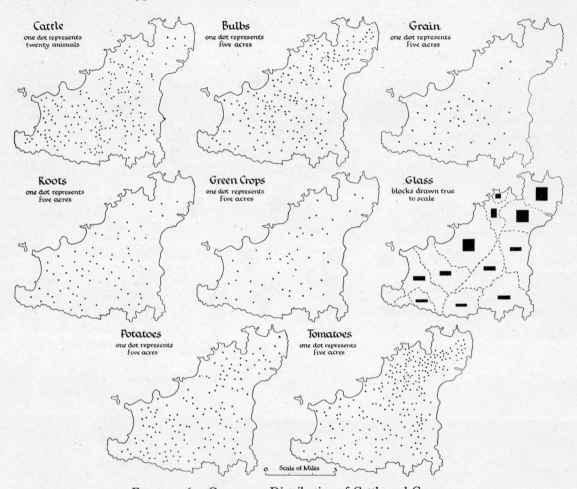

FIGS. 19–26.—Guernsey—Distribution of Cattle and Crops.

In detail, the distribution shows the influence of certain controls. On the shelf, glass occurs on flat land where there is no danger of waterlogging, while in the south it is densest along the highest part of the plateau. In the western enclaves of low land, the belt of glass along the foot of the plateau slope is everywhere thicker on the eastern sides of the niches than on the less sunny southern.

Paradoxically enough, Guernsey's unfavourable aspect contributed directly to the development of cultivation under glass, which enabled Guernsey growers to offset Jersey's climatic advantage while at the same time forcing them to concentrate on a crop other than the potato which Jersey raised out of doors in such large quantities. On the other hand, the difference between the natural climate and the artificial conditions in glasshouses is small, as it must be for economical working. The optimum temperature in hot-houses is 60° (compare the atmospheric temperature figures in a previous section) ; cold-house working is favoured by the long hours of direct sunlight. Hail is rarely sufficient to damage glass, while perfect protection is obtained from the strong winds.

Most glasshouses are now heated (with South Wales anthracite) and workers in the glass areas include many stokers as well as actual cultivators. Without counting those indirectly affected, such as drivers and mechanics, the amount of labour required averages one man for 300 square feet of glass.

Bulbs (Fig. 20)

Daffodils and narcissi account for three-quarters of the bulb acreage (938). Whole fields at a time are planted, the cut flowers being marketed chiefly in London. There is an important exchange of bulbs between Guernsey and Holland.

Flower cultivation is widespread throughout the island, being densest on the central shelf. Although the land in the latter area is largely Arable it carries many glasshouses, so that bulbs are evidently very frequently grown in the unglazed enclosures.

Potatoes (Fig. 25)

The area under potatoes is diminishing, and in 1939 they accounted for only 748 acres, thus ranking third by area in the list of crops. In the Arable parts they are well distributed, with greatest density on the central shelf and the plateau top, especially in the south-west. The main crop is the more extensive, except in parishes with a western exposure—St. Saviour and St. Peter in the Wood both carry more earlies. Although the potato is no longer among the chief exports, it receives official (and compulsory) protection in the form of spraying to prevent the Colorado beetle from establishing itself.

Fruit

The absence of separate figures for orchard fruit, soft fruit and outdoor tomatoes precludes an adequate discussion of the extent of fruit crops. It may be said however that orchards have dwindled greatly since the heyday of the cider trade, and most of the trees now require replacement ; on the Land Utilisation Survey map they are included with Gardens. Fruit growing is mainly carried on in the east and south.

Roots (Fig. 22)

In 1939 the root acreage was composed as follows :—

Swedes, etc.	.	.	66 acres
Parsnips and carrots	.	.	146 ,,
Mangolds	.	.	178 ,,
Total	.	.	390 acres

The map brings out the contrast of the growing districts of the shelf and the farmland of the high land to the south, where roots are much more densely scattered. *Green Crops* and *Grain*, which are minor crops, are, of course, also chiefly found on the plateau (Figs. 23 and 21). Oats account for three-quarters of the grain land.

Grassland (See Land Utilisation Survey map).

Grass, both permanent and rotation, extends over 4,527 acres, that is, rather more than half of the land worked. The Land Utilisation Survey map, recording rotation grass as Arable, does not present a true picture of the extent of grassland since the ratio of temporary to permanent grass is about 1 : 1 and is increasing. Temporary leys are rarely embodied in a fixed rotation scheme, however. Meadow, as in Jersey, occurs mostly on the less workable lands—the sides of incised valleys, low-lying and badly drained areas, and the western niches. There are patches of Meadow at the foot of the plateau slope where streams descend on the low land.

Livestock

The Guernsey herd in 1939 stood at 4,252 head, of which 2,250 were cows in milk or calf ; about one animal per acre of grassland (grazing and hay combined).[1] In this connection the long growing season due to the peculiarities of local climate must be remembered. Little need be added to the comments made above in the discussion of Jersey, except to say that cattle distribution (Fig. 19) is expectedly similar to that of roots.

The figures for poultry, pigs and goats are given in the livestock table.

E. GUERNSEY—OTHER LAND

Figures are issued only for buildings and furze-brakes, which account only for 1,345 and 447 acres of land out of the uncultivated total of 6,914 acres (nearly 45 per cent. of the island). The problem of accounting for this land here presents somewhat different aspects from the same problem in Jersey, for not only is the area proportionately greater but also the larger constituent categories occur in different ratios.

Forest appears on the coloured Land Utilisation Survey map in a few tiny patches, which mostly indicate very small plantations of conifers on shady slopes in the south. Gardens are again widespread throughout the island, with a belt round the town and a smaller concentration at St. Sampson almost linked by Garden along the shore of Belle Grève Bay. Gardens as shown on the Land Utilisation Survey map do not, however, correspond very closely with the distribution of population, for two reasons ; individual gardens tend to be largest in the south-east, which is a " desirable residential district," while in the north-west especially many small enclosures attached to houses raise growers' produce for the market instead of kitchen garden crops and have, therefore, been mapped as Arable. In this respect the survey is more precise than the official returns.

Along the southern coast high Heath corresponds to the similar feature in the north of Jersey ; the dune sands have their counterpart in L'Ancresse Common. Here the land, although low-lying, is yet high enough for the water-table to be well below the surface and the Heath to be dry. Elsewhere minute patches of damp Heath mark points of poor drainage, and dry Heath is found on many of the hougues and promontories of the shelf, often in association with Waste and Inland Water. The conjunction of these three types of land use is found at so many points in the Clos du Valle, around St. Sampson and south-west of Grand Havre, that it may be looked on as a typical feature of these districts. It has been occasioned by the opening, working and abandonment of quarries which impart to much of the shelf a truly remarkabe variety of detail and which contain practically all the Inland Water to be found on the island.[2]

Apart from the much greater number of quarries, the occurrence of Waste on Guernsey is essentially similar to that on Jersey.

See statistics for summary of findings.

---

[1] Five or six per farm of fourteen acres (averages).   [2] The dam was to store water covering a square mile.

F. THE SMALLER ISLANDS

Alderney, Sark, Herm and Jethou are very small indeed, small even compared with Jersey and Guernsey. They are in fact not large enough to maintain their own trade connections with the outside world, being for the most part served by Guernsey in this respect, and it is not surprising that their cultivation should be directed chiefly towards raising farm crops, including grass, which amount in each case to over nine-tenths of the worked area. This does not mean that land use is identical in these islands ; there are contrasts, which will appear in the following passages.

Alderney

Although the deep indentations of Braye and Longy Bays give Alderney a rather irregular shape, the general effect of an elongated block is easily to be seen. Block structure is most apparent in the western two-thirds of the island, where cliffs rise from the sea on the south and west to heights of 150–200 feet. The plateau just fails to reach 300 feet at its highest point ; it falls away very gently to the north and north-west to about 200 feet O.D., where the surface steps down old cliffs to a narrow shelf less than 50 feet above sea-level ; this is the counterpart of the niches of Jersey and Guernsey (Fig. 27).

The plateau is attacked in the normal manner by tiny streams, but the effects of erosion are most marked in north-eastern Alderney, where four hills are separated from one another by well-defined cols. There is a marshy patch behind Longy Bay ; quarrying has had considerable effect of the relief of the hills.

The geological structure of Alderney may be dealt with briefly. As the map shows (Fig. 28) exposures may be grouped under two heads, the igneous and the sedimentary ; the sedimentary rocks are the younger, and consist of reddish or grey grit formed of the debris of the igneous masses, possibly in Cambrian times. The chief exposure occurs north-east and south-west of Longy Bay, and it is in this rock that the extensive quarries referred to above were opened. The igneous outcrops include dioritic and granitic masses, with their upper surfaces decomposed to varying degrees, and various intrusions. The main rock bodies are all ascribed to the pre-Cambrian.

Surface deposits include the residual materials resulting from weathering, brick-earth, raised beach materials, and, to the north of Longy Bay, more recent sands. The soils of Alderney are probably in general lighter than those of the other Channel Islands, although they exhibit the same main characteristics.

There has always been a contrast between the cultivated and uncultivated parts of Alderney. The cultivated area, the Blaye, lies on the plateau, mostly above 250 feet O.D. Its soils are deep, and Arable practically excludes all other forms of land use. This well-defined nucleus is in one respect different from the plateau Arable of the other islands ; that is to say, it is almost all unfenced, and the land is not broken up into the multitude of tiny enclosures which have been described elsewhere. The reason is that the three-field system of working persisted on Alderney long after it had been abandoned on the other islands, probably because of the ease with which all parts of the island could be reached from St. Anne's (where nearly all the islanders still live) which formed a settlement of a convenient size. A contributory factor was most probably the difficult sea approach, which rendered contact with the outside world less frequent and thus helped the local tradition to maintain itself.

c

The solid block of Arable[1] which remains is largely laid to grass, and it is probable that temporary leys are not being ploughed up but are being allowed to form permanent grassland. The minor position held by tillage crops is sufficiently evident from Fig. 30 and the tables to need no comment; it is obvious that Alderney's former participation in the potato trade has ceased.

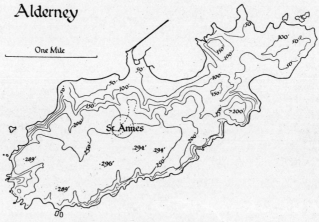

FIG. 27.—Alderney—Physical.

According to the published statistics, more than half Alderney is under crops or grass, the latter making up 87 per cent. of the worked area. There is a discrepancy between the official returns and the results of the Survey recorded on the Land Utilisation Survey map, which is due to the inclusion in the returns of grassland of much unfenced rough grazing—a form of

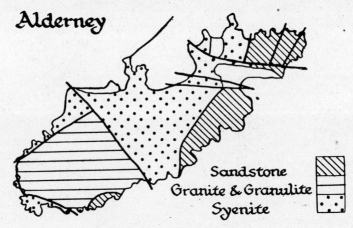

FIG. 28.—Alderney—Geological.

land use which is not often met on the other islands. It occurs in those areas marked as Heath in the west and north-east. Meadow is restricted in extent by the pressure of Arable above and Heath below, and along the south coast there is in places no intervening Meadow between the tillage of the flat land and the heath-grown upper slopes of the present cliffs; to the north

[1] Cut into by the airfield.

of St. Anne's, the step down to the low ledge has been enclosed, and here Meadow and Heath dispute possession.

The herd of "Alderneys" (Guernseys) numbered only 475 in 1939; there had been a rapid fall from 735 in 1927. In the same period cultivation lost only 70 acres, about half each from grass and tillage. It may be assumed that the cattle export trade has declined.

Sark

Sark is usually taken to include Great and Little Sark and the adjacent island of Brecqhou. They are peculiar in not having been niched; there are no shelves, no enclaves, and very little

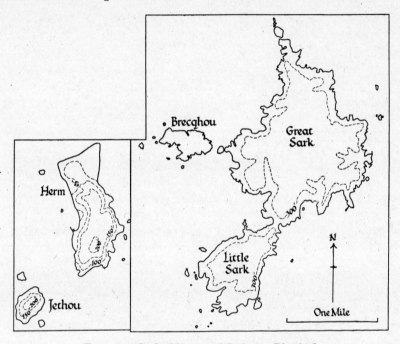

FIG. 29.—Sark, Herm and Jethou—Physical.

development of valley, so that the plateau surface is largely unbroken. The descent to the sea is precipitous in all parts, while the plateau is remarkably flat and even, lying at over 300 feet O.D., and not passing the 350-feet level. Sark is composed entirely of metamorphic rocks of great age, similar to the more ancient igneous masses in Jersey and Guernsey. Great Sark is mostly micaschist, Little Sark mostly granitic, while Brecqhou has rocks of both types. Little is known of the superficial deposits, but it is safe to assume that here, too, they are made up of residual sands and brick-earth.

On the Land Utilisation Survey map, Sark resembles the plateau of Jersey, in that Arable covers most of the area. Some 35 per cent. of the island was worked in 1939; the low proportion is accounted for by the small size of the island and the relatively large coastline which makes Heath a large item. Rotation grass here is not so prominent as in Alderney, although grassland as a whole takes 58 per cent. of cultivated land; again, the number of cattle is dwindling and appears small for the amount of grass available. Among tillage crops grain occupies first place (Fig. 30 and Table).

It is interesting to note that Great Sark reproduces on a minute scale the distribution of woodland typical of the Channel Islands ; that is, shade trees, and wooded belts on the valley sides.

Herm and Jethou

These two islands between them cover about the same area as the average English farm. Even within this tiny space features may be recognised corresponding to those which are now familiar. Herm, like Guernsey, has a southern plateau, reaching up to 210 feet, and a northern lowland, about 50 feet O.D. The gentle northward slope of the plateau is also repeated here. The whole island is of very old granitic rocks with black micaceous dikes ; quarrying has removed or reduced in places deposits which in any case are thinner on the whole than in the island's larger neighbours, and the solid rock beneath is for the most part very close to the surface.

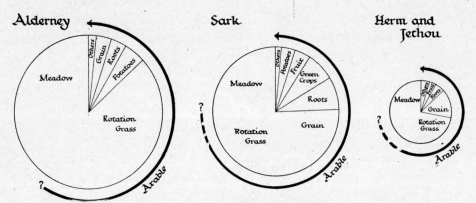

Fig. 30.—Alderney, Sark, Herm and Jethou—Proportions of Crop Acreages.

For this reason Heath is found on the highest land, as well as over the whole of the low-lying northern part, but Arable and Meadow are both firmly established. . Grass is nearly three-quarters of the cultivated total, which itself is about a third of the whole area. Grain is the chief tillage crop (Fig. 29 and Table). On Herm again, the amount of land worked is decreasing.

Jethou is little more than a flat-topped rock, but nevertheless it carries three enclosures, a house, two little patches of trees, and the usual cliff Heath. Both these islands afford striking testimony to the manner in which cultivation in the Channel Islands is pushed to the limits of possibility.

CROPPING AND LIVESTOCK STATISTICS FOR ALDERNEY, SARK, HERM & JETHOU
1939 (Acres).

	Grain	Roots[1]	Green crops	Potatoes	Fruit	Misc.	Grass	Total	Cattle	Sheep
Alderney . .	34	37	3	43	7	$1\frac{1}{2}$	856	892	475	50
Sark . .	78	36	32	16	17	$\frac{1}{2}$	250	430	160	27
Herm and Jethou .	9	3	1	1	2	$\frac{1}{2}$	44	61	2[2]	—

[1] Includes swedes, mangolds, parsnips, carrots, etc.   [2] 1936.

IV. LAND-USE REGIONS

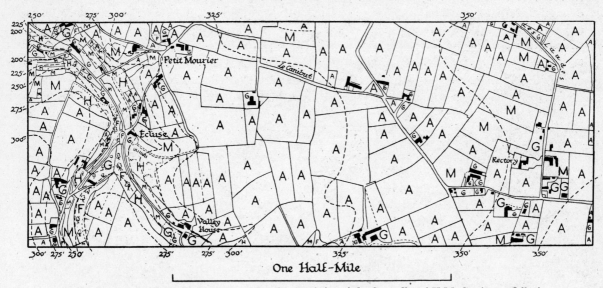

(*Reproduced from the Ordnance Survey Map, by permission of the Controller of H.M. Stationery Office.*)

FIG. 31.—Portion of a Field Sheet in Jersey—the Main Plateau.

Here, close to the centre of the north coast, the plateau surface is more than 300 feet O.D. The sample presents all the typical features of the plateau region—scattered settlement, very widespread Arable, and small development of Meadow. The portion of incised valley in the west shows how Heath and Forest on the steepest slopes pass into Meadow on the valley bottom. Where Meadow and Arable have become established on the sides, it is in places with the assistance of terracing.

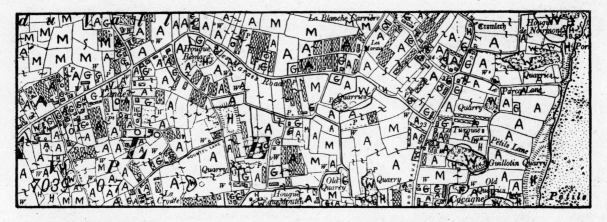

(*Reproduced from the Ordnance Survey Map, by permission of the Controller of H.M. Stationery Office.*)

FIG. 32.—Portion of a Field Sheet in Guernsey—Arable of the Clos du Valle.

In this sample, taken from the northern part of the shelf, all other land-use forms serve only to point up the wide spread of Arable. The small patches of Meadow represent low-lying ground, while igneous outcrops appear as Heath, with Waste and Inland Water where quarrying has taken place. The scatter of Gardens emphasises the unnucleated settlement characteristic of the rural areas. Scale, 6 inches to one mile.

BECAUSE of their common interest in market-gardening and dairying, in produce and stock export, the Channel Islands should be considered as parts of a single land-use region. There are sufficient contrasts between members of the group to warrant taking each as a sub-region, which gives a unit already so small, and moreover so dominated by one or two crops, that further sub-division is undesirable. There is, of course, in every island a range from most intensively

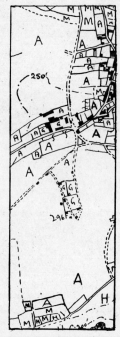

FIG. 33.—Portion of a Field Sheet in Alderney— Nucleated Settlement and the Arable Plateau.

Here the unfenced Arable typical of the plateau of Alderney is well brought out, and can be seen to pass abruptly into Heath and the edge of the flat land, in places without the intervention of Meadow. St. Anne's lies mainly in a small valley and provides no exception to the general Arable nature of the plateau. The large waste area is part of the airfield, which, like those of Jersey and Guernsey, is on the platform top. Scale, 4 inches to one mile.

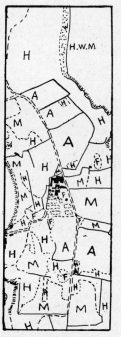

FIG. 34.—Portion of a Field Sheet in Herm— Sub-marginal Land.

This map portrays so much of Herm that nothing need be added to the comments already made. Scale 4 inches to one mile.

worked land to obstinate Heath and bare rock Waste, the differences between the farming and the growing areas, and between high and low land, but if boundaries were drawn to take account of these facts the result would necessarily be to split the total area into too great a number of parts, some of which would be very small indeed.

It seems better, therefore, to provide samples of some typical land-use forms, and this has been attempted in the small sections of field maps reproduced as Figs. 31 to 34.

V. HISTORY OF LAND USE

IT is most probable that Guernsey and Jersey, at least, have been continuously occupied from neolithic times to the present day. The inhabitants who lived among the megaliths appear to have settled originally on fertile patches ; they practised ploughing, and even in those early days maintained flourishing trade connections with both the French and English mainlands. The present state of agriculture in the islands is, therefore, the last stage reached in a long process of farming evolution ; and although agriculture has always formed as it were a permanent background to island life, it has suffered various changes of fortune because of political events.

To understand fully the impact of political changes, one must appreciate the factor of insularity, for the islands are all small and each one has tended to operate as a single economic unit, with its interests less varied than those of a larger community lacking such a definite boundary as the seashore. The result has been that at any one time each island has concentrated chiefly on agriculture or chiefly on trade, in the latter case, it must be said, to the detriment of agriculture.

The political union of the islands with England was achieved by the Norman Conquest. Very little is known of their state in the preceding centuries, although it is thought that the three-field system of agriculture was practised on all the larger islands at one stage. However, already in 1030 the present organisation of parishes existed, and it may be taken that the present inheritance law was in operation under the Normans. That is to say, a landowner had the greatest difficulty in disposing of his land during his lifetime (some recent changes have been made here) and on his death it was partitioned among his kin in a somewhat complicated manner which involved the constant sub-division of property and which accounts for the tiny size of the present-day fields.

An event of major importance which can be dated is the granting in 1482 or 1483 of a privilege of neutrality, which was conferred on the islands by Pope Sixtus IV at the request of Edward IV of England. This had the effect of checking to a great extent French expeditions against them, except for a few sporadic irruptions, and assured peace in which to develop agriculture and to ply trade, the latter probably encouraged by the reception of religious refugees from France. By the early seventeenth century Guernsey, which lay on the Spain–St. Malo–Paris shipping routes, had established a flourishing entrepôt trade. As a result, agriculture suffered, according to a contemporary observer. Although the island produced enough bread to feed itself, and a sufficient surplus of meat to provision its ships, the less commercially favoured Jersey was agriculturally the better favoured and more productive, with an export of both corn and cider— a fine early example of produce cultivation for sale abroad. By 1651, Guernsey appears to have been overtaken by some disaster, whose cause is obscure, but was possibly in part due to heavy taxation on wheat and in part also the economic upheaval of the Civil War. The population declined, and in the year mentioned two-thirds of the land was out of production and nineteen-twentieths of the inhabitants were living in poverty.

The latter half of the seventeenth century saw the spread of sheep-farming, which supplemented the supply of wool for the domestic knitting industry. Some notion of the size of this industry and also of the relative populations of the islands may be gained from the following figures, which at the same time show that Alderney and Sark were not at all thinly peopled :

Wool shipments from Southampton authorised by James II (tods of 28lbs.) :

Jersey	Guernsey	Alderney	Sark
4,000	2,000	400	200

The cider trade of Jersey, which was to continue for so long, had developed on the basis of trees planted on the earthen banks between enclosures. As the trade grew, orchards were set, and this example was followed in Guernsey, which came to share the trade by 1750. In the meantime, an event of great importance had taken place; in 1689, William III, wishing to isolate the Jacobite factions in the islands from French influence, refused to renew the concession of neutrality so long in force, and forbade trade with France. The way lay open to privateering in war and to smuggling at all times, with profits so great that agriculture was faced with keen competition and considerable numbers deserted their fields. It was more so in Guernsey than in Jersey, which accentuated the already existing differences in agricultural usage in the two islands. This fact, and the more plentiful information forthcoming for the succeeding period, makes it desirable to consider the two separately from this point onwards.

Heathland in Guernsey
1787
from a map in Guille Allés library.
St. Peter Port.

former Braye du Valle

0   Scale of Miles   2

FIG. 35.—Guernsey—Heathland, 1787.

Commencing with Guernsey : that island, by 1750, had extended its trade connections to include wine shipping and storage for the trade between England and Portugal, and the wine traffic was to prove most profitable before the century ended. The cider export trade already referred to called for land which was turned over from farming. Sheep and cattle grazing were more popular than tillage, and as a result the wheat yield was no longer sufficient for the island. One must assume that the population was increasing steadily, for land was being brought in and reclaimed. Heath still persisted along the south coast, on the sands in the north, in the valleys of the plateau and in low-lying areas—that is, in places that were over-dry or over-wet (see Fig. 35); but the proportion of arable and meadow combined rose from 35 per cent. of the island area in 1650 to 50 per cent. in 1775.

The protracted wars which ended the eighteenth and began the nineteenth centuries initiated great changes in the use of the land. Knitwear had still been a major export in 1750; but now sheep farming received a severe blow and was no longer to be of any great importance. Agriculture was more neglected than ever, for illicit traders in wine and other commodities flourished as never before. On the other hand, roads constructed for military purposes did a great deal to open up the remote parts of the island and in the years of peace greatly aided the improvement of fresh land and the development of the produce market in the town. The influx of English traders, too, was not without its effect in lowering a little the language barrier which was so great an obstacle to the reception of ideas from the outside world.

In 1815 the first detailed report of agricultural conditions in the Channel Islands was published. It shows that the twenty years of wartime neglect had seen no expansion of the cultivated area, which was still some 50 per cent. of the island, and it was clear that a great deal of workable land was unnecessarily lying waste. True, the tidal channel between Grand Havre and St. Sampson, the Braye du Valle, had been diked off and reclaimed by 1812, but much land was still unenclosed in the south-west, much drainage was needed in low-lying areas, and the light soils in some parts of the north promised good returns if they were improved. Cultivation in 1815 was concentrated on the naturally productive areas, especially on the deep loam to the north-west of St. Peter Port. The plateau, although heavy and retentive of moisture, yielded well both in grain and grass; the north (in direct contrast to the present day) was predominantly grazing land. The system of rotation generally adopted was as follows: wheat; barley and clover after vraic (kelp) and three ploughings; parsnips, after ploughing and harrowing in September and October followed by couch-burning, and digging or deep ploughing or harrowing in January. Manuring took place in the second year, the whole rotation lasting five. Fallow did not figure; it was precluded by high rents, short leases, the ready supply of vraic for fertilisation and the rapid spread of couch grass. There were few exceptions to the five-year rotation; potatoes, although frequently grown, did not yet enter into a regular system of cropping. Farmers found them profitable, and some successive crops had been taken with heavy manuring, but the root crop on which attention was still mainly centred was the parsnip. This crop was principally raised as a winter feed for milkers, and for fattening oxen and hogs. Lifting commenced in September, the yield amounting commonly to 18,000 lb. of clean root per acre. The deep, light loam was found to suit the parsnip, which was held in such high regard that heavy land was lightened with sea sand for its benefit. The grande kerue—the great plough—was introduced for parsnip cultivation; it was jointly operated by a number of farmers who pooled their draught animals to provide the four oxen and six horses required, in addition to the animals for the common plough which went before the grande kerue to open up the furrow.

Wheat was still the main cash crop, and continued to be so for some years after 1815. Its yield was sufficient in some years to provide a small surplus for export, although in others an import was necessary, and it may be said that the island was barely self-sufficient in this respect. Carrots were known as a field crop; lucerne, although introduced as long ago as 1650, and yielding four crops a year, was however considered unsuitable for grazing cattle, which were increasing in numbers.

To review the position when peace was concluded: Guernsey farmers adhered to a five-year rotation, wheat and parsnips were the principal crops, and cattle were of both the beef and dairy varieties.

The end of the war brought in its train notable economic changes. Blockade-running came to an end; smuggling was at last suppressed; the local shipbuilding industry declined sharply, and trade was hit by a severe slump. As a result, the capital accumulated during the war sought other outlets, and a period of industrial experiments ensued, among which was the distillation of potato spirit, for export. This traffic gave a fillip to potato planting, and the acreage under potatoes rose steadily. There was a general improvement in agriculture under the influence of the new Agricultural Society. More and more land was improved, one feature being the lessened need for furze grown for fuel, as it had been during the war. It is interesting to note that this peculiar crop was used not only as domestic fuel, but also for partially charring ships' bottoms to give the contrabanders an extra turn of speed, and that furze brakes are still recorded in the published statistics.

By 1840, dairying, dairy breeding for export, and potato growing shared with wheat the dominance of Guernsey's agriculture. The export of cattle may be said to have commenced in 1810, and the new trade increased in the following manner : 1810, 67 cows and calves exported ; 1812, 101 ; 1822-7, an average of 465 head per year ; 1834, 708. The acreage of cider apples was now declining, and the cider export falling off. Instead, besides the potato spirit already mentioned, potatoes themselves came to be sent out ; from small beginnings, the amount exported grew to 376,160 bushels[1] by 1839-40. The cultivation of fruit under glass, for export, had also commenced. The first crop thus to be raised was the grape, of which 3,474 lb. were sent to England in 1830. Fruit growing in general was on the increase, and an observer in 1810 noted that, in addition to the grape, the peach, apricot, apple, pear, fig, strawberry and raspberry were all to be found on the island.

Here, then, are the beginnings of cultivation and stockbreeding primarily for export. The trade in produce was greatly helped by the coming of steam navigation between the islands and England shortly before the end of the wars, while the collapse of Guernsey's shipbuilding industry referred to above made available a number of carpenters whose skill could be turned to glasshouse construction, with the result that large glasshouses were gradually added to the existing numerous small conservatories. Among the traditional crops there were also changes. Parsnips were being replaced as a winter feed by turnip and beet. The deficiency in wheat, although this was a major crop, increased from year to year and imports rose correspondingly. At the same time better use was made of the land in general, and cultivated acreage expanded rapidly, in spite of the inroads of stone quarries (see Fig 32) ; for a steady pressure was exerted by a rising population (16,000 in 1800, 24,000 in 1830, and 30,000 in 1870).

The year 1840 marked a stage in the history of land use in Guernsey ; it was shortly after that date that the blight disaster overtook potato growers, and production fell so far that by 1853 imports exceeded exports. Although recovery was sufficient to make the potato again the main cash crop, and in 1875 5,000 tons were exported, mostly for the London market, it never regained its eminence of 1840. In the meantime the improvement of land reached a peak about 1865, when 65 per cent. of the island was worked, more than half of this area being accounted for by grassland. Farming methods had however scarcely advanced in step with enclosure and the great plough was still in use ; it is possible that the soil was showing signs of exhaustion, and that the wheat yield was below that of 1815. Wheat, however, was no longer of prime importance. Grain had long given way before roots, and a typical farm was divided as follows :

Hay and pasture :   one-half
Wheat :   .   one-sixth
Turnips and potatoes :   one-tenth
Remainder (almost one-quarter), mangolds, parsnips and carrots.

Guernsey experienced competition in all branches of the export trade. The failure of potatoes to re-establish themselves permanently was due to the rivalry of Jersey, which with its southern aspect was better placed to raise primeurs. In the fruit line, competition came chiefly from the

[1] About 11,400 tons.

nearby coast of France, and in this case Guernsey was the more favourably situated and more than able to hold its own. To the fruits already mentioned were added the plum, cherry, mulberry and orange, but the grape continued to lead, and its production was organised on modern lines after 1874, in which year a limited liability company for vineries was formed. In the export of dairy cattle Guernsey continued to take its share (about 2,000 head per annum).

By the end of the century there had been some decline in the total of worked land, with tillage the chief loser ; in fact, the numbers of cattle remained fairly steady, and after 1900 some extra land was laid to Meadow ; rotation grass showed little change. Grain and potatoes were the crops to be restricted, the one facing competition from imports for the local market and the other competition from Jersey produce for the export trade. The most significant change of all was the switch from grapes to tomatoes by growers, who were faced with such severe competition from English grape producers that they were forced to look for an alternative crop suitable for raising under glass. The tomato had already been raised as a catch crop under

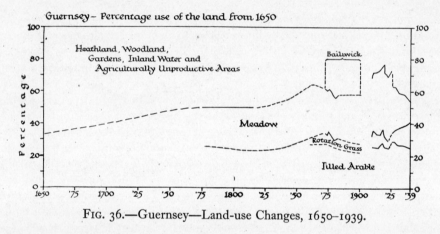

FIG. 36.—Guernsey—Land-use Changes, 1650–1939.

vines ; it was so successful that many glasshouses built as vineries never carried grapes at all. Tomatoes became and have remained ever since the principal growers' crop.

Some caution is necessary in reading Fig. 36, which illustrates the changes in land use in Guernsey ; the statistics on which it is based relate, for the years 1872–1900 inclusive, to the entire Bailiwick, and consequently over this period the proportion of worked land shown may be rather too low. The discrepancy thus introduced will not however be serious as Guernsey represents so large a proportion of the total area—about four-fifths.

At the time when the later series of statistics begins, that is in 1909, the worked area was spreading, and continued to do so throughout the first world war until in 1918 a new peak of 79 per cent. of the island was under crops or grass. Both Arable and Meadow received additions during the war, although the size of the herd changed little. The emphasis during the war years was more on subsistence crops, and for a brief period potatoes regained a little of their lost importance.

Immediately after the war there was a sharp temporary fall in the rotation grass acreage, which did not recover until about 1928. Since then it has grown steadily, occupying four times as much land in 1939 as in 1925. The shrinkage in the total cultivated area which has gone on fairly regularly of recent years has been at the expense of Meadow, which has diminished rapidly, and of tillage, which has also declined although with less speed ; between 1918 and 1939 almost a third of the total went out of cultivation—3,831 acres in all ; tillage lost over a thousand acres, Meadow over four thousand, with a gain of only about a thousand acres of rotation to mitigate the loss to grassland. In the same years the Guernsey herd lost 1,800 of its numbers, scarcely a proportionate fall ; it is clear from this fact and from the increase in rotation grass which has been noted that dairying methods have vastly changed. This change is reflected in the figures of feed import (see table). Despite improvements, the local dairy industry is not capable of producing sufficient butter, or of producing at a low enough price, to exclude large quantities of imported standardised produce from the local market (see import figures). The export trade in dairy stock has also suffered severely and the present annual demand from overseas markets is of some 600 head only.

Farming proper is now most definitely secondary to growing, even though growers' crops do not occupy such a large share of the land as they do in Jersey. Grain crops are no longer of importance, sheep have practically disappeared, and the pig population has dwindled with great speed.

The trade figures for fertilisers and other agricultural chemicals show the same trends that have been noted in the case of Jersey on pp. 9–10. The coal import figures (not included in the trade table) reflect an increase in the amount of glass heated, which is part of the larger increase of the glass total. The two-way traffic in bulbs has developed strongly of recent years.

A comparison of the statistics for various items in 1938 will show that the export of flowers is now about three times that of potatoes *by weight* ; the disparity in cash value may be imagined. It is the factor of cash yield per acre that has so greatly restricted the farming acreage, for growers' employees are better paid than farm workers, so that market-gardening, whose glasshouses absorb so much labour, dominates the man-power market as well as the trade in produce.

In the foregoing discussion of recent developments of land use in Guernsey, the fact has not been lost sight of that some land has been taken out of cultivation by new building, the airport, and playing-fields ; but in Jersey, too, the same demands have been made without a similar reduction in the worked acreage, and the conclusion must be that in Guernsey, farming proper brings so little return that land is being allowed to revert. It remains to be seen whether growing will in time be able to recover the lost acres.

JERSEY AFTER 1750

It has already been shown above that in 1750 Jersey was concentrating rather on arable than on pastoral farming, and that cider export was the chief item of trade. In the following discussion, which will trace the development of land use during the last two centuries, it will scarcely be necessary to deal with the subject in such detail as in the case of Guernsey ; the historical background for example was the same for both, but the differences in their agricultural histories are great and significant, and must be recorded.

The wars between 1793 and 1815 had an adverse effect on sheep raising, in Jersey as in Guernsey ; but in other respects farming was not so badly hit, in spite of a shortage of labour. Jerseymen were less preoccupied with the contraband trade, and had shown themselves readier to co-operate in suppressing smuggling. Although the tilled area fell somewhat, agriculture was not neglected : in 1815 about a quarter of the whole island was under the plough, with wheat and barley acreages about equal. There had been a concentration on cattle and grain during the war, when produce was scarce ; peace allowed French produce to be imported, and prices fell (a striking contrast to the inflation in Guernsey) so that farmers turned their attention to cash crops for export.

Military roads recently constructed had the same effect as in Guernsey of enabling the remoter parts to be exploited, and the improved area spread. Dairy cattle export was already being carried on before the end of the wars ; an average of 750 head each year was despatched in 1810–3, rising to 1,440 in 1830–2. The cider trade flourished, and potato export increased twenty-five times between 1813 and 1832 (in 1830, over 10,000 tons; 1835, rather less than 7,000). There was in addition a large export of both fresh and salted butter by the early 1830s.

In 1835, a rotation was still usual. The typical farm was adapted to mixed working, with barns, byre, and hay stack for the stock, a cider press to cater for the increasing trade, and raised hogs and steers which were fattened on parsnips. In order of area, the principal crops were : apples, potatoes, lucerne, and wheat. Foreign labour was being regularly imported for the harvest, from England, Ireland and France. Conditions generally were improving ; there

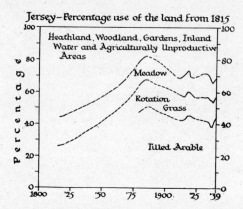

FIG. 37.—Jersey—Land-use Changes, 1815–1939.

were changes in cropping, despite the persistence of the five-year rotation, and in method—the grande kerue was being displaced—and the standard of living on the island was rising.

The potato blight hit Jersey also ; in fact, it affected all the islands. In 1861, the potato export had fallen to some 3,000 tons, and was more than balanced by imports. Export produce consisted chiefly of cider, whose orchards now covered a quarter of the Arable, and of dairy cattle (about 1,500 head per annum). The setback to potatoes was not permanent, however, and five years later they were the principal crop and the cider trade was finally on the decline.

The subsequent changes in the land use of Jersey have been simpler than corresponding changes in Guernsey, for the potato has remained the leading crop and growers have not been driven from one expedient to another. This is not to say, however, that changes have not taken place. Towards the end of the nineteenth century the sharp increase in the amount of worked land (see Fig. 37) came to a halt; in a short time there was an actual decline, up to the time of the first world war. Over 3,000 acres were lost between 1880 and 1914, chiefly at the expense of farmland, for in the same period potatoes increased from 4,761 acres to 8,967, thereafter changing relatively little before the 1930s. Grassland also fell off somewhat, losing about 1,000 acres in the thirty-five years after 1880 ; within the grassland, rotation grass constantly accounted for something over 50 per cent. Despite the constriction of grassland there was no decline in the herd : in fact, its numbers rose from 11,000 in 1880 to 12,000 in 1914.

The main development was once again the ousting of farming by growing, here demonstrated by the increased potato acreage. With this went the breaking down of the rotation system, which still persisted in 1880. There was at that time still a five-year course, as follows : turnips, potatoes or parsnips, wheat, hay, hay, but it was evidently not followed by all cultivators as potatoes even then occupied a quarter of the total Arable.

The first world war disturbed the trends which had been perceptible. Arable increased again for a brief period, and the total of worked land rose, but soon after peace was re-established there was a return to former conditions. Cattle on the other hand were reduced in numbers by the war, and the loss was not subsequently made good.

No statistics are available for the years 1922–9. It may be noted, however, that there was no great change over this period. Later developments have already been described.

APPENDIX I

STATISTICAL SUMMARY

The Land Utilisation of Jersey According to Available Statistics

Year	Total area (acres)[1]	Area under crops and grass[2]	Arable land[2]	Permanent grass[2]
1880	28,665	23,097	18,950	4,087
1909	—	19,440	16,340	3,100
1910	—	19,197	16,031	3,166
1912	—	19,495	16,184	3,275
1913	—	19,666	15,922	3,744
1914	—	19,687	16,118	3,569
1916	—	19,399	15,628	3,771
1917	—	20,344	16,451	3,983
1918	—	20,349	16,726	3,623
1919	—	20,838	16,726	4,112
1920	—	19,597	16,073	3,524
1922	—	19,412	15,941	3,471
1930	—	20,000[3]	15,900[4]	4,129[5]
1931	—	20,000[3]	15,350	4,645
1932	—	20,000[3]	15,400	4,584
1933	—	20,104	15,740	4,364
1934	—	19,241	15,111	4,130
1935	—	19,002	15,118	3,883
1936	—	19,103	15,277	3,826
1937	—	18,507	14,685	3,822
1938	—	18,620	15,116	3,504
1939	—	19,375	16,011	8,526

[1] Area calculated from map; excludes offshore rocks and islets.

[2] 1880, *Encyclopædia Britannica*. 1909–22, *Statesman's Year Book*. 1930 onwards, figures published by the States of Jersey.

[3] Approximate totals.

[4] Calculated from the published figures, allowing for double-cropping.

[5] Meadow, for 1930 and later years, taken as half the total grassland; the figure thus arrived at is very close to the true figure for Meadow.

47

JERSEY
Analysis of Crop Returns, 1918, 1930–9, in Acres

	1918	1930	1931	1932	1933	1934	1935	1936	1937	1938	1939
Grain	2,994	1,830	2,040	1,419	1,088	905	643	520	505	514	404
Roots	—	3,900	3,595	3,730	3,950	3,720	3,675	3,880	4,030	3,980	3,573
Green crops	—	173	232	250	363	430	674	1,037	1,163	1,017	1,446
Potatoes	8,531	7,865	6,990	8,308	8,804	9,342	9,837	10,080	10,387	10,328	10,614
Tomatoes	—	1,405	1,728	1,668	2,040	2,410	2,270	2,230	2,290	2,514	3,008
Soft fruit	—	—	—	—	—	25	24	20	23	20	21
Miscellaneous	—	638	490	488	550	433	474	554	415	435	405
Grass	7,880	8,257	9,290	9,168	8,728	8,260	7,768	7,652	7,643	7,008	6,728
Fallow	—	1,772	1,480	1,250	1,510	1,610	1,630	1,590	1,770	1,650	1,702
Total	20,450	25,840	25,845	26,281	27,033	27,135	26,995	27,563	28,226	27,376	27,901
Total area cultivated	20,344	20,000[1]	20,000[1]	20,000[1]	20,104	19,241	19,002	19,103	18,507	18,620	19,375
Meadow	3,894	4,129	4,645	4,584	4,364	4,130	3,884	3,826	3,822	3,504	3,364
Arable	16,450	15,900	15,350	15,400	15,740	15,111	15,118	15,277	14,685	15,116	16,011

Notes.—These figures relate to holdings of over one vergee (= four-ninths acre). Total of crop returns refers to crop acres.

[1] Approximate.

JERSEY
Crop Acreages, 1939

Parish	Grain	Roots	Green crops	Potatoes	Tomatoes	Soft fruit	Miscellaneous	Grass	Fallow	Total	2nd crop	Area cultivated	Land area
St. Ouen	62	530	183	1,421	244	·22	13	765	219	3,437	1,055	2,382	3,740
Grouville	9	84	55	674	699	1·33	42	305	62	1,931	578	1,353	1,985
St. John	34	394	157	980	41	·11	28	693	55	2,382	826	1,556	2,015
St. Clement	·67	15	1	282	424	·44	27	89	14	854	228	626	1,000
Trinity	40	509	226	1,343	131	·44	44	937	99	3,330	1,092	2,238	3,125
St. Martin	41	339	196	1,051	301	1·11	40	733	162	2,864	891	1,973	2,330
St. Saviour	27	277	120	804	341	6·44	75	665	97	2,413	701	1,712	2,210
St. Mary	44	321	73	683	40	2·44	10	499	265	1,937	569	1,368	1,665
St. Brelade	24	134	97	631	254	—	13	359	203	1,716	439	1,277	3,190
St. Helier	9	204	97	644	171	4·33	46	327	117	1,620	569	1,051	2,190
St. Peter	67	364	78	995	192	—	13	730	227	2,667	742	1,926	2,865
St. Lawrence	47	403	163	1,105	170	3·67	53	625	181	2,750	834	1,916	2,350
Total	404	3,573	1,446	10,614	3,008	20·6	405	6,728	1,702	27,901	8,526	19,375	28,665

Notes.—1. Figures relate to holdings of over one vergee (= four-ninths acre).
2. Correction is to nearest acre except for soft fruit.
From statistics published by the States of Jersey.

JERSEY

Livestock, 1918, 1930–9
Agricultural Workers and Machinery, 1930–9

1918		1930	1931	1932	1933	1934	1935	1936	1937	1938	1939
Cattle (herd book)											
Cattle (not in herd book)	} 9,657	11,928	12,580	12,233	11,467	10,559	9,911	10,019	10,164	10,037	9,662
		178	149	158	144	123	137	173	154	146	111
Sheep .	127	23	20	52	58	49	36	51	4	1	1
Goats . .	—	259	269	254	235	236	221	254	242	229	—
Pigs .	2,883	3,818	4,864	4,994	4,555	4,001	4,532	5,675	5,716	3,320	3,336
Horses .	—	1,619	1,549	1,539	1,500	1,498	1,462	1,446	1,424	1,329	1,334
Poultry . .	—	53,751	61,253	67,757	68,185	78,588	66,488	82,896	64,337	69,878	62,858
Agricultural Workers (regular) .		2,802	2,569	2,450	2,064	2,051	1,863	2,051	1,901	1,758	1,839
Agricultural Machinery and Transport											
Tractors . .		71	66	76	83	96	119	174	248	289	372
Lorries . .		244	321	405	456	592	694	772	836	850	914
Horse sprayers . .		—	—	—	—	—	—	—	—	110	122
Mechanical potato diggers . .		—	—	—	—	—	—	—	—	—	312

JERSEY

Cattle, 1939

Parish	Cows and heifers in milk or calf	Other females	Bulls	TOTAL	Not Herd Book Stock[1]
St. Ouen . .	659	364	40	1,063	10
Grouville . .	263	140	17	420	2
St. John . .	684	375	41	1,100	13
St. Clement . .	114	42	12	168	1
Trinity . . .	912	481	42	1,435	4
St. Martin . .	673	339	51	1,063	25
St. Saviour . .	663	346	49	1,058	11
St. Mary . .	450	275	31	756	4
St. Brelade . .	222	100	7	329	14
St. Helier . .	324	174	16	514	3
St. Peter . .	553	302	25	880	17
St. Lawrence . .	552	294	30	876	7
Total .	6,069	3,232	361	9,662	111

[1] Additional to total in preceding column.

All the Jersey cattle are Jerseys; those recorded as "not herd book stock" are the few exceptions to the general rule that all the island stock is pedigree.

D

THE LAND UTILISATION OF THE ISLANDS OF THE BAILIWICK OF GUERNSEY ACCORDING TO AVAILABLE STATISTICS

Year		Total area (acres)[1]	Area under crops and grass[2]	Arable land	Permanent grass
1872			12,007	6,846	5,161
1873			11,830	6,419	5,421
1875			12,060	7,160	4,900
1880	Bailiwick	19,617	11,123	6,123[3]	5,000[3]
1883			11,425	6,330	5,195
1899			11,672	5,672[3]	6,000[3]
1900			11,665	—	—
1909			11,007	5,142	5,865
1910			11,412	5,881	5,531
1912			11,438	5,535	5,903
1913			11,565	5,321	6,244
1914			11,616	5,374	6,242
1916		15,750	11,588	5,410	6,178
1917			11,990	5,797	6,193
1918			12,437	6,023	6,414
1919			11,453	5,172	6,281
1922			11,137	4,714	6,424
1925			11,890	5,660	6,230
1926			9,939	5,444[4]	4,495[4]
1927			10,010	5,735	4,275
1928			9,853	5,863	3,990
1931		15,520	9,425	5,855	3,570
1934			9,242	6,162	3,080
1936			9,103	6,351	2,752
1939			8,606	6,343	2,264

[1] 1872–1900, figures from various encyclopædias; includes whole of the Bailiwick. 1909–25, *Statesman's Year Book*, "Guernsey, etc." 1926 onwards, figures published by the States of Guernsey. It is possible that for the earlier series, vergees were incorrectly converted to acres.

[2] Figures from the same sources.

[3] Approximate only.

[4] For 1926 and later years no separate figures are available for rotation grass, and the proportions of Arable and Meadow are approximate.

GUERNSEY
CROP ACREAGES, 1939

Parish	All grain	Pota-toes	Roots	Green crops	Fruit, etc.	Bulbs	Miscel-laneous	Glass	Grass	Total culti-vated	Total land area
St. Peter Port	4·5	39	22	15	82	36	11	55	296	560·5	1,630
St. Sampson	5·5	70	15	13	56	136	35	189	277	769·5	1,475
Vale	2	95	24	24	74	157	22	220	324	942	2,185
Catel	57	110	69	63	75	235	21	161	888	1,679	2,490
St. Saviour	49	111	61	27	30	122	14	59	660	1,133	1,557
St. Peter in the Wood	37	104	54	33	27	62	6	57	596	976	1,527
Torteval	15	42	25	12	9	26	3	26	246	404	760
Forest	15	47	32	13	20	29	1	40	308	505	1,003
St. Martin	18·5	65	44	20	47	54	11	56	528	843·5	1,792
St. Andrew	18·5	65	43	26	42	82	33	52	405	766·5	1,101
Total 1939	222	748	390	246	462	938	157	915	4,527	8,606	15,520
Total 1936	265	753	440	278	479	1,032	240	864	4,752	9,103	15,520

Notes.—1. Conversion from vergees (one vergee = two-fifths acre) to nearest acre in most cases.
2. Buildings other than glasshouses, 1939 : 1,270 acres. Furze brakes, 1939 : 424 acres.

GUERNSEY
LIVESTOCK, 1939 and 1936 (head)

Parish—	Cows in milk/ calf	Total cattle	Pigs	Sheep	Horses & ponies	Goats	Poultry
St. Peter Port	186	311	—	—	—	—	—
St. Sampson	137	287	—	—	—	—	—
Vale	160	352	—	—	—	—	—
Catel	409	799	—	—	—	—	—
St. Saviour	283	521	—	—	—	—	—
St. Peter in the Wood	260	478	—	—	—	—	—
Torteval	103	240	—	—	—	—	—
Forest	189	353	—	—	—	—	—
St. Martin	231	379	—	—	—	—	—
St. Andrew	292	532	—	—	—	—	—
Total 1939	2,250	4,252	1,174	33	414	235	32,849
Total 1936	2,377	4,482	2,378	12	504	251	37,392

ALDERNEY, SARK, HERM AND JETHOU
Area Under Crops and Grass[1]

Year	ALDERNEY (Total area: acres)[2]	SARK (Total area: acres)[2]	HERM AND JETHOU (Total area: acres)[2]
1926	1,090	403	111[3]
1927	1,051	430	107[3]
1928	1,064	356	118[3]
1931	1,039	407	—
1934	1,055	400	100
1936	956	372	61
1939	982	430	—

[1] Figures from those published by the States of Guernsey. It is not possible to divide the total into Arable and Meadow.
[2] Calculated from maps.
[3] Herm only.

APPENDIX II

SELECTED TRADE FIGURES

JERSEY
EXPORTS, 1929–39 (*tons*)

	1929	1930	1931	1932	1933	1934	1935	1936	1937	1938	1939
Apples and pears	16[1]	3[1]	68	551	248	159	66	90	45	526	83
Tomatoes	17,070	19,852	16,989	18,914	33,433	30,640	27,281	22,607	29,281	26,284	30,671
Potatoes	70,624	53,475	47,971	54,732	71,976	63,031	88,186	61,014	59,401	57,441	75,570
Other vegetables	—	—	74	81	143	168	93	234	251	159	75
Flowers	21	31	37	31	23	25	14	13	19	5	11
Bulls[2]	100	81	64	64	48	48	78	81	111	76	83
Cows[2]	691	535	522	500	274	456	309	320	454	312	339
Calves[2]	22	75	21	10	18	19	16	47	21	20	67
Heifers[2]	533	318	396	709	728	729	704	690	724	698	698
Total cattle[2]	1,346	1,009	1,003	1,283	1,068	1,252	1,107	1,138	1,310	1,106	1,187

[1] Apples only.　　　[2] Head.

JERSEY
IMPORTS, 1929–39 (*tons*)

	1929	1930	1931	1932	1933	1934	1935	1936	1937	1938	1939
Barley	34	112	118	100	137	141	176	114	70	136	187
Oats	510	569	665	692	972	587	711	565	903	229	288
Maize	716	551	624	753	914	1,258	918	815	1,056	998	800
Other grains and seeds	469	434	613	434	906	54	54	74	73	61	78
Bran and cattle food	4,444	4,857	6,039	7,448	5,505	5,864	6,234	7,080	6,709	6,315	7,100
Flour	4,940	5,132	5,150	5,136	4,967	5,064	5,168	5,166	4,832	4,659	5,858
Hay[1]	1,536	1,671	1,065	3,064	2,822	4,137	2,246	4,410	4,032	5,437	3,548
Straw[1]	2,405	3,613	2,588	3,441	4,042	4,479	5,863	6,036	6,464	8,830	5,872
Meat	2,092	2,267	2,340	2,334	2,302	2,519	2,332	2,654	2,333	2,471	2,527
Eggs	234	281	259	43	228	258	188	108	77	202	327
Fruit and nuts	506	643	640	608	1,428	2,022	2,048	2,280	2,552	2,410	2,082
Potatoes	1,185	1,951	2,994	936	287	1,815	1,879	2,653	2,043	2,005	1,680
Manures	11,624	9,633	11,376	11,196	13,267	14,070	15,146	14,656	16,548	15,943	21,519
Sprays, etc.	—	—	—	54	61	28	214	164	—	180	217
Cider, gallons	22,704	16,113	21,311	19,655	18,777	18,751	18,411	22,854	24,181	30,225	27,585
Cider, dozens	674	254	1,053	1,415	2,204	2,790	2,018	1,739	1,290	1,294	1,330
Horses (head)[2]	46	67	69	74	90	101	108	70	104	51	59

[1] Largely ex Norway and Sweden.　　　[2] Net imports : in 1939, 54 horses were exported, 113 imported.

GUERNSEY
EXPORTS, 1928–38 (*tons*)

	1928	1929	1930	1931	1932	1933	1934	1935	1936	1937	1938
Tomatoes .	25,068	24,946	26,907	25,830	23,069[1]	27,359[1]	27,000[1]	28,045[1]	28,648[1]	—	—
Grapes .	1,280	1,131	1,107	925	912	879	908	747	577	—	—
Total fruit .	26,440	—	—	—	—	28,331	27,974	28,873	29,286	32,439	35,708
Potatoes .	537	314	346	274	670	675	715	1,179	1,333	1,498	1,330
Other Vegetables .	602	921	736	1,031	1,034	1,218	1,408	550	629	—	—
Bulbs .	408	913	474	215	217	386	527	445	358	—	—
Flowers .	3,204	3,743	3,318	3,878	3,896	4,977	4,728	3,968	4,367	4,091	3,721
Cattle[2] .	761	—	—	—	—	611	701	876	—	613	628

[1] Net.   [2] Head.

GUERNSEY
IMPORTS, 1929–38 (*tons*)

	1929	1930	1931	1932	1933	1934	1935	1936	1937	1938
Wheat .	1,020	1,093	1,117	940	1,266	989	1,080	983	878	920
Bran and cattle foods .	3,366	3,518	3,942	4,138	3,838	4,085	3,720	—	—	—
Total grain and forage .	6,718	7,346	7,248	7,235	7,231	7,749	7,768	7,228	7,374	6,975
Meat and poultry .	1,691	1,672	1,652	1,600	1,680	1,631	1,745	1,816	1,818	1,868
Butter .	291	310	348	377	434	494	521	525	531	515
Flour .	3,715	3,369	3,791	3,737	3,664	3,871	3,705	—	—	—
Potatoes .	2,122	1,626	2,485	1,692	1,102	2,138	2,363	1,936	1,772	1,900
Bulbs .	106	—	90	—	833	857	1,087	1,006	1,121	1,373
Manures, etc. .	4,119	4,086	3,816	4,488	4,435	4,584	4,800	4,548	5,584	5,152
Plant washes, etc. .	271	264	297	275	346	329	387	491	501	549